POWER SYSTEM PROTECTION

3 Application

POWER SYSTEM PROTECTION

3 Application

Edited by
The Electricity Council

PETER PEREGRINUS LTD.

Published by: Peter Peregrinus Ltd., Stevenage, UK, and New York

British Library Cataloguing in Publication Data

Power system protection — 2nd ed.
    Vol. 3: Application
    1. Electric power transmission — Safety appliances
    I. Electricity Council
    621.319   TK3091

ISBN: 0-906048-54-0

Printed in England by A. Wheaton & Co., Ltd., Exeter

Contents

Foreword

The three volumes which make up this publication owe their origin to a correspondence tuition course launched in the Electricity Supply Industry in Britain in 1966, written by expert engineers in the Electricity Boards and with electrical manufacturers, and administered by the Education and Training Branch of the Electricity Council. The correspondence course continues to be provided to meet the needs of staff in the Electricity Supply Industry.

It became apparent soon after its inception, however, that the work met a widespread need in Britain and overseas as a standard text on a speciaised subject. Accordingly, the first edition of Power System Protection was published in book form in 1969, and has since come to be recognised as a comprehensive and valuable guide to concepts, practices and equipment in this important field of engineering. Because the books are designed not only to provide a grounding in theory but to cover the range of applications, it was recognised that changes in protection technology required a process of up-dating, and this second edition therefore presents a revision of the original material to take account of recent developments in the field.

The three revised volumes comprise 18 chapters, each with bibliography. The aim remains that of providing sufficient knowledge of protection for those concerned with design, planning, construction and operation to understand the function of protection in those fields, and to meet the basic needs of the engineer intending to specialise in the subject.

In the use of symbols, abbreviations and diagram conventions, the aim has been to comply with British Standards.

The Electricity Council wishes to acknowledge the work of both the original authors, and those new contributors who have undertaken the revision work in preparation for this new edition. They are referred to at the head of the appropriate chapter. The Council also acknowledges the valuable assistance of the CEGB's Transmission and Technical Services Division Drawing Office at Guildford and its staff in preparing the diagrams; and the help of the following in permitting reproduction of illustrations and other relevant material:

Allen West & Co. Limited, ASEA, Brown Boveri Company Limited, BICC Limited, Electrical Apparatus Company, ERA Technology Limited, GEC Measurements Limited, GEC Switchgear Limited, GEC Transformers Limited, Price and Belsham Limited, Reyrolle Protection Limited.

Extracts from certain British Standards are reproduced by permission of the British Standards Institution, from whom copies of the complete standards may be obtained.

A particular indebtedness is acknowledged to the Chairman and members of the Editorial Panel, who directed and co-ordinated the work of revision for publication.

Chapter authors

N. Ashton	C.Eng., F.I.E.E., A.R.T.C.(S) (deceased)
K.A.J. Coates	C.Eng., M.I.E.E.
P.C. Colbrook	B.Sc.Tech., A.M.C.S.T., C.Eng., M.I.E.E.
L. Csuros	Dipl. Eng., C.Eng., F.I.E.E.
P.M. Dolby	C.Eng., M.I.E.E.
L.C.W. Frerk	B.Sc.(Eng.), C.Eng., M.I.E.E., F.I.Nuc.E.
F.L. Hamilton	B.Eng., C.Eng., F.I.E.E., (deceased)
J. Harris	C.Eng., M.I.E.E.
D. Hay	B.Sc., C.Eng., M.I.E.E.
J.W. Hodgkiss	M.Sc.Tech., C.Eng., M.I.E.E.
L. Jackson	B.Sc., Ph.D., C.Eng., F.I.E.E.
G.S.H. Jarrett	Wh.Sc., B.Sc.(Eng.), C.Eng., F.I.E.E.
M. Kaufmann	C.Eng., F.I.E.E., (deceased)
E.J. Mellor	T.D.
K.G. Mewes	Dip.E.E., C.Eng., M.I.E.E.
J.H. Naylor	B.Sc.(Eng.), C.Eng., F.I.E.E., A.M.C.T., D.I.C.
H.S Petch	B.Sc.(Eng.), M.I.E.E., M. Amer.I.E.E. (deceased)
J. Rushton	Ph.D., F.M.C.S.T., C.Eng., F.I.E.E.
E.C. Smith	A.M.C.T., C.Eng., F.I.E.E.
C. Turner	D.Sc., F.Inst.P.
H.W. Turner	B.Sc., F.Inst.P.
J.C. Whittaker	B.Sc.(Eng.), C.Eng., F.I.E.E.

Editorial Panel

J.H. Naylor	B.Sc.(Eng.), C.Eng., F.I.E.E., A.M.C.T., D.I.C. (Chairman)
G.S.H. Jarrett	Wh. Sc., B.Sc.(Eng.), C.Eng., F.I.E.E.
J. Rushton	Ph.D., F.M.C.S.T., C.Eng., F.I.E.E.
P.M. Dolby	C.Eng., M.I.E.E.
J. Harris	C.Eng., M.I.E.E.
W. Looney	T.Eng.(CEI)., M.I.E.E.T.E.

Protection symbols used in circuit diagrams

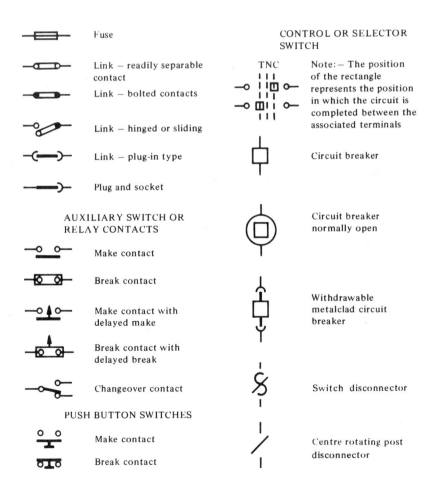

	Fuse
	Link — readily separable contact
	Link — bolted contacts
	Link — hinged or sliding
	Link — plug-in type
	Plug and socket

AUXILIARY SWITCH OR RELAY CONTACTS

	Make contact
	Break contact
	Make contact with delayed make
	Break contact with delayed break
	Changeover contact

PUSH BUTTON SWITCHES

	Make contact
	Break contact

CONTROL OR SELECTOR SWITCH

TNC

Note:— The position of the rectangle represents the position in which the circuit is completed between the associated terminals

Circuit breaker

Circuit breaker normally open

Withdrawable metalclad circuit breaker

Switch disconnector

Centre rotating post disconnector

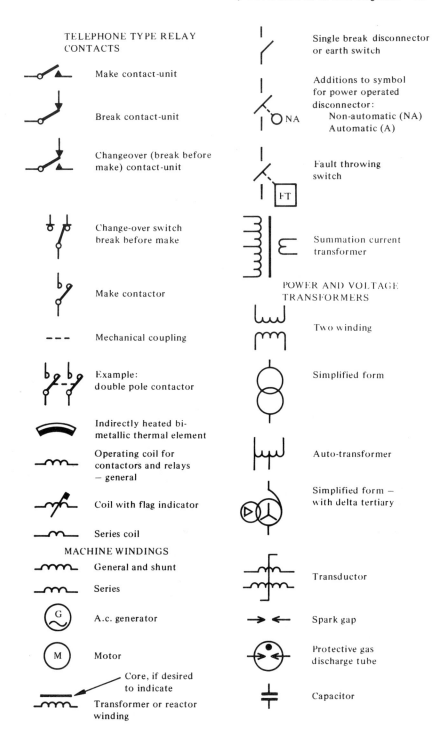

TELEPHONE TYPE RELAY CONTACTS

Make contact-unit

Break contact-unit

Changeover (break before make) contact-unit

Change-over switch break before make

Make contactor

Mechanical coupling

Example: double pole contactor

Indirectly heated bimetallic thermal element

Operating coil for contactors and relays — general

Coil with flag indicator

Series coil

MACHINE WINDINGS

General and shunt

Series

A.c. generator

Motor

Core, if desired to indicate

Transformer or reactor winding

Single break disconnector or earth switch

Additions to symbol for power operated disconnector:
  Non-automatic (NA)
  Automatic (A)

Fault throwing switch

Summation current transformer

POWER AND VOLTAGE TRANSFORMERS

Two winding

Simplified form

Auto-transformer

Simplified form — with delta tertiary

Transductor

Spark gap

Protective gas discharge tube

Capacitor

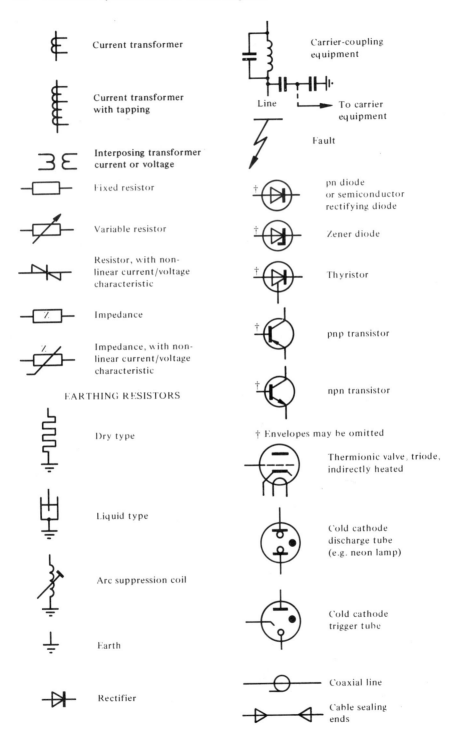

Current transformer

Current transformer with tapping

Interposing transformer current or voltage

Fixed resistor

Variable resistor

Resistor, with non-linear current/voltage characteristic

Impedance

Impedance, with non-linear current/voltage characteristic

EARTHING RESISTORS

Dry type

Liquid type

Arc suppression coil

Earth

Rectifier

Carrier-coupling equipment

Line

To carrier equipment

Fault

pn diode or semiconductor rectifying diode

Zener diode

Thyristor

pnp transistor

npn transistor

† Envelopes may be omitted

Thermionic valve, triode, indirectly heated

Cold cathode discharge tube (e.g. neon lamp)

Cold cathode trigger tube

Coaxial line

Cable sealing ends

	Rectifier equipment in bridge connection
	Amplifier
B	Buchholz — single float
B	Buchholz — two float
WT	Winding temperature single switch
WT	Winding temperature double switch
HSA	High speed ammeter
	Alarm flag relay
	Trip flag relay
R	Relay general symbol
FP	Feeder protection
PLC PC	Power line carrier phase comparison protection
Z	Distance protection
MHO	High speed distance (Mho) protection
	Electric bell
	Signal lamp
E	Electro-motive force e.m.f.
PP	Private pilot protection
POP	Post office pilot protection
TP	Transformer protection
DB	Biased differential protection
PB D	Plain balance differential protection
T HVC	Transformer h.v. connection protection
CC	Circulating current
BB	Busbar protection
MCP	Mesh corner protection
HAR	High speed auto-close relay
OV	Over voltage relay

X	High speed distance (reactance) protection
3OC I	3-pole overcurrent relay (inverse definite minimum time)
2OC I EI	2-pole overcurrent and single pole earth-fault relay (inverse definite minimum time)
OC I	1-pole overcurrent relay (inverse definite minimum time)
EI	Earth-fault relay (inverse definite minimum time)
3OC 2S I	3-pole two stage overcurrent relay (inverse definite minimum time)
3OC DI	3-pole directional overcurrent relay (inverse definite minimum time)
3OC	3-pole overcurrent relay (instantaneous)
3OC XI	3-pole overcurrent relay (extremely inverse definite minimum time)
E	Earth-fault relay (instantaneous)
3OC HS	3-pole high set overcurrent relay
E SB LTI	Standby earth-fault relay (long time inverse definite minimum time)
E2S SB LTI	Two stage standby earth-fault relay (long time inverse definite minimum time)
RP	Reverse power relay
E RES	Restricted earth-fault relay
T	Tripping relay
INT	Intertrip relay
INT S	Intertrip relay (send)
INT R	Intertrip relay (receive)
TD	Definite time relay
NEG PH SEQ	Negative phase sequence
LE	Lost excitation
3OC VC I	3-pole voltage controlled overcurrent relay (inverse definite minimum time)
3OC INT I	3-pole overcurrent, interlocked relay (inverse definite minimum time)
BF C CK	Breaker fail current check
LVC	L.V. connection protection

Protection of generators, transformers, generator-transformer units and transformer feeders

by J. Rushton, revised by K.G.M.Mewes

12.1 Introduction

In the early days of electricity, supply generators were operated by the Supply Company to supply a local load. Economically it was desirable to generate at the distribution system voltage. As the size of local networks grew, higher distribution voltages became necessary, and by the time the 132 kV National Grid was established many of the larger supply companies were generating and distributing at a voltage of 33 kV.

With the development of the 132/275/400kV systems, the overall pattern of generation changed resulting in larger stations sited to take advantage of fuel and cooling water supplies, and operated over an interconnected transmission network to give lowest cost and maximum efficiency. Generators were connected to the main transmission busbar via an associated transformer, and this arrangement permitted the additional facility of voltage and power factor control by transformer tappings.

Optimisation of machine design has resulted in standard machine ratings, of which the following is a typical selection:

Generator output MW	Voltage of h.v. connection	Generated voltage
60	132 kV	11·8 kV
120	132 kV	13·8 kV
500	275/400 kV	22 kV
660	400 kV	22 kV

Increase in outputs has been achieved without proportional increase in frame size by employing more efficient cooling methods. The protective systems applied to small directly connected generators are equally applicable to large transformer connected units, but the smaller operating margins available with these units (due

to their smaller frame size) require more comprehensive schemes of high performance protection.

12.2   Performance requirements

The high costs associated with large generating and transforming plants accentuate
the need for reliable, high speed schemes of protection to:

(*a*)   minimise fault damage and so reduce the possible need to replace the plant
(capital outlay)
(*b*)   reduce repair outage time and so minimise the need to run lower merit (less
cost-efficient) plant in order to meet the demand (revenue expenditure)
(*c*)   assist in maintaining system stability.

The degree of protection to be provided for the plant is determined by protection
engineers in consultation with plant designers and system operation engineers,
the objective being to provide a minimum of protection consistent with adequate
coverage of all conditions liable to cause damage or affect the continuity of supply.
Before considering in detail the many forms of protection fitted to generators and
transformers, it is desirable to consider the origin and effects of faults and other
system disturbances so that the significance of the protection arrangements may be
appreciated.

12.2.1   Generator faults

(*a*)   *Stator faults:* Stator faults involve the main current carrying conductors and
must therefore be cleared quickly from the power system by a complete shutdown
of the generator. They may be faults to earth, between phases or between turns of a
phase, singly or in combination. The great danger from all faults is the possibility of
damage to the laminations of the stator core and stator windings due to the heat
generated at the point of fault. If the damage so caused is other than superficial, the
stator would have to be dismantled, the damaged laminations and windings replaced
and the stator rebuilt, all of which is a lengthy and costly process.

Limitation of generator stator earth-fault current by means of resistance earthing
is normal practice (see Chapter 1) and serves, among other things, to minimise core
burning.

Phase-to-phase faults and interturn faults are both less common than earth faults.
It is relatively easy to provide protection for phase-to-phase faults, but interturn
faults are, on the other hand more difficult to detect and protection is not usually
provided. Generally speaking, interturn faults quickly involve contact with earth via
the stator core and are then tripped by stator earth-fault protection.

(*b*)   *Rotor faults:* Rotor faults may be either to earth or between turns and may
be caused by the severe mechanical and thermal stresses acting upon the winding
insulation; these are aggravated by a variable load cycle.

The field system is not normally connected to earth so that a single earth fault does not give rise to any fault current. However, a second fault to earth would short circuit part of the field winding and thereby produce an asymmetrical field system, and unbalanced forces on the rotor. Such forces will cause excess pressure on bearings and shaft distortion, if not quickly removed.

Under the general heading of rotor faults can be included loss of excitation. This may be caused by an open circuit in the main field winding or a failure elsewhere in the excitation system.

Loss of excitation in a generator connected to a large interconnected power system results in a loss of synchronism and slightly increased generator speed, since the power input to the machine is unchanged. The machine behaves as an induction generator drawing its exciting current from the remainder of the system in the form of wattless current whose magnitude approximates to that of the full load rating of the machine. This may cause overheating of the stator winding and increased rotor losses due to the currents induced in the rotor body and damper winding. This condition should not be allowed to persist indefinitely and corrective action either to restore the field, or to off-load and shut down the machine should be taken.

With generator outputs above half rated load, pole-slipping caused by weak field condition, would cause severe voltage variations which may, in turn, cause operation of the undervoltage protection on the boiler auxiliaries. The resultant operation of 'loss of boiler firing' protection would then shut down the generator unit. Other generators connected to the same busbar may also be caused to 'swing' and system instability would result. Pole slipping may also result from insufficiently fast clearance of a system fault and require the tripping of the unit.

(*c*)　*Mechanical conditions:* The mechanical conditions requiring consideration are overspeed due to sudden loss of load, loss of drive due to prime mover failure and loss of condenser vacuum.

The problem of overspeed limitation, particularly in relation to sudden load changes, is considered later. With modern large units it is essential to anticipate overspeed and take corrective action. Mechanical overspeed devices which operate on the steam stop valves are invariably fitted.

In the event of failure of the prime mover, a generator will continue to run synchronously drawing power from the system. This can sometimes lead to a dangerous mechanical condition if allowed to persist, although the condition is immediately obvious to the attendant.

Sets having an internal combustion prime mover must be protected against engine failure, where, if the alternator continues to motor serious engine damage may result.

Vacuum failure (or low vacuum) detection is necessary to prevent a rise of condenser pressure which might lead to shattering of l.p. casing and condensers.

(*d*)　*External faults:* Turboalternators must be protected against the effects of sustained external faults, for example faults on lines or busbars which are not cleared by the appropriate protection. The main condition of interest is that of an unsymmetrical fault producing negative phase sequence currents in the stator winding. The effect of these currents is to produce a field rotating in opposite sense to the d.c. field system producing a flux which cuts the rotor at twice the rotational frequency thereby inducing double frequency currents in the field system and the rotor body. These currents produce severe rotor heating and modern machines have a limited negative phase sequence current capability.

Automatic tripping is therefore required for the higher negative phase sequence current conditions.

This capability limit applies to all modern hydrogen-cooled machines and many air-cooled machines, but some of the older air-cooled machines are designed to withstand full negative sequence currents continuously. In large modern alternators, particularly those employing direct cooling of the stator and rotor conductors, the temperature rise caused by abnormally high stator currents is more rapid than in the less highly rated machines and the capability limit is therefore lower.

12.2.2.   Transformer faults

(a)   *Faults within the transformer tank:* These may comprise phase-to-earth, phase-to-phase, or interturn faults on the windings, interwinding faults, tap changer faults, insulator bushing failure and core overheating due to failure of core insulation. The possibility of damage is high for these faults as is the risk of fire, and short fault clearance times are advantageous.

The connections of the power transformer and the method of earthing play an important part in determining current magnitude available for relay operation, and each case requires separate consideration. Figs. 12.2.2A and B give the current distribution under fault conditions for various transformer arrangements based on the performance of typical transformers.

For a resistance earthed, star-connected winding, a winding-to-earth fault will give rise to a current dependent on the value of the earthing resistor and the distance of the fault from the neutral end of the winding. The effective ratio of transformation between the primary winding and the short circuited portion of the secondary winding varies with the fault position. The current flowing through the transformer terminals is therefore, for all practical purposes, proportional to the square of the percentage of the winding short circuited. This is illustrated in Fig. 12.2.2A(a).

For a solidly earthed star winding, the fault current bears no simple relationship to the distance of the fault from the neutral end since the effective reactance of the fault path changes with fault position. Fig. 12.2.2A(b) shows that the minimum value of fault current occurs for a fault 30 to 40% from the neutral end.

For a delta connected winding the minimum voltage on the delta winding is at the centre of one phase and is 50% normal phase-to-earth voltage, and an illustration of the approximate method of calculation is given in Fig. 12.2.2B. The range of values of fault current varies less than with the star connected winding. The value of fault current depends upon system earthing arrangements, and the curves of

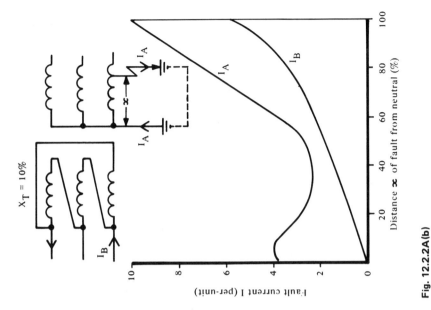

Fig. 12.2.2A(b)

Transformer fault current for solidly earthed star winding

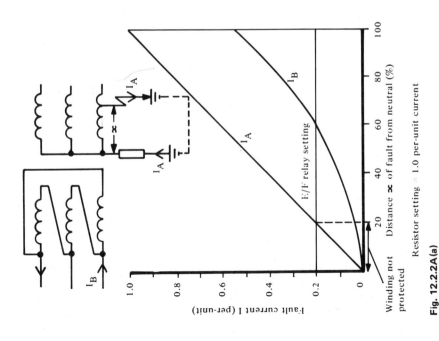

Fig. 12.2.2A(a)

Transformer fault current for resistance earthed star winding

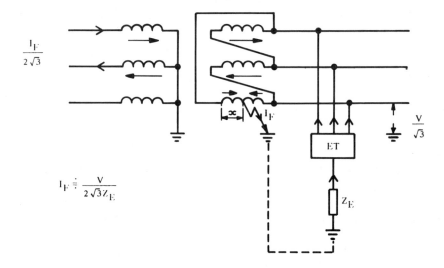

(a) Approximate method for calculating fault current

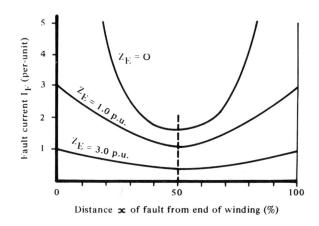

(b) Typical fault current values

Fig. 12.2.2B   *Transformer fault current for delta winding*

Fig. 12.2.2B(*b*) show that the minimum value of fault current occurs for a fault at the centre of one phase winding. The impedance of the winding under such conditions will be between two and four times the normal value.

Phase-to-phase faults rarely occur on a power transformer. Clearly such faults will give rise to large currents.

Interturn faults are more likely to occur than phase-to-phase faults. The interturn insulation on a power transformer is not so great as the interwinding insulation, and the possibility exists of breakdown between turns.

A short circuit of a few turns of the winding will produce a heavy current in the faulted loop and a very small terminal current. In this respect it has some similarity to a neutral end fault on a solidly earthed star winding.

Core faults can occur due to lamination insulation becoming short circuited. This can cause serious overheating due to eddy current losses. Core clamping bolts must always be insulated to prevent this trouble. If core insulation becomes defective (due, possibly, to the failure of core bolt insulation or debris in the tank), it must be detected quickly.

(*b*)   *Faults on transformer connections:* These may comprise any type of normal system fault on open copperwork connections or flashover of co-ordinating gaps. Damage due to such faults is not usually great though they may constitute a serious hazard to power system stability if not cleared quickly. Faults between the current transformers and the associated circuit breaker have to be included in this category.

(*c*)   *Overheating:* Failure of the cooling system will cause overheating and consequent danger of damage to the windings.

(*d*)   *Faults external to the transformer zone:* These will be of the usual range of system earth and phase faults to be cleared by appropriate external protection systems. They will affect, therefore, only the requirement of transformer back-up protection.

12.3   Generator protection systems

A generator is invariably protected against phase-to-phase faults by overall differential protection using either a biased or unbiased relay. The unbiased relay is usually of the attracted armature pattern and the biased relay uses either an induction-disc or rectifier moving coil element. In all cases a high speed relay is used.

12.3.1   Unbiased differential protection

The basic circuit for generator differential protection shown in Fig. 12.3.1A is the simplest arrangement of a balanced current system in which only two current transformers per phase are required to balance together. The theory of balanced systems is discussed in Chapter 4 which gives the design parameters for the correct operation of an unbiased relay system under power system transient conditions. For most applications to the protection of a direct-connected generator, an instantaneous unbiased relay is used and this gives an adequate and predictable performance.

The fault setting required from the differential protection is determined by the value of the neutral earthing resistor and also by the amount of winding to be protected. For the winding fault shown in Fig. 12.3.1A the earth-fault current is

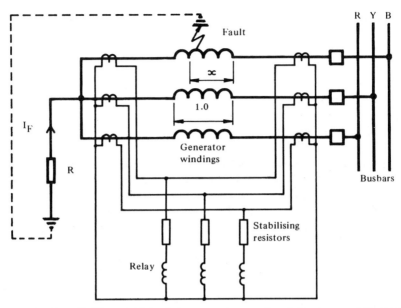

Fig. 12.3.1A   *Overall differential (circulating current) protection of direct-connected generator*

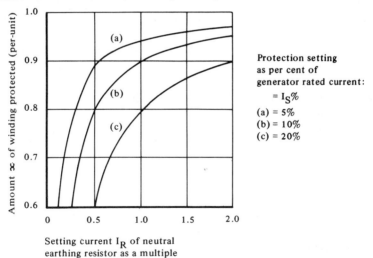

Fig. 12.3.1B   *Relation between neutral resistor setting, protection sensitivity and amount of generator winding protected*

$I_F = (1 - x)E/R$ which must equal the primary fault setting of the differential protection, I_S, for minimum operating current.

Thus,

$$I_S = (1 - x)\frac{E}{R} \text{ and } I_R = \frac{E}{R}$$

whence $x = (1 - I_S/I_R)$, I_R being the earthing resistor current setting.

The relationship is shown graphically in Fig. 12.3.1B.

With a resistor designed to pass rated current of the machine on a fault at the machine terminals, it is clear that a differential protection setting of 10% will protect 90% of the machine winding, the unprotected portion being the 10% at the neutral end where fault risk is reduced.

The differential protection will give greater than 90% cover for phase-to-phase faults since the fault current is limited only by the machine impedance which is small when the faulted portion of the winding is small.

12.3.2   Biased differential protection

Occasionally, there is some advantage in using a biased differential relay. The effect of the bias feature is to enable the impedance of the relay operating coil circuit to be reduced for a given value of through fault stability. The voltage drop across the current transformers at setting is correspondingly reduced and the magnetising currents have a negligible effect on the primary fault setting. The bias feature is obtained by circulating the through fault current through an additional winding which exerts a restraining force on the relay. The basic circuit connections are shown in Fig. 12.3.2A. Nominally no current flows in the operating coil under through fault conditions but, due to imperfect matching of the current transformers, some spill current may be present. This spill current will flow in the relay operating circuit but will not cause operation unless the relay operating/bias setting ratio is exceeded. The magnitude of relay operating coil current to cause operation thus increases as the circulating current increases in a fixed relationship determined by the fundamental constants of the relay circuit. This is illustrated in Fig. 12.3.2B.

Referring to Fig. 12.3.2A

$$\text{relay operating force} = K(I_1 - I_2)N_o$$

$$\text{relay restraining force} = K\frac{(I_1 + I_2)}{2}N_r + S$$

where N_o and N_r are the operating and restraint coil turns, respectively, and S is the spring restraint force.

The electrical operating and restraint forces are equal at the balance point of the relay when the spring restraint is zero, whence

$$\frac{I_1 - I_2}{\frac{1}{2}(I_1 + I_2)} = \frac{N_r}{N_o}$$

This equation shows that the characteristic has a slope determined by the ratio N_r/N_o, and the relay bias is defined as the difference current $(I_1 - I_2)$ divided by the mean circulating current, which is fundamentally a constant ratio for all current magnitudes. This is plotted in Fig. 12.3.2C.

The percentage bias feature reduces c.t. requirements under transient through fault conditions. With the correct combination of bias and operating circuit resistance, through fault stability can be obtained for any value of through fault current. The required value of stabilising resistance is invariably quite low, thus giving a lower relay operating voltage than that required for an unbiased relay. The

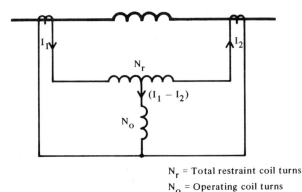

N_r = Total restraint coil turns
N_o = Operating coil turns

Fig. 12.3.2A   *Basic circuit connection for biased differential protection*

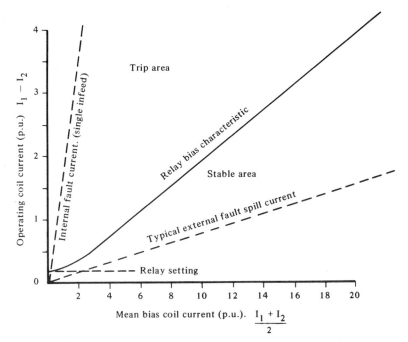

Fig. 12.3.2B   *Biased relay characteristic illustrating performance under internal and external faults*

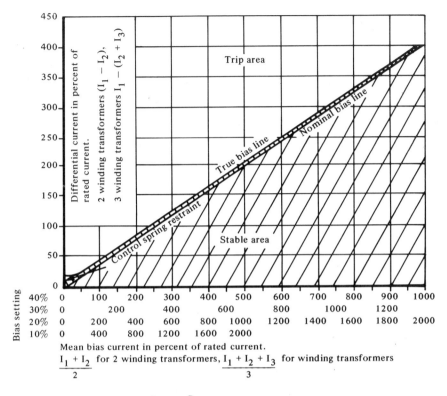

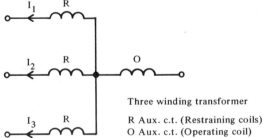

Fig. 12.3.2C   *Percentage differential relay restraint characteristic*

biased relay is thus most suitable for cases where c.t. performance is limited or where leads are long.

Care must be taken that the c.t.s do not saturate too severely under high current internal fault conditions since any magnetising current will flow through the relay bias coils and may inhibit operation.

High speed biased differential protection may be particularly suitable when it is necessary to use existing current transformers and their design is not suited to an unbiased system.

12.3.3   Back-up overcurrent and earth-fault protection

Inverse, definite minimum time relays are generally fitted to provide back-up over-current and earth-fault protection of a generator, and its h.v. connections, primarily to provide 'last resort' tripping in the event of failure of the main protection. Ideally, it should be set to trip in the shortest possible time so as to minimise the risk of loss of system stability.

The minimum permissible relay setting is determined by the requirement that tripping must not occur for external h.v. system faults which may be more discriminatively cleared by other forms of protection. The relay setting should be

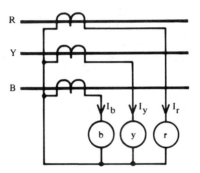

Fig. 12.3.3A   *Direct connection of overcurrent protection*

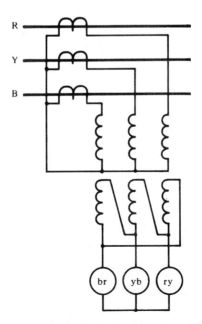

Fig. 12.3.3B   *Interposed connection of overcurrent protection*

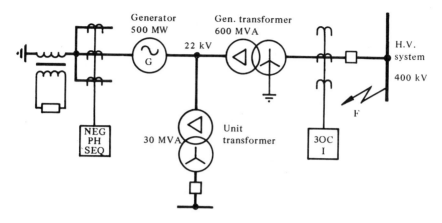

Fig. 12.3.3C *Diagram of transformer connected generator showing overcurrent and n.p.s. relays*

chosen to provide adequate grading margins with negative phase sequence back-up protection.

Overcurrent protection normally uses c.t.s in the h.v. circuit breaker which, in the case of a transformer connected generator, is on the star-connected side of the generator transformer. Two types of relay connection may be used, either:

(*a*) direct connection to star-connected current transformers (Fig. 12.3.3A) where the relay is supplied with the phase currents, or

(*b*) connection to star-delta interposing current transformers (ratio 1/0·578) (Fig. 12.3.3B) where the relay is supplied with phase-difference currents so avoiding any zero-sequence currents present in the primary fault current.

Generally, the star-connected c.t. arrangement is used, but it may be seen from Fig. 12.3.3D that the star-delta interposed connection appears to give a more acceptable range of operating times for the more severe types of external h.v. system fault. It also appears to provide better back-up to the negative phase sequence protection described in Section 12.3.4.

The following analysis refers particularly to the generator-transformer connected unit illustrated in Fig. 12.3.3C

External-system faults: The overcurrent relay must not operate for external-system faults for which the generator will remain in synchronism, and settings chosen on the basis of 2·0 s minimum operating time will embody high safety margins. The relay-fault-current curves for both cases are shown in Fig. 12.3.3D. The highest fault current for star-connected current transformers is obtained for the single-phase-to-earth fault, while, for delta-connected current transformers, the phase-to-phase fault gives the worst case. Fault settings for the two types of relay connection are determined in Table 12.3.3A for a minimum operating time of 2 s under external-system-fault conditions.

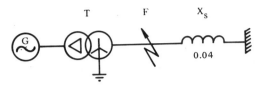

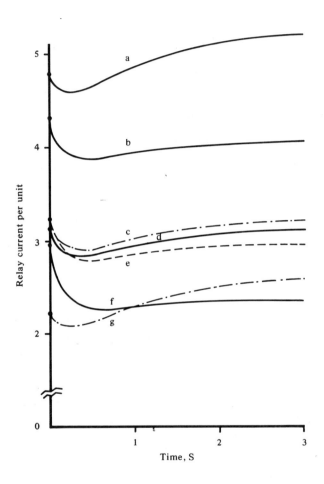

a and g	Phase-to-earth fault
b and e	Phase-to-phase-to-earth fault
c and d	Phase-to-phase fault
f	3-phase fault
– – – –	delta-connected auxiliary current transformers
——	star-connected current transformers

Fig. 12.3.3D   *Variation of relay current for star- and delta-connected current transformers under external-fault conditions*

Table 12.3.3A   *Determination of protection settings and operating times for external h.v. system faults*

Fault	Average current over 2 s from Fig. 12.3.3D (transformer)		P.S.M. on 1.5 p.u. plug setting (transformer)		T.M.S. to give minimum operating time of 2 s (transformer)		Operating time of relay with appropriate t.m.s. setting for various faults (transformer)		Time of n.p.s. relay $1\frac{1}{2}t = 2.5$
	star	delta	star	delta	star	delta	star	delta	
	p.u.	p.u.					s	s	s
3-phase	2.3	2.3	1.54	1.54			5.7	3.4	
Phase-to-phase	3.0	3.1	2.0	2.06		0.2	3.3	2.0	1.6
Phase-to-phase-to-earth	4.0	2.9	2.68	1.93			2.3	2.2	3.1
Phase-to-earth	4.8	2.2	3.2	1.46	0.33		2.0	4.0	5.0

Average values of current are used to illustrate the principle rather than an integration of relay current with time to determine incremental disc travel. This is permissible in this case because the fault-current variation in Fig. 12.3.3D does not give significant differences in relay operating time over the period of interest.

Generator: 500 MW; 588 MVA = 1.0 p.u.

Current transformer: ratio 1000/1A, plug setting 125% = 1250A (865 MVA)

Equivalent plug setting = $\dfrac{865}{588}$ = 1.47, say 1.5 p.u.

It is seen from Table 12.3.3A that a lower time-multiplier setting is possible with the delta-connected current transformers because the effect of the delta connection is to reduce the variations in relay-current level for different types of fault. Thus, with delta-connected current transformers, the maximum operating time for an external fault, using conventional inverse-definite-minimum-time-lag (i.d.m.t.l.) relay characteristics is 4·0 s (for a single phase-to-earth fault), while the maximum operating time with star-connected current transformers is 5·7 (for the 3-phase-fault case). Since longer fault-clearance times can be accepted for single-phase-to-earth faults, the use of delta-connected current transformers seems preferable.

Faults internal to generator: The back-up protection should operate quickly for internal generator faults, since it then provides discriminative tripping in the event of failure of the main protection. Fault currents for an internal fault will usually be higher than those for external-system faults. Fig. 12.3.3E shows the relay-operating-time curves for different types of fault. The curves apply to a simple system which

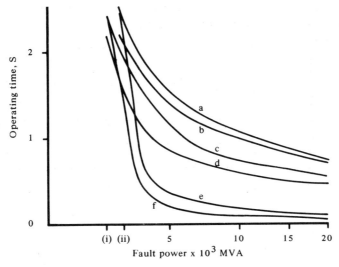

a   Star-connected current transformers: all faults except phase-to-phase
b   Star-connected current transformers: phase-to-phase fault
c   Delta-connected current transformers: phase-to-earth fault
d   Delta-connected current transformers: all faults except
   phase-to-earth
e   Extremely inverse relay characteristic for condition a
f   Extremely inverse relay characteristic for condition d

Note: Curves a—d apply for a conventional i.d.m.t.l. relay to
BS 142: 1966

(i) Maximum external-fault power for delta-connected current
   transformers
(ii) Maximum external-fault power for star-connected current
   transformers

Fig. 12.3.3E   *Relay operating times for generator internal faults fed from h.v. system*

neglects the infeed of the faulted generator and assumes an equivalent system having equal positive-, negative- and zero-sequence infeed at the busbar. For the star-connected current transformers, the infeed from the phase-to-phase fault will be lower than for other faults, while, for delta-connected current transformers, the phase-to-earth fault will give the lower infeed.

It is seen from the curves that the tripping times obtained from the use of delta-connected current transformers are lower because of the lower t.m.s. setting needed for external fault grading.

Fig. 12.3.3E also shows the characteristics of typical extremely inverse overcurrent relays. This type of characteristic gives greatly reduced fault-clearance times at the higher current levels, and, where delta-connected current transformers are used, the back-up-clearance times for faults within the generator could greatly assist in meeting the system-stability requirements.

12.3.4 Negative phase-sequence protection

As previously mentioned, there is a limit to the degree of stator-current unbalance a turboalternator can withstand before it suffers serious rotor overheating. Faults

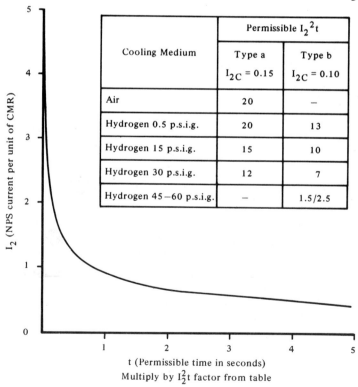

Cooling Medium	Permissible $I_2{}^2 t$	
	Type a $I_{2C} = 0.15$	Type b $I_{2C} = 0.10$
Air	20	–
Hydrogen 0.5 p.s.i.g.	20	13
Hydrogen 15 p.s.i.g.	15	10
Hydrogen 30 p.s.i.g.	12	7
Hydrogen 45–60 p.s.i.g.	–	1.5/2.5

t (Permissible time in seconds)
Multiply by $I_2^2 t$ factor from table

Type (a). Machines without directly cooled rotor copper.
Type (b). Machines with directly cooled rotor copper.

Fig. 12.3.4A   *Negative phase-sequence current capability for modern alternators*

external to the generator are usually cleared quickly by circuit protection, but failure of remote protection to operate, or its associated circuit breaker to trip, would leave the faulted circuit connected to the generator. All faults other than one involving all three phases of the primary system give rise to a system of un-balanced currents which may be resolved into its positive-, negative- and zero-sequence components. By definition, the negative sequence components rotate in a direction contrary to the d.c. field system of the generator. The stator flux thus produced therefore cuts the rotor at *twice* its rotational velocity, thereby inducing double-frequency currents in the field system and rotor body. The resultant eddy

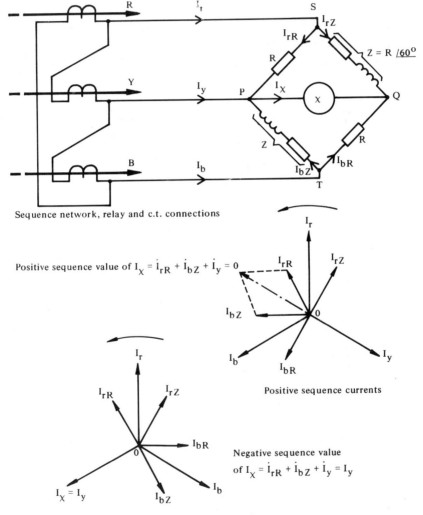

Sequence network, relay and c.t. connections

Positive sequence value of $I_\chi = \dot{I}_{rR} + \dot{I}_{bZ} + \dot{I}_y = 0$

Positive sequence currents

Negative sequence value of $I_\chi = \dot{I}_{rR} + \dot{I}_{bZ} + \dot{I}_y = I_y$

Negative sequence currents. (Relay impedance χ = 0)

Fig. 12.3.4B   *Generator negative phase-sequence protection using simple bridge network*

currents may be very large, so causing severe overheating of the rotor at those points where the circulating eddy current is concentrated by winding slots. To disconnect the machine before damaging temperatures are attained, a negative

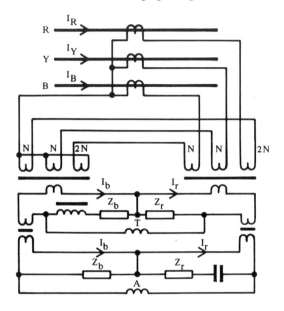

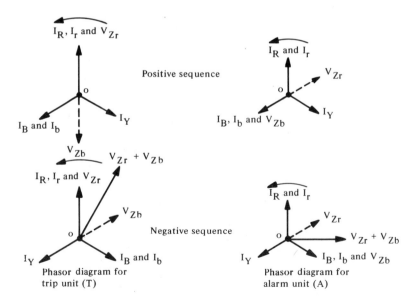

Fig. 12.3.4C *Generator negative phase-sequence relay (General Electric Company Ltd.)*

phase sequence (n.p.s) current measuring relay is applied whose (n.p.s. current)^2 x time characteristic matches that of the machine. The relay is so designed as to give warning when the maximum continuous n.p.s. current rating of the generator is

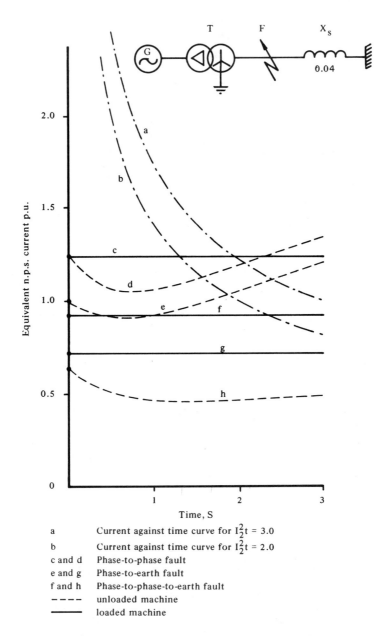

a	Current against time curve for $I_2^2t = 3.0$
b	Current against time curve for $I_2^2t = 2.0$
c and d	Phase-to-phase fault
e and g	Phase-to-earth fault
f and h	Phase-to-phase-to-earth fault
– – – –	unloaded machine
———	loaded machine

Fig. 12.3.4D   *Generator n.p.s-current/time curves for 500 MW generator loaded and unloaded (h.v.. circuit breaker open), including effect of a.v.r.*

exceeded (I_{2c}) and to trip when the value of $(I_2)^2\ t$, where $t < 100$ s exceeds the capability of the generator. Fig. 12.3.4A shows the capabilities of modern British turboalternator sets.

Typical n.p.s. networks are shown in Figs. 12.3.4B, C and D.

The output of the network is proportional to the generator n.p.s. current in each case and is fed into a relay with an inverse square law characteristic. The overall arrangement is matched to the generator n.p.s. current capability curve such that tripping occurs when the curve value is reached. An alarm unit may also be provided with a range of settings to cover the required range of I_{2c}. The required inverse square law characteristic is obtained by use of an appropriately designed

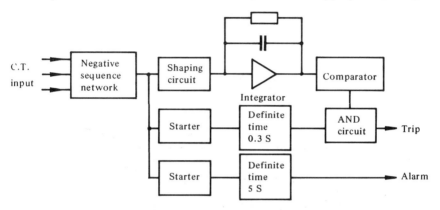

Fig. 12.3.4E *Static n.p.s. relay (Type CTN, GEC Measurements)*

induction disc relay, a thermal replica relay (Fig. 12.3.4C) or a 'static' relay in which the characteristic is shaped by a resistor/Zener diode circuit. (Fig. 12.3.4E)

The settings of the n.p.s. relay are determined by the stator n.p.s. current capability of the generator. Fig. 12.3.4D shows the n.p.s. currents for a typical 500 MW machine for different types of fault condition. The unloaded case (shown dotted) gives lower n.p.s. currents than the loaded case, except for a phase-to-earth fault, and the maximum current, and therefore the minimum operating time, are given for a phase-to-phase fault on a loaded machine. This gives a required tripping time of 1·3 s for $I_2^2 t = 2·0$ and 1·9 s for $I_2^2 t = 3·0$.

12.3.5 Interturn fault protection

The differential current protection described in Section 12.3.1 cannot detect interturn faults which remain clear of earth, since there is a balance of the currents entering and leaving the winding despite the presence of a large current circulating the shorted turns. Interturn faults are not normally protected against because of the technical difficulty of so doing. If interturn faults occur in the stator slots, they quickly develop into faults to earth and are cleared by the stator earth fault protection. There is, however, the possibility that they may occur at the winding ends and so cause extensive damage to the generator before the fault evolves to one detectable by other protection.

12.3.6   Loss of excitation (field failure) protection

Loss of excitation results in a generator losing synchronism and running above synchronous speed. Operating as an induction generator, it would produce its main flux from wattless stator current drawn from the power system to which it was still connected. Excitation under these conditions requires components of reactive current which may well exceed the rating of the generator and so overload the stator

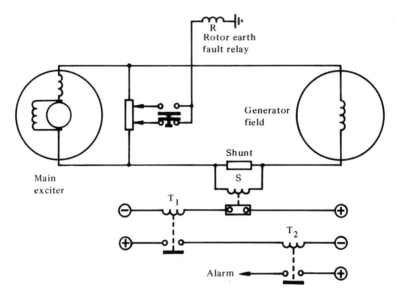

Fig. 12.3.6A   *Generator field failure protection using sensitive relay (Diagram also shows simple rotor E/F scheme)*

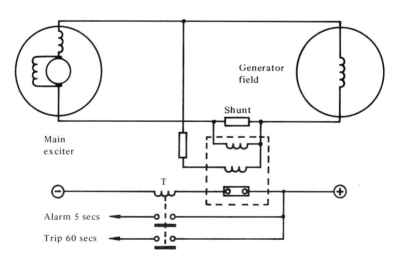

Fig. 12.3.6B   *Generator field failure protection using underpower relay*

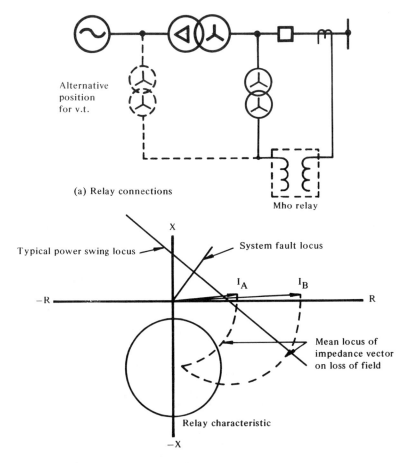

(a) Relay connections

Mho relay

(b) Relay characteristic showing mean locus of input
impedance at generator terminals under loss of excitation
conditions. N.B. Effects of rotor saliency not included.

I_A – Lagging current (heavy load)
I_B – Lagging current (light load)

Fig. 12.3.6C *Loss of excitation protection using offset impedance measuring relay at generator terminals*

winding. Additionally the slip frequency currents induced in the damper windings
of the rotor would cause abnormal heating of the rotor.

Operation as an induction generator does not, therefore, damage the set immediately, but, as the higher ratings of modern machines are obtained by advanced
cooling techniques rather than increased frame size, the short thermal time constants
require the machine to be deloaded and tripped in a matter of seconds.

Fig. 12.3.6A illustrates a method commonly used to provide field failure and
rotor earth-fault protection on the smaller generators of a decade ago. The relay

combination operates when the field current is zero (or cyclically passing through a zero during asynchronous running) and trips or alarms after a predetermined time delay set on relay T_2.

An alternative method employed a d.c. underpower relay in the field circuit as shown in Fig. 12.3.6B. This relay is responsive to power flow and is held inoperative by the normal flow of current from the main exciter to the field windings. Should the power fall below a certain level, or reverse its direction (due to induced a.c. at slip frequency) the relay contacts would close after a time lag to give an alarm.

As modern large generators may be required to operate with very low values of excitation, both of the above schemes would be unsuitable. When a generator loses synchronism, the quantity which changes most is its impedance as measured at the stator terminals. Loss of field will cause the terminal voltage of the generator to begin to fall, while the current begins to increase. The apparent impedance of the machine will therefore be seen to decrease and its power factor to change. A relay designed to detect the change of impedance from the normal load value may therefore be used to provide protection against asynchronous operation resulting from the loss of excitation (Fig. 12.3.6C).

12.3.7 Protection against pole-slipping

Generally speaking, pole-slipping protection was not provided on earlier, small machines but on larger, modern sets, the severe mechanical torque oscillations accompanying pole slipping conditions require prompt action to be taken if damage to the generating plant is to be prevented and power-system disturbance minimised. Pole-slipping conditions do not normally occur for system faults correctly cleared by high speed main protection

Pole slipping, either between generators and the system, or between two sections of the system, results in a flow of synchronising power, which reverses in direction twice every slip cycle. When displayed in the complex impedance plane, this flow of synchronising power is characterised by a cyclic change in the effective load impedance V/I as measured at the terminals of the two asynchronous systems and the load impedance locus passes between the +R and −R quadrants as the real power flow reverses in direction. The transition point on the jX axis corresponds approximately to the instant when the two systems are 180° out of phase (assuming the load impedances are largely reactive). At this instant only reactive power is flowing and the system voltage collapses to zero at the electrical midpoint of the two systems. This midpoint is the centre about which pole-slipping can be considered to be taking place and its location, with respect to the relaying point, can be determined from the apparent load impedance to the point where the locus crosses the jX axis. The load impedances seen from the terminals of individual generators either side of the pole-slipping centre will depend on their respective contributions to the total synchronising power flowing at any instant. Measurement of the magnitude, direction and rate of change of load impedance relative to a generator's terminals provides a convenient and generally reliable means of detecting whether pole

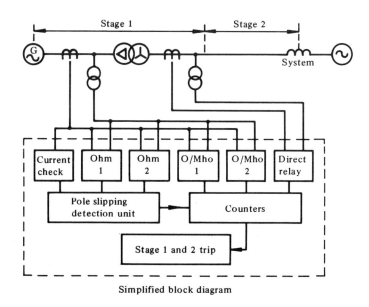

Simplified block diagram

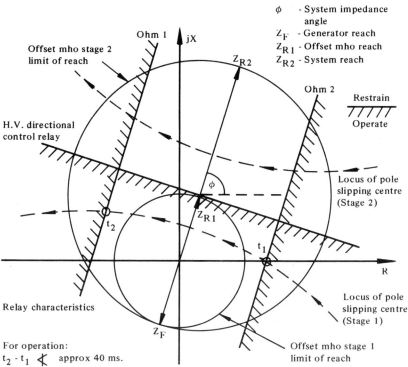

Fig. 12.3.7A *Offset mho type pole slipping protection (GEC Measurements Ltd.)*

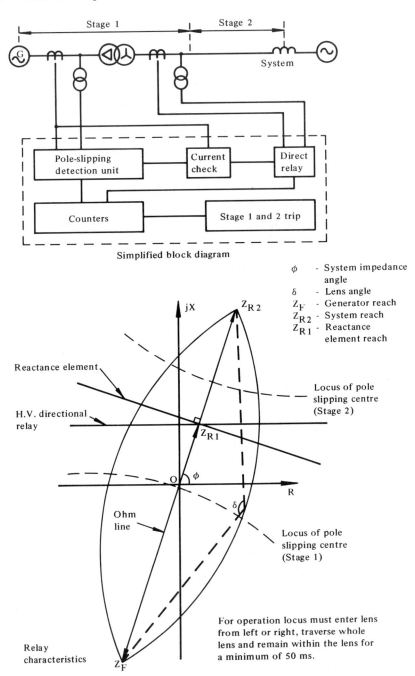

Simplified block diagram

ϕ - System impedance angle
δ - Lens angle
Z_F - Generator reach
Z_{R2} - System reach
Z_{R1} - Reactance element reach

For operation locus must enter lens from left or right, traverse whole lens and remain within the lens for a minimum of 50 ms.

Fig. 12.3.7B   *Lenticular type pole slipping protection (Brown Boveri)*

slipping is taking place. Individual generators, generally those on the side of the larger system, although contributing synchronising power will not see a pole slipping centre (i.e. their impedance loci will not cross the jX axis) if their real power output remains positive, but care needs to be exercised in designing and setting pole-slipping protection based on load impedance measurement if satisfactory discrimination is to be obtained.

The pole-slipping detection relays are connected to c.t.s and v.t.s on the l.v. side of the generator transformer and the directional control relay to c.t.s and v.t.s fitted on the h.v. side of the transformer. Schematic diagrams of two manufacturer's schemes are illustrated in Fig. 12.3.7A and B.

In both cases, the protection is of the impedance-measuring type, having two stages:

Stage 1 reaching through the generator to the neutral point and into the transformer to cover the entire winding as far as, but not beyond, the h.v. terminals (the directional control relay inhibiting operation if the system centre occurs beyond the transformer h.v. terminals).; and

Stage 2 operating after an adjustable number of pole slips, whether the system centre is within the generator transformer unit or out on the system.

The pole-slipping relays are capable of detecting the first pole-slip condition when a slip, corresponding to the speed of pole-slipping is in the range ±0·1% to ±10% on a 50 Hz basis. The protection must, of course, remain unoperated for steady state loading, power swinging and correctly cleared system fault conditions, although some of its component relays may operate.

12.3.8   Rotor earth-fault protection

Two methods are available for the detection of earth faults in the rotor circuit. One method utilises a high resistance connected across the rotor circuit, the centre point of which is connected to earth through the coil of a sensitive relay (Fig. 12.3.6A). This relay will detect earth faults over most of the rotor circuit. There is, however, a blind spot at the centre point of the field winding which is at equipotential with the midpoint of the resistor under earth-fault conditions. This blind spot can be examined by arranging a tapping switch which, when operated, shifts the relay connection from the centre of the resistor to a point a little to one side. Alternatively, one half of the resistor can be replaced by a nonlinear resistor which, since it will change its value for different values of rotor voltage, will continuously vary the effective resistor tapping voltage as the field conditions change. This method has been used in the USA.

A second method utilises a small power pack connected to the positive pole of the field circuit, in series with which is connected the fault detecting relay and a high resistance (Fig. 12.3.8A). A fault at any point in the field system will pass a current of sufficient magnitude through the relay to cause operation. The field winding earth-fault relays are usually instantaneous in operation and are connected

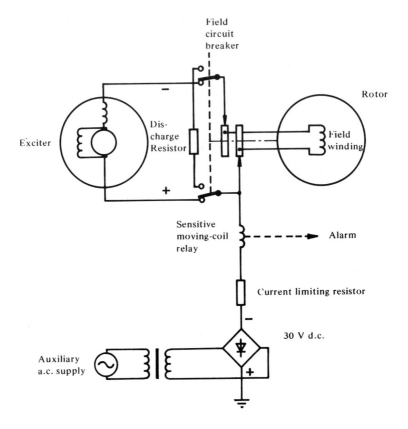

Fig. 12.3.8A   *Rotor earth-fault detection using negative-potential biasing device*

for alarm only as there is no immediate danger to the set. This device is similar in principle to the battery negative biasing device referred to in Section 7.2.

It will be seen that with both of these schemes the earth return path is through the body of the rotor. Since, however, the contact between rotor and stator is through the bearing oil film which is non- (or intermittently) conducting, it is essential to earth the rotor shaft by an additional earthed brush. This also serves the essential purpose of discharging static electricity induced in the turbine rotor by steam friction, thereby preventing the bearing surfaces from pitting.

In some modern machines the traditional direct current exciter is replaced by an alternator with a rotating armature, the field winding of the main generator being supplied through rectifiers carried on the rotor, and a 'brushless' design is thereby achieved. The inaccessibility of the main d.c. field circuit makes direct detection of rotor earth-faults impossible.

The single earth-fault (or diode open circuit) would produce little change in the level of excitation. A more severe interturn fault (or diode short circuit) would, in all probability, tend to cause abnormal vibration of the set and a vibration detector is sometimes employed to initiate deloading and tripping. The diodes are themselves protected by fuses and a fuse failure protection relay is normally included.

12.3.9   Sensitive power protection

Reverse power protection has in the past been fitted to detect failure of the prime mover (that is the engine or turbine) which it does by measuring the power drawn from the system by the generator when it is motoring.

The power taken by the generator under such conditions is very low, being from about 10% for engine driven sets to 2% for turboalternators. The power factor of the current depends, of course, upon the excitation level and may thus be either leading or lagging. The wattmetric relay must, therefore, be highly sensitive and have an accurate quadrature adjustment. It must also be connected as a 'true' wattmeter and not be fitted with phase angle or low voltage compensation, as are directional relays for fault power applications.

The wattmetric relay must be associated with a time lag relay to prevent operation due to power swings.

12.3.10   Low forward power interlock

A more recent application of a sensitive power relay is on large modern alternators where it is desirable to delay tripping of the electrical load on the generator until after the steam has been tripped, so that the steam entrained in the turbine is used in supplying electrical power rather than causing the set to overspeed, that is the generator acts as a 'brake'. This feature is only provided for 'non-urgent' tripping conditions. The contact of the wattmetric relay is associated with a time lag relay whose contact is connected in series with the 'non-urgent' tripping contacts, and with this arrangement the generator is not allowed to trip until the power output of the generator falls below a small preset value. (Fig. 12.3.13A).

Operation of the relay at low levels of forward power permits full protection during run up and prior to synchronising, since the relay contacts will be closed during this period.

To provide the highest degree of security under all conditions the relay contacts are arranged to close when the generated power falls to 0·5% of full load output. Such an accurate setting requires the current and voltage transformers to be of high accuracy. Two relays are normally used and have their contacts connected in parallel.

The generator internal fault tripping devices (for example differential protection, etc.) are arranged to trip independently of this sensitive power interlock.

An alternative method of preventing the electrical tripping of a generator until after its steam supply had been cut off was to use a pressure operated switch connected into a suitable point on the turbine. The setting of such a switch had to be not appreciably higher than the no-load steam pressure and the contacts were set to be on the point of opening under no-load conditions.

Two pressure switches with parallel connected contacts were sometimes used to give additional safeguard against mechanical failure. A time delay relay was associated with the pressure switch so that transient overshoot of the switch would not permit tripping of the generator circuit breaker under unsafe conditions.

The method was recommended only for non-reheat machines in view of the additional complications where reheat is used. In the case of reheat machines, three possible contingencies must be guarded against:

(*a*)   failure to close of the main steam supply valves
(*b*)   failure to close of the valves after the reheater, and
(*c*)   failure of both sets of valves.

Two series-connected pressure switches were required to cover these contingencies; one operated by the pressure difference across the h.p. cylinder, and the other by the pressure at some point in the turbine down-stream of the reheat valves. In view of these additional complications the use of pressure switches is not now recommended for reheat machines.

12.3.11   Overspeed protection

It is essential for the governing system of a turbine generator to incorporate safety devices to prevent dangerous overspeeding. The importance of these devices is such that routine testing facilities should be included to check the correct functioning of the valve gear on normal load, and normal operating procedure should verify the operation of all safety devices prior to going on load and after removal of load before shut down.

Most large turbines are now fitted with overspeed limiting gear designed to detect sudden loss of load and to close emergency valves immediately, to limit the magnitude of the temporary speed rise.

In a typical scheme this is achieved by monitoring the electrical output of the generator using a wattmetric relay. This relay will detect a sudden loss of output and operate instantaneously to close its contacts. A second relay monitors the steam input to the turbines at a chosen stage and the contacts are held closed when the steam pressure is in the full load region.

A sudden loss of load will give instantaneous operation of the output relay but the steam input relay does not operate immediately because steam is being admitted to and expanding in the turbine. Under this condition the emergency valve solenoids are energised giving instantaneous control of steam admission. The emergency valves remain closed until falling pressure or restoration of load restores the machines to normal control.

The action of this equipment is clearly much faster than that obtainable from the governing system which requires an actual overspeed to produce a response and take corrective action. It is for this reason that overspeed limiting equipment of the type described is often installed where reheat turbines are used, because the long steam pipes of relatively large bore interconnecting each reheater and the reheat sections of the associated boiler plant present special problems due to the large volume of steam entrained.

The overspeed limiting equipment then operates additionally into the interceptor emergency stop valves associated with each interceptor steam chest to give instantaneous control of the steam entering the turbine at all stages.

In the ultimate, overspeeding of the machine beyond the safe limit (10%) will cause operation of the overspeed bolts, and shut the stop valves.

12.3.12 Underexcitation limiting

The operating characteristics of a cylindrical rotor a.c. generator feeding an interconnected system are such that a definite positive minimum of rotor excitation must be maintained to ensure synchronous stability.

From the design criteria this limit can be described and is usually termed the 'theoretical stability limit'. To guarantee stability in service a safety margin is added to the theoretical limit to make a 'practical stability limit'.

If the control of excitation is by manual adjustment the operating point of the generator is usually maintained by observation and adjustment within an area bounded by the practical stability limit in the leading (underexcited) reactive zone, the stator and rotor heating limits in the lagging (overexcited) zone, the kW limit being set by the turbine capacity or steam conditions.

When an automatic voltage regulator is employed to control excitation, measures must be taken to ensure that excitation is not reduced below a safe limit. This limit will depend upon the form of voltage regulator and will correspond to the practical stability limit for most electromechanical regulators, but may approach the theoretical stability limit for regulators having no dead band and a high speed of response. If the level of excitation approaches the limit a subsidiary control loop is employed to feed a modifying signal into the automatic voltage regulator control loop to prevent further lowering, and in certain cases, to raise excitation in addition to giving an alarm.

The initiating signal for the under excitation limiting device may be taken from a measure of rotor angle, or of rotor excitation current, or of a derivation of the generator operating point from a measure of watts, revs and terminal voltage.

12.3.13 Mechanical and hydraulic trips

In addition to the electrical protection discussed earlier in the chapter, various mechanical and hydraulic devices are employed to detect abnormalities in the turbine and its boiler. Some of the devices intiate alarms to the operator, and these are not dealt with here, but others trip the unit automatically and so, to illustrate complete protection of a modern, large, turbo-generator, they have been included in Fig. 12.3.13A.

(*a*) *Local turbine trip level:* a grab-handle on the turbine pillar enabling an

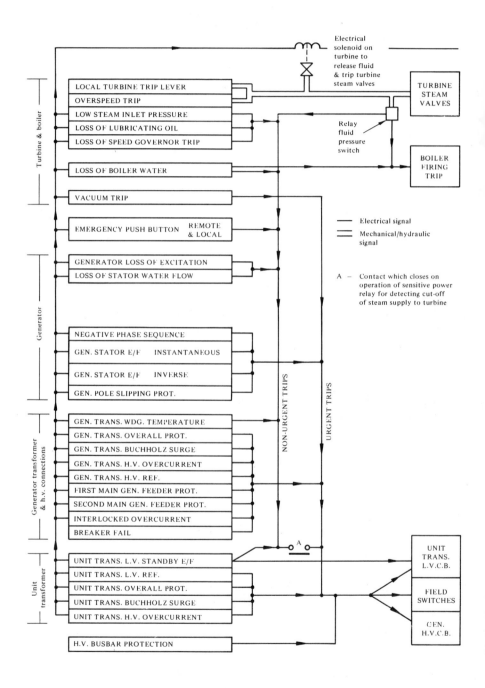

Fig. 12.3.13A   *Tripping logic for a modern large turbogenerator*

attendant to shut-down the set locally should the need arise.

(*b*)   *Overspeed trip:* a centrifugal device initiating tripping if the turbine speed rises 10% above the synchronous speed.

(*c*)   *Low steam inlet pressure:* a device sensing loss of turbine steam pressure due to loss of boiler firing.

(*d*)   *Loss of lubricating oil:* an oil-pressure device monitoring the supply of lubricating oil to the turbine bearings.

(*e*)   *Loss of boiler water:* a water-level detector initiating boiler firing tripping to prevent extensive damage being done to the boiler tubing due to overheating.

(*f*)   *Vacuum trip:* independent vacuum-operated unloading control and tripping devices. The control progressively reduces the steam flow into the turbine as the vacuum falls over a predetermined range, but if the vacuum falls below a pre-determined minimum value a vacuum operated switch initiates tripping.

(*g*)   *Emergency push button:* operation of an emergency push button initiates tripping of the turbine steam valves. The remaining main plant will trip via the low power interlock contact A.

To enchance the integrity of modern turbogenerator protection tripping, the trip-initiating devices are divided between several, independent d.c. tripping supplies, typically, as follows:

H.V. switchgear, first supply
   Busbar protection
   Generator feeder, first main protection relay 1
   Interlocked overcurrent relay
   Generator transformer h.v. overcurrent relay

H.V. switchgear, second supply
   Breaker fail protection
   Generator feeder, second main protection relay 1

Power station, first supply
   Generator feeder, first main protection relay 2
   Unit transformer overall protection
   Unit transformer Buchholz surge
   Generator stator E/F relay (instantaneous, low resistance)
   Generator transformer overall protection

Negative phase-sequence protection
Generator transformer Buchholz surge
Generator transformer winding temperature trip
Emergency push button
Generator stator E/F relay (1st i.d.m.t., high resistance)
Loss of excitation protection
Loss of vacuum trip
Low steam inlet pressure trip
Unit transformer l.v. standby E/F
Pole-slipping protection
Loss of stator water flow
Loss of lubricating oil
Loss of speed governor trip
Loss of boiler water

Power station, second supply
Generator feeder, second main protection relay 2
Unit transformer l.v. restricted E/F
Unit transformer h.v. overcurrent
Generator stator E/F relay (2nd i.d.m.t., high resistance)
Generator stator E/F relay (i.d.m.t., low resistance)
Generator transformer, h.v. restricted E/F
Negative phase-sequence protection

12.4   Gas-turbine driven generators

12.4.1   Direct connected, gas-turbine sets

At all modern power stations in the United Kingdom, gas-turbine powered generators have been installed to provide:

(a)   an independent supply to the auxiliaries of the main steam driven units in the event of unacceptably low frequency on the grid system

(b)   additional generation into the grid system if required by system conditions

(c)   start-up supplies to a station detached from the grid system

(d)   independent supply to ensure operation of essential drives, e.g. main bearing lubricating oil in the event of loss of normal supplied. This duty is, in effect, a back-up to the d.c. battery system.

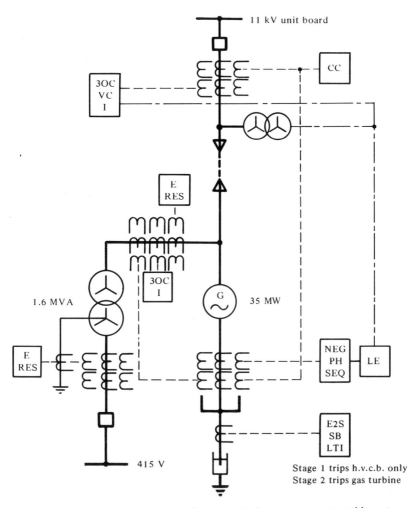

Fig. 12.4.1A *Protective relay a.c. circuits for power station emergency gas-turbine set*

Fig. 12.4.1A shows the protection of a 35 MW, 11kV generator and its connections (but not the gas-turbine). It comprises:

differential current protection covering the generator and its outgoing connections
loss of excitation protection
standby earth-fault protection (2 stages)
     – stage 1 trips the h.v. circuit breaker only
     – stage 2 trips gas-turbine
voltage-controlled overcurrent protection
negative phase-sequence protection

The teed unit transformer and its h.v. connections are protected by overcurrent and restricted earth-fault relays.

12.4.2   Transformer connected, gas-turbine sets

The functions of main gas-turbine generating plant are to provide:

(*a*)   Normal, economic generation close to load centres, giving added security to load demand by reducing its dependence on remote generation and its associated transmission system

(*b*)   Emergency generation at times when severe system disturbances cause a local generation deficit

(*c*)   Peak-lopping capacity for system frequency regulation purposes, thereby reducing the amount of national spinning reserve required

(*d*)   Reactive compensation whilst running on load, or synchronous compensation (with clutch disengaged).

Typically gas-turbine sets are each of 70 MW capacity powered by either two 35 MW or four 17·5 MW power turbines (Fig. 12.4.2A). The protection arrangement and tripping logic are illustrated in Figs. 12.4.2B and 12.4.2C respectively. A particular point of interest in Fig. 12.4.2B is the absence of biased differential c.t.s in the unit transformer tee-off connections. In this case the low rating (high impedance) of the unit transformer limits through fault currents on the 415 volt system to a value well below the differential protection fault setting.

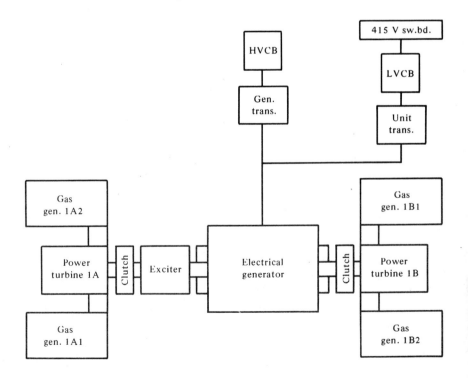

Fig. 12.4.2A   *Key diagram of gas-turbine generator*

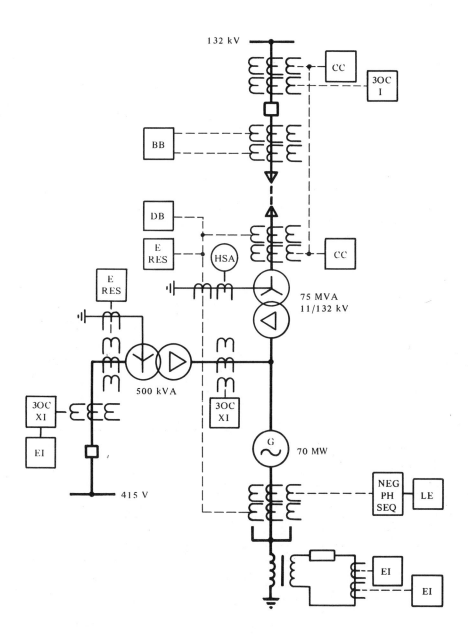

Fig. 12.4.2B *Protective relay a.c. circuits for main gas-turbine generator unit*

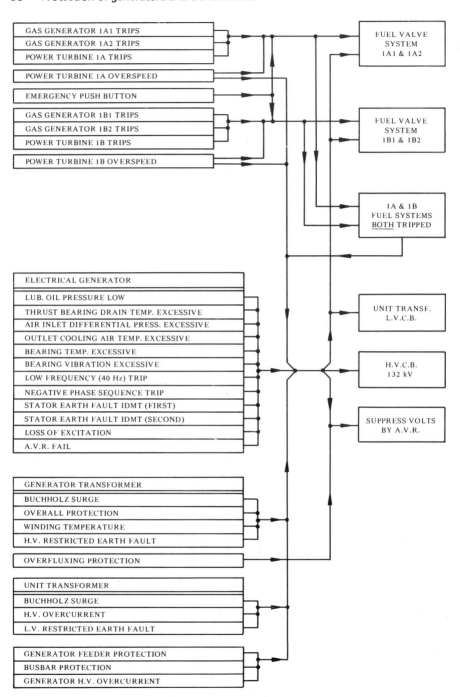

Fig. 12.4.2C *Protection tripping logic for main gas-turbine generator*

12.5   Transformer protection

The protection provided for a power transformer depends to some extent upon its size and rating, and will comprise a number of systems each designed to provide the requisite degree of protection for the different fault conditions outlined in Section 12.2.2. For large units high speed protection is essential.

12.5.1   Unbiased differential protection

The unbiased differential overall transformer protection system is similar in principle to that for a generator. In this case, however, the differential protection system compares h.v. and l.v. currents, which are in a known relationship under healthy conditions, rather than the same current entering and leaving the protected apparatus, as for generator protection. It is for this reason that the transformer differential protection system is capable of detecting interturn short circuits since these change the effective overall transformation ratio of the power transformers.

The c.t. connections must be arranged to give a through fault balance taking into account the transformer vector group reference with respect to windings, connections, and turns ratio. The guiding principles in establishing c.t. connections are that (*a*) zero-sequence currents should be eliminated from or correctly compensated in the relay circuits since, almost invariably, the transformer connections will not permit transformation of zero-sequence currents, and (*b*) the phase shift due to the through transformation of positive and negative-sequence currents must be correctly compensated.

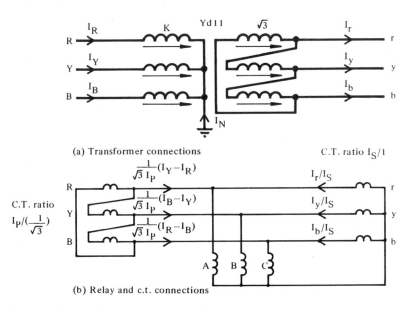

(a) Transformer connections

C.T. ratio $I_S/1$

(b) Relay and c.t. connections

Fig. 12.5.1A   *Overall differential protection of star/delta power transformer*

The elimination of zero-sequence currents from the relay circuits is usually achieved by associating a delta c.t. connection with a star connected transformer winding.

Considering the typical example of a star-delta transformer (Fig. 12.5.1A) having a star/delta voltage transformation ratio of $K:1$, then the line currents on the delta side I_r, I_y and I_b are

$$I_r = \frac{K}{\sqrt{3}} (I_R - I_Y)$$

$$I_y = \frac{K}{\sqrt{3}} (I_Y - I_B)$$

$$I_b = \frac{K}{\sqrt{3}} (I_B - I_R)$$

when I_R, I_Y and I_B are the line currents on the star side. Balance is therefore obtained using star connected c.t.s on the delta side of the transformer and delta connected c.t.s on the star side of the transformer, as shown in Fig. 12.5.1A, since with turns ratio $K: \sqrt{3}$ and $I_S = KI_P$

$$\frac{I_r}{I_S} = \frac{1}{\sqrt{3}I_p} (I_y - I_R) \text{ etc.}$$

If similar reasoning is applied to the transformer and earthing transformer combination of Fig. 12.5.1B, the following relations are obtained

$$\frac{K}{\sqrt{3}} (I_R - I_Y) = I_r - \frac{I_n}{3}$$

$$\frac{K}{\sqrt{3}} (I_Y - I_B) = I_y - \frac{I_n}{3}$$

$$\frac{K}{\sqrt{3}} (I_B - I_R) = I_b - \frac{I_n}{3}$$

which shows that through fault balance is obtained by the addition of neutral c.t.s to the delta side of the transformer, as shown in Fig. 12.5.1B. It will be noted that the additional neutral c.t.s have a ratio which is three times that of the star connected c.t.s in the delta side of the power transformer.

In Figs. 12.5.1A and B, I_P and I_S are, respectively, the primary and secondary winding rated currents.

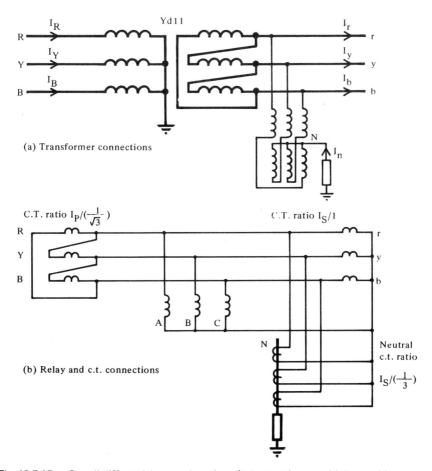

(a) Transformer connections

(b) Relay and c.t. connections

Fig. 12.5.1B *Overall differential protection of star/delta transformer with l.v. earthing transformer*

The effect of tap changing equipment upon the overall transformer ratio must also be borne in mind in the application of a differential protection system. This, in effect, changes the ratio of the transformer according to tap position so that a differential protection system using a fixed c.t. ratio cannot give adequate balance. The unbalance current resulting from inaccurate matching of transformer and c.t. ratio will increase in magnitude as the through current increases, so that, for example, a ratio difference producing 15% spill current at rated load will give rise to a spill current of 150% for a through fault of 10 times rated load. An unbiased high speed relay would require a fault setting in excess of this if stability is to be achieved under through fault conditions. In practice, for optimum performance, the c.t.s ratios are based on the transformer turns ratio at the mid-tap position.

An inverse time lag relay is used for unbiased differential protection systems, often in conjunction with a high set instantaneous relay operating at a higher level than the maximum through current spill. The relay current and time settings are adjusted so that it will grade correctly with back-up protection under maximum unbalance conditions. Where both the inverse and high set relays are employed typical current settings are 50% for the inverse time lag relay and 600% for the high set relay.

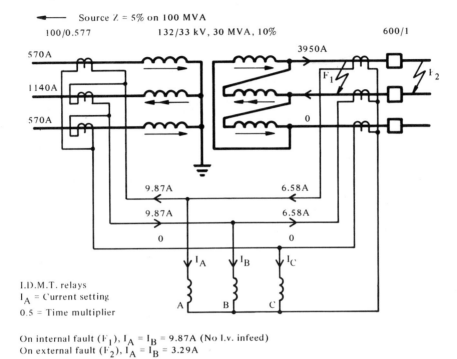

Fig. 12.5.1C   *Rough-balance system of transformer differential protection showing relay currents under internal and external fault conditions*

An interesting extension of this system is the 'rough balance' protection, in which the h.v. and l.v. c.t. ratios are deliberately mismatched. The induction pattern relay thus provides low speed differential protection and also a more positive measure of back-up protection for external fault conditions.

A typical application of the scheme is shown in Fig. 12.5.1C.

Where high-speed protection is required with a low fault setting it is essential to use a percentage bias relay to overcome the unbalance current effects due to tap changing.

12.5.2   Biased differential protection

In protecting power transformers equipped with on load tap changing facilities the overall differential protection must incorporate a bias feature if a low fault setting and high operating speed are to be obtained. For smaller transformers the percentage differential (biased) induction-disc relay depicted in Fig. 12.5.2A gives

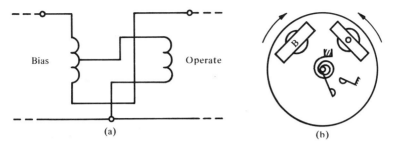

Fig. 12.5.2A   *Induction-type biased-differential relay for overall transformer, generator or generator/transformer protection*

some improvement on the unbiased schemes described in the previous Section, but is slow in operation. With the larger and more important transformers, the relay current and time settings necessary to ensure stability on the magnetising inrush currents produced by switching in the transformer are inadequate to provide high-speed protection.

A high speed biased differential relay incorporating a harmonic restraint feature will prevent relay operation under magnetising inrush current conditions. A typical oscillogram of transformer magnetising inrush currents is shown in Fig. 12.5.2B, the initial peak value of the inrush current in any phase depending on such factors as the instant of switching, and the magnetic condition of the core. Maximum peak values equal to 6-8 times the rated current of the transformer can occur. Insofar as inrush current affects the operation of transformer differential protection relays two aspects are of significance. First, that this current flows in one winding only of

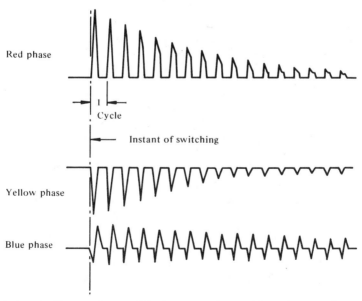

Fig. 12.5.2B   *Oscillogram of magnetising-inrush currents on a three-phase transformer*

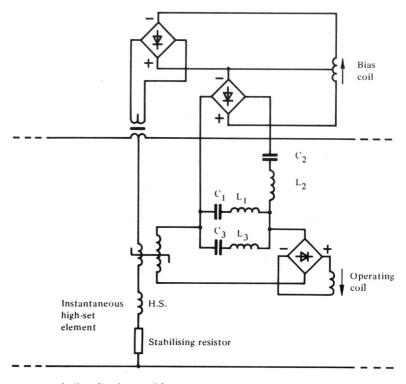

L_1C_1 = Fundamental frequency acceptor circuit

L_2C_2 = Second harmonic acceptor circuit

L_3C_3 = Third harmonic acceptor circuit

Fig. 12.5.2C   *GEC biased-differential transformer protection with harmonic restraint feature (only one phase shown)*

the power transformer (the winding being energised) and therefore appears to the protection as an internal fault condition. Second, that this current differs from an internal fault current insofar as its wave form comprises a high percentage of harmonics. Of these, the second harmonic has particular prominence under all 'switching in' conditions, as Fig. 12.5.2B shows.

It thus follows that a relay designed to detect the second harmonic component in the magnetising inrush current can be made to utilise this as a means of discrimination between internal fault currents and magnetising inrush conditions. This is achieved by the use of a second-harmonic filter which is arranged to inject an additional bias current in the relay circuit proportional to the second-harmonic component. Typical arrangements of practical schemes are shown in Figs. 12.5.2C and 12.5.2D.

In Fig. 12.5.2C, the harmonic restraint feature is added to each phase separately,

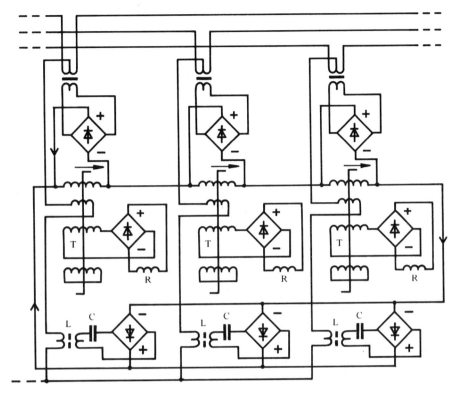

LC = Second harmonic restraint circuit
T   = Transductor
R   = Relay

Fig. 12.5.2D *Reyrolle 'Duobias' biased differential transformer protection with harmonic restraint feature*

as shown, whereas in Fig. 12.5.2D a transductor relay is used with the harmonic restraint derived from all three phases and used to bias all three transductors.

A sensitive relay element is essential to reduce c.t. burdens to a minimum, and modern harmonic restrained relays utilise a sensitive moving coil or transductor type relay as the basic comparator. Typical current settings for biased differential transformer protection relays are 50-100% for the low-speed induction-disc relay and 20-30% for the harmonic restraint relays. In both cases a range from 10-40% is usually provided for the through current bias.

12.5.3   Restricted earth-fault protection

The difficulties inherent in the provision of an adequate earth fault sensitivity in the overall differential protection system often require that restricted earth-fault protection should be added to both windings of the transformer. Separate c.t.s can

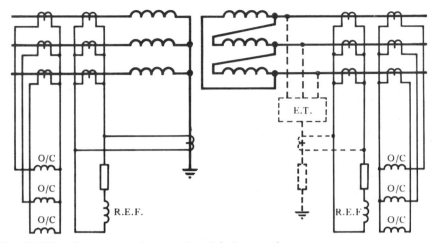

Fig. 12.5.3A   *Overcurrent and restricted earth-fault protection*

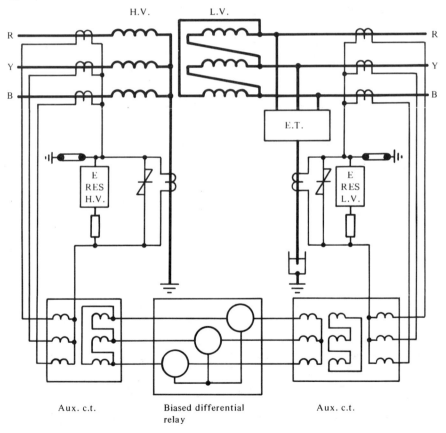

Fig. 12.5.3B   *C.T. circuit diagram for combined biased differential and restricted earth-fault protection*

be used for this purpose, as shown in Fig. 12.5.3A, or the restricted earth-fault protection may be operated from the c.t.s associated with the overall differential protection. A typical arrangement is shown in Fig. 12.5.3B.

It will be seen that compensation for the power transformers h.v./l.v. star delta connection is achieved by a similar star/delta connection of the auxiliary c.t. associated with the h.v., c.t.s. The star/delta/star auxiliary c.t. associated with the l.v., c.t.s provides the four-wire connection of the line c.t.s (necessary to connect with the l.v. neutral c.t. to give l.v.. restricted earth-fault protection) whilst eliminating the zero sequence components of l.v. earth-fault current from the three-wire connection required by the phase fault differential relay. Ratio correction for a mismatch of h.v. and l.v. line c.t. ratios may be accommodated in either, or both, sets of auxiliary c.t.s. For solidly earthed, star-connected transformer windings, an effective setting of greater than 50% but less than 100% of rated current is usually specified. For transformer delta windings connected to resistance earthed systems, the setting specified should lie between 20 and 25% of the neutral resistor current setting.

12.5.4 Overcurrent protection

The degree of protection afforded by an overcurrent relay of the i.d.m.t. type is somewhat limited when applied to a transformer. Since the relay must not operate under emergency loading conditions it requires a high current setting (often about 200% rating). Also, the time setting may have to be high in order to grade with other overcurrent relays on the system. Clearly overcurrent relays provide negligible protection for faults inside the transformer tank, and may be very slow even for terminal faults where high fault currents are involved.

On large transformers, therefore, overcurrent relays are usually employed only as back-up protection for terminal faults, or uncleared l.v. system faults. In such cases the overcurrent relays may be installed on one or both sides of the transformer, according to requirements. Moreover the relays may trip only the side of the transformer with which they are associated, or they may trip both.

Two-stage overcurrent protection is sometimes employed instead of separate i.d.m.t. overcurrent on both sides of a transformer. The two-stage scheme comprises one i.d.m.t. overcurrent relay and one time-lag relay. The i.d.m.t. relay is usually energised from current transformers on the h.v. side of the transformer, the source of infeed. Operation of this relay trips the l.v. breaker and starts the time-lag relay. The latter requires a time setting, say 0·3 sec., so that it does not operate before the l.v . breaker trips. If the fault persists the time-lag relay completes its operation and trips the h.v. breaker. Since the contacts of most i.d.m.t. relays have a long reset time it is usually necessary to connect in series with them the contact of an instantaneous overcurrent element which has a high speed of reset, so that the time-lag relay is de-energised as soon as the fault is cleared. The instantaneous elements would have the same current setting range, and prescribed setting as the i.d.m.t. relay. The advantages of two-stage overcurrent protection are mainly economic, the chief saving being the cost of a set of three current transformers.

A disadvantage of this arrangement is, however, that it does not provide discriminative back up protection for faults on the transformer l.v. connections. Frequently, supergrid transformers have their l.v. connections separately protected by differential protection (Fig. 12.6.4B) but if this protection should fail to operate correctly, the two stage, h.v. overcurrent protection on the transformers feeding the l.v. system would operate and randomly trip their l.v. breakers. If however each transformer is equipped with l.v. overcurrent protection, breaker tripping would be discriminative since individual l.v. system infeeds would aggregate in the overcurrent protection of the faulted transformer to give it fastest operation.

12.5.5   Directional overcurrent protection

Directional overcurrent relays may be used to provide discriminative phase fault protection for two parallel transformers where there is no l.v. source infeed. Where an l.v. source infeed exists care must be taken to ensure correct discrimination for faults on the h.v. system external to the transformers.

An analysis of the various fault conditions on transformer circuits shows that the $(90° - 45°)$ arrangement obtained with a $90°$ connection of a $45°$ relay gives best discrimination. Fig. 12.5.5A shows the basic connections for the directional overcurrent relay, and Fig. 12.5.5B illustrates the performance of the relay under phase-fault conditions. The circuit diagram illustrates the current flow in the

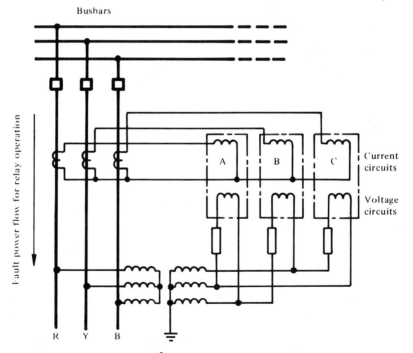

Fig. 12.5.5A   *Relay connections (90°) for directional overcurrent protection*

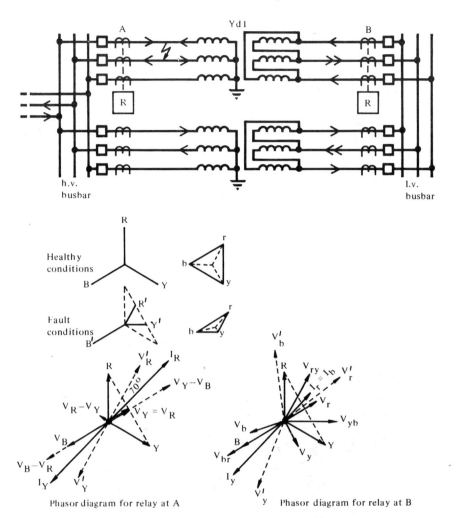

$V_R V_Y V_B$ = Star side voltages

$V'_R V'_Y V'_B$ = Star side relay coil voltages (not to scale)

$I_R I_Y$ = Star side fault (and relay) currents

$V_r V_y V_b$ = Delta side voltages

$V'_r V'_y V'_b$ = Delta side relay coil voltages (not to scale)

$I_r I_y I_b$ = Delta side fault (and relay) currents

Assumed fault impedance angle = 70°

Fig. 12.5.5B *Use of 90° connection of 45° relay for parallel transformers showing fault performance*

parallel transformers and the phasor diagrams for the primary system voltages under both the healthy and the faulty conditions are shown separately.

From a study of the phasor diagrams for the relays at A and B, it is seen that the use of the $(90° -45°)$ arrangement gives positive operating torque for the relays on all three phases of the faulty circuit; it being assumed that positive torque occurs when the angle between the relay coil voltage and the relay current is within the range of $+90°$ to $-90°$. On the healthy circuit the currents are in the opposite direction, and it is clear that all three relays will restrain in this case. If a similar study is made for relays using the $30°$ connection (see Chapter 8) it is found that one of the end B relays on the healthy circuit will operate incorrectly, thereby causing tripping of the healthy circuit, and one of the relays on the faulty circuit will restrain when it should in fact operate.

Directional overcurrent protection is also fitted to the l.v. side of transformer feeders to detect reverse flow of current through the transformer, such as will occur for h.v. feeder faults. Typical applications are discussed under transformer feeder protection (Section 12.9).

Directional overcurrent protection cannot normally be applied where generation exists on the l.v. side of the power transformer since reverse load flow is possible under healthy system conditions. In such cases, however, the directional element of the relay can be arranged to have an additional voltage restraint feature such that relay operation only occurs for reverse current flow associated with a voltage collapse denoting a fault condition.

12.5.6   Interlocked overcurrent protection

Where for economic reasons it is necessary to locate the protective current transformers on one side of the circuit breaker only, a fault occurring between the circuit breaker and its associated current transformer may not be adequately guarded against.

In Fig. 12.5.6A, for example, a fault occurring at point F is detected by the busbar protection which trips the circuit breaker. It is clear, therefore, that the fault will not be disconnected, except possibly by back-up protection involving a long clearance time. One solution would be to arrange the busbar protection to trip both sides of the transformer. This would not be acceptable if the other side of the transformer were connected, for example, to a single-switch or mesh substation, or if the transformer was banked with another. In the case of the genuine busbar fault it would cause unnecessary disconnection of healthy equipment.

To discriminate between a busbar fault and the fault at F, busbar protection trip relay contacts are used to start an induction disc relay. If fault infeed persists for more than its operating time (about 0·5s), the relay initiates tripping to the backing breakers.

A later development of the interlocked overcurrent principle is now being installed on the supergrid system. Known as 'circuit-breaker fail protection' its role is to ensure selective automatic tripping of the breakers 'backing' a circuit breaker that fails to clear a fault. If c.t.s associated with a circuit breaker carry current after

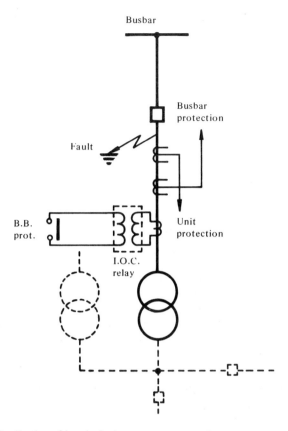

Fig. 12.5.6A *Application of interlocked overcurrent protection*

an interval marginally longer than designed tripping time of the breaker, it must be assumed it has either,

(a)   failed to trip correctly, or that

(b)   fault current continues to be fed into the protected zone from a remote end. (In either case, a minimum number of additional breakers have to be tripped to clear the fault from the system and this is achieved by the breaker fail protection. The scheme is dealt with at greater length in Chapter 13).

12.5.7   Standby earth-fault protection

Back-up protection against l.v. earth faults can be provided by an induction pattern relay energised from a current transformer connected in the power transformer l.v. neutral. For resistance earthed systems the relay should have a time setting high enough to discriminate with the l.v. network protection, and be arranged to trip the transformer in the event of a sustained l.v. fault. The relay also serves to protect the neutral earthing resistor against the effects of a sustained fault.

Duplicate relays may be used, the coils being connected in series. The first (Stage 1) relay should have the shorter time setting, say 5 s, and should trip the transformer l.v. circuit breaker. The Stage 2 relay, say 7 s should trip the h.v. circuit breakers either directly or, where appropriate, via intertripping equipment.

Where the transformer has an individual h.v. circuit breaker, as for example, at a double busbar substation, there is no necessity to provide discriminative tripping between h.v. and l.v. circuit breakers and only one stage is required. On mesh connected substations, banked transformers, and transformer feeders, it is usual to provide two stages and discriminative tripping.

12.5.8 Tank earth-fault protection

Where banked transformers are protected by a single overall differential protection system there is no indication given by the protection regarding which transformer is faulty. This indication can conveniently be provided by means of a tank earth-fault relay.

The transformer tank is lightly insulated from earth and all earthed cable sheaths, and then bonded to earth via a single copper strap, over which is mounted a current transformer connected to a relay. Any earth fault within the transformer tank will produce a current in the earthing strap which operates the relay.

Faults external to the transformer and its bushings are not covered by this device, but these can usually be located by inspection.

This is the principle of frame-leakage protection which has been applied in the past for the earth-fault protection of distribution transformers, as an alternative to restricted earth-fault protection.

12.5.9 Winding temperature protection

Large transformers with forced cooling are usually fitted with winding temperature devices to detect overloading of the transformer or failure of the cooling equipment.

The winding temperature device is of the type described in Chapter 6. The bulb is situated in a special pocket located in the flow of hot oil and is, in addition, heated by a small heater energised from a current transformer connected to measure the transformer winding current. The device thus indicates the top oil temperature of the transformer plus an increment proportional to the load on the transformer, this increment being arranged to match the difference between top oil and winding hot spot temperatures. Full use is made of the transformer overload capability by arranging the thermal time constant of the equipment to be similar to that of the transformer.

Two winding temperature instruments are generally fitted to each transformer; each instrument is fitted with two mercury switch contacts. Operation of one instrument is arranged to start cooling fans and pumps, and to give an alarm. The other instrument is arranged to give the same alarm and to trip the l.v. circuit breaker.

Typical settings employed are:

	Instrument 1		Instrument 2
Coolers	In: 90°C	Alarm	110°C
	Out: 65°C		
Alarm	110°C	Trip	125°C

At one time, transformers were fitted with separate oil and winding temperature instruments. The former measured the oil temperature only which did not give a reliable indication of hot spot temperatures because of the long thermal time constant of the oil (approximately 10 times that of the winding).

In the case of transformers without forced cooling, an oil temperature alarm only is sometimes fitted.

12.5.10   Gas generation and oil-surge protection

All faults within the transformer tank give rise to generation of gas, which may be, slow for minor or incipient faults or violent in the case of heavy faults.

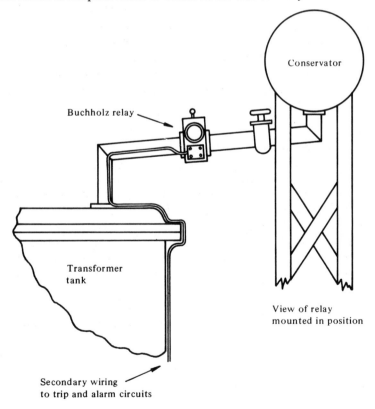

Fig. 12.5.10A   *Installation of Buchholz gas- and oil-actuated relay*

The generation of gas is used as a means of fault detection in the gas and oil-operated relay which comprises one or two hinged floats, buckets, or similar buoyant masses which are inserted in the pipework (Fig. 12.5.10A) between transformer tank and conservator and which are normally held in equilibrium by the oil (see Chapter 6).

The rising bubbles produced by the slow generation of gas, due to a minor fault, pass upwards towards the conservator but are trapped in the relay chamber causing a fall in oil level inside it. This disturbs the equilibrium of the gas float, thereby closing its contacts which would normally be connected to give an alarm.

A heavy fault will produce a rapid generation of gas causing violent displacement of the oil which moves the surge float system of the relay in passing to the conservator. This will result in closure of the surge float contacts which are arranged to trip the transformer.

To relieve the violent surging of oil which may cause splitting of the transformer tank wall and the ejection of its bushings, transformers of small rating are fitted with explosion vents taking the form of a 'chimney' capped by a bursting-disc diaphragm. For transformers of larger rating it becomes impossible to accommodate the explosion vents and maintain their earth fault clearance from the live conductors. The solution to the problem is to fit a spring-loaded pressure relief diaphragm in the tank wall through which surging oil may escape into the bund surrounding the transformer. 'Qualitrol devices' as they are called are equipped with contacts which may be used for alarm or trip initiation.

The gas- and oil-operated relay gives the best possible protection against such conditions as defective coil bolt insulation and short-circuited laminations, and incipient failure of the main insulation. The alarm element will also operate for low oil conditions etc., as will the trip element if the condition deteriorates.

Analysis of the gas collected in the Buchholz relay chamber may frequently assist in the diagnosis of the type of fault, and the rate of gas generation gives an indication of the severity.

Where the tap changer selector switches are in a separate oil compartment from the main transformer, protection can be provided by either a separate gas- and oil-operated relay, or by arranging the oil pipework so that the tap change compartment is connected to the transformer conservator via the main oil- and gas-operated relays.

12.6   Protection schemes for typical transformers

The degree of protection provided depends to a great extent upon the size and functional importance of the unit. A further important factor is the economic aspect. The cost of protection for power transformers tends to be proportionally higher than the cost of protection for other items of plant.

12.6.1   Distribution transformers

With distribution transformers the economic considerations are predominant, and the minimum protection is usually provided consistent with acceptable overall performance. High speed protection is not always necessary, particularly for phase-faults as power system stability problems have rarely to be considered.

The larger sizes of distribution transformers, say about 5 or 10 MVA, are equipped with on-load tap changing and may have forced cooling. The smaller sizes generally have neither and are often equipped with fuses rather than circuit breakers.

Larger distribution transformers are protected by overcurrent and earth-fault protection. Where fault current can be fed from h.v. and l.v. sides the overcurrent protection is usually fitted to both sides of the transformer. Fig. 12.6.1A shows a typical arrangement.

Larger distribution transformers may also have overall differential protection in which the restricted earth fault protection is incorporated. The protection of such transformers in practice may differ little from transmission transformers described in Section 12.6.2.

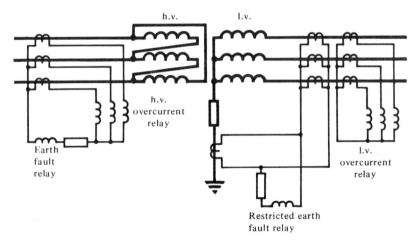

Fig. 12.6.1A *Overcurrent and earth-fault protection for a delta/star distribution transformer*

12.6.2 Two-winding transmission transformers

Economic considerations in the protection of transformers connected to the 132 kV, 275 kV and 400 kV grid system tend to be outweighed by the need for high speed fault clearance, necessary for system stability reasons, and the need to minimise fault damage.

The two-winding transmission transformer normally has the h.v. winding solidly earthed, and the l.v. winding resistance earthed through an interconnected-star earthing transformer. On-load tap changing and forced cooling are always provided.

To achieve high-speed discriminative fault clearance for both phase faults and earth-faults differential protection with h.v. and l.v. restricted earth fault is fitted. The differential protection usually incorporates load bias and harmonic restraint features.

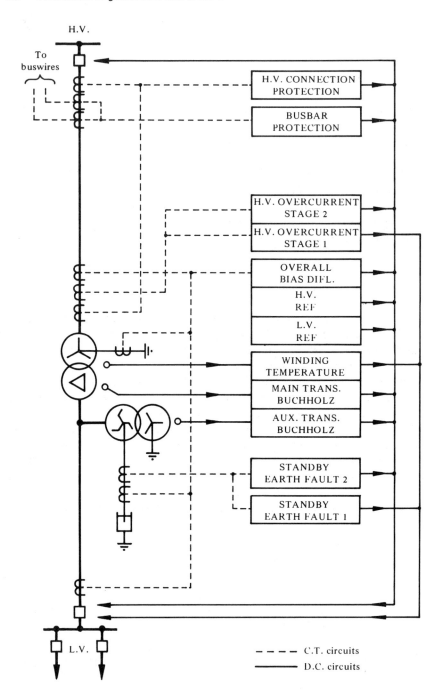

Fig. 12.6.2A   *Typical grid transformer protection arrangement*

Gas- and oil-actuated relays are fitted to both the main transformer and its associated earthing (auxiliary) transformer. Duplicate winding temperature instruments are fitted for starting the cooling, and for alarm and trip.

Back-up protection is provided by overcurrent relays and l.v. standby earth-fault relays (one or two stages).

A typical 132 kV grid transformer protection arrangement is shown in Fig. 12.6.2A.

On a single transformer installation the h.v. connections are normally included in the zone of the overall differential and balanced earth-fault protections. Where transformers are banked it is preferable to have separate overall differential and balanced earth-fault protection for each transformer, and a separate circulating current system for the protection of the h.v. interconnections. This requires current transformers in the transformer h.v. bushings.

Banked transformers will invariably be fitted with two stage standby earth fault protection.

12.6.3 Station transformers

At most major generating stations transformers are installed to provide a supply to the station auxiliaries from the grid system. Though their MVA rating may be comparatively low, these station transformers are important units, and their protection is governed by technical rather than economic considerations.

Station transformers normally have on-load tap changing; but forced cooling is not employed. The windings are usually star/delta/star, the h.v. winding being solidly earthed and the l.v. winding resistance earthed.

Since these transformers are connected to the grid system, internal fault currents can reach very high multiples of transformer rating (for example 300 times c.t. rating), and the protection arrangements must be capable of correct operation at these high currents.

The protection fitted to a station transformer is similar to that applied to a grid transformer except that winding temperature indicators may be omitted.

12.6.4 Autotransformers for transmission

The use of an autotransformer rather than a two winding transformer has economical advantages where the h.v./l.v. voltage ratio is low, since in these circumstances the autotransformer will be smaller for a given MVA rating. Auto-transformers are used to interconnect the British 400 kV, 275 kV and 132 kV systems, thus making possible the installation of units of high rating in situations where the use of a two winding transformer would introduce transportation difficulties. Both h.v. and l.v. systems have common neutral earthing arrangements (solid earthing in the case of the 400 kV, 275 kV and 132 kV systems).

Most autotransformers are fitted with delta-connected tertiary windings (voltage typically 13 kV) and these tertiary windings may be used for the connection of a

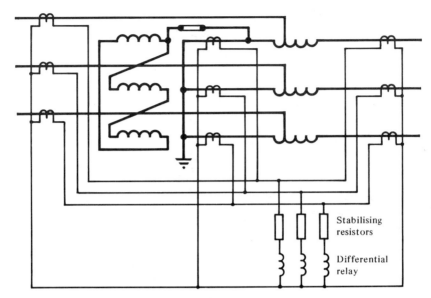

Fig. 12.6.4A   *Circulating current protection for an autotransformer*
(Note: All c.t.s. have identical ratios)

synchronous compensator. The protection of synchronous compensators is described in Chapter 14.

Large autotransformers are fitted with 'on-load' tap changing and forced cooling equipment. The tap changing is generally carried out at the lower voltage terminals, and in consequence the tap changer has to be fully insulated and the diverter switches are therefore mounted on top of the lower voltage terminal bushings.

The protection arrangements for large autotransformers are similar in most respects to the protection of two winding transformers. A simpler differential protection scheme, however, can usually be employed. Typical of the differential protection for an autotransformer is the circulating current system shown in Fig. 12.6.4A. Each phase winding forms a three-ended protection zone, and the c.t.s in the l.v., h.v. and neutral ends are connected in parallel to form a circulating current system.

All c.t.s have the same ratio and a simple instantaneous relay is used since the protection is not affected by either magnetising inrush currents or tap changing. The earth connection of the tertiary winding is normally taken from inside the zone of the circulating current protection so that operation occurs for earth faults on the tertiary winding.

With banked transformers it is usual to provide separate circulating current protection for each transformer using a further circulating current scheme to cover faults on the connections between the h.v. circuit breaker and transformer h.v. bushings. (Fig. 12.6.4B). This arrangement has the advantage of distinguishing co-ordinating gap flash-overs and h.v. connection faults and provides basic logic for the automatic isolation of a faulty transformer and the restoration of healthy plant.

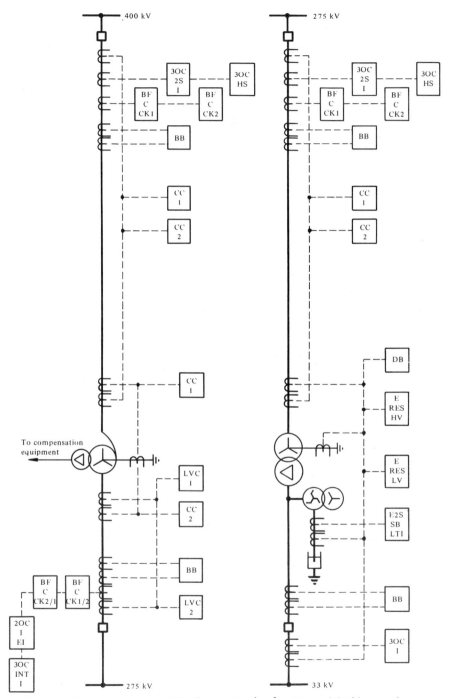

Fig. 12.6.4B *Circulating current and back-up protection for auto and double-wound transformers*

12.7   Protection system for generator transformer units

All large modern generators are directly connected to an individual power transformer and the combination is switched on the h.v. side of the transformer at the main transmission voltage. A unit transformer, which supplies the generator auxiliary system, is connected at the generator terminals.

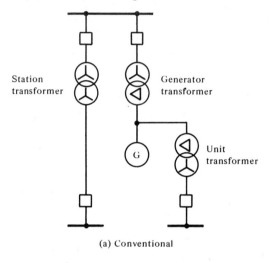

(a) Conventional

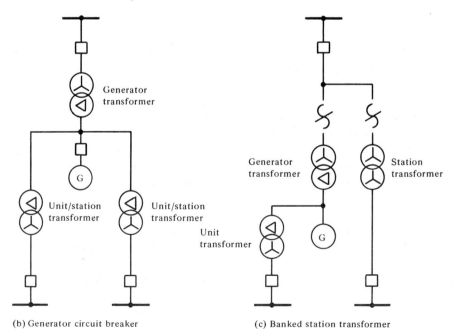

(b) Generator circuit breaker

(c) Banked station transformer

Fig. 12.7A   *Alternative methods of connecting generators*

Alternative methods of connecting generators are shown in Fig. 12.7A but for each of the arrangements shown, the principles of protection are similar. In the following discussion the conventional arrangement shown in Fig. 12.7A(*a*) is assumed.

The generator winding and transformer l.v. windings form an isolated system which therefore requires its own neutral earth. Common methods of earthing use a low resistance, a high resistance (possibly using a distribution transformer and secondary loading resistor) or a resistance-loaded voltage transformer. The earth-fault current is usually limited to 200-300 A in the case of low resistance earthing, to 1-10 A in the case of high resistance earthing, and to a negligible value in the case of v.t.s earthing. Care must be taken with v.t. earthing to avoid ferroresonance effects between the voltage transformer and the transformer winding capacitances. The virtue claimed for this method is that the generator can be left in service with an earth fault on the winding until it is convenient to transfer the load, and arrange a planned shut down.

Modern practice in the United Kingdom tends toward the use of high resistance earthing set to limit earth-fault current to 10A.

The protection systems for the generator transformer unit are generally similar in principle to those applied individually to generators and transformers. Since the generator stator and the transformer l.v. (delta) windings form an isolated zone of protection for earth faults, however, a simple stator earth-fault protection scheme can be used. The differential protection system, moreover, can be arranged to cover both the generator and main transformer.(Figs. 12.3.13A and 12.7B).

12.7.1   Biased differential protection

When generator and transformer are solidly connected there are no problems due to magnetising current inrush, since both the generator and its transformer are excited gradually up to their full operational values.

Through fault conditions can result in collapse of voltage, but the subsequent inrush due to the recovery of the voltage is far less onerous than the switching-inrush. Inrush current conditions being relatively light, no special harmonic restraint feature need be applied to the overall differential protection as long as the fault setting is not too low.

A biased differential relay with a setting of 20% and a bias of 20% is generally satisfactory; the bias is required, of course, to cover transformer on load tap changing.

The generator-transformer overall differential protection does not include the unit transformer for which, because of its low rating, a separate overall differential protection is provided (Fig. 12.7A). The fault settings of the unit transformer differential protection can thus be related to its own rating rather than the rating of the main generator.

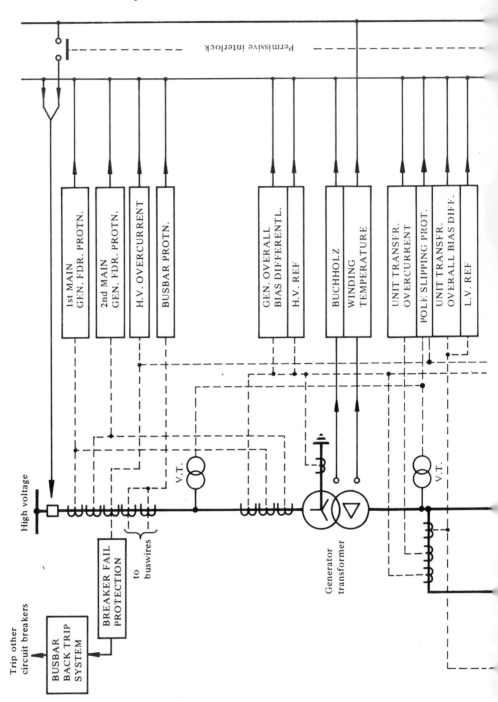

Fig. 12.7B   Basic arrangement of generator protection

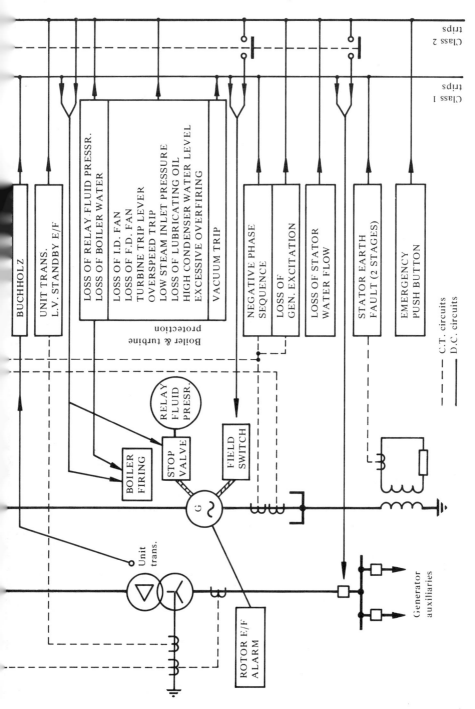

12.7.2 Stator earth-fault protection

A simple earth-fault protection can be applied using a relay operated from a current transformer in the generator neutral connection, or in the secondary winding of the distribution transformer, or from the secondary winding of the voltage transformer in the case of v.t. earthing.

Where a low value earthing resistance is used to limit earth-fault current to 200 to 300 A, high-speed tripping from instantaneous relays is required to minimise damage. A setting of 10% of maximum earth-fault current is the minimum permissible if the possibility of relay operation, due to the zero sequence currents transmitted by generator-transformer inter winding capacitance during external h.v. earth-fault conditions is to be avoided. The protection arrangement, therefore, usually comprises two relays, an instantaneous relay having a setting of 10% and an i.d.m.t. induction disc relay, having a setting of 5%.

When the generator is earthed through a high resistance (limiting the maximum stator earth-fault current to approximately 10 A) a longer time delay is permissible. Duplicated i.d.m.t. relays, having 5% settings, are used in such cases.

Both of the above systems of protection leave the neutral ends of the stator windings unprotected against earth faults (typically the bottom 5-10% of the windings) and, although earth faults near the neutral ends are unlikely to be caused by electrical stressing, faults due to mechanical stressing cannot be ruled out and 100% winding protection is required and two systems are available.

One method injects coded a.c. current into the generator neutral connection and monitors its amplitude, as drawn by the total system to earth capacitance (i.e. that of the generator stator, generator transformer l.v. and unit transformer h.v. windings and connections). The effect of an earth fault on the windings would be to reduce the system impedance and so increase the level of injected current and trip the set if the deviation from the datum level exceeded a predetermined value.

A second method makes use of the third harmonic voltages normally present on the neutral connection of the generator. A fault near the neutral end of the machine would reduce this voltage to near zero and so identify faults in those sections of the windings not protected by the associated 50 Hz voltage sensing protection, set to cover the upper 90-95% of the windings. A system of filters reject unwanted frequencies from the complementary systems, so as to provide substantial overlap in the zones covered by the two relays.

The first of the two described methods has the advantage of enabling a check for low resistance to be made on the machine before it is run up - a significant facility, particularly when returning a set to service after a long shutdown or maintenance outage.

Where v.t. earthing is used, earth-fault current is negligible and an i.d.m.t. relay may be used to give alarm only.

It should be noted that neither the direct nor the indirect connected generators are provided with interturn fault protection. Such faults occur rarely in modern generators but when they do, they rapidly involve earth and are cleared by the earth-fault protection.

12.7.3   Tripping arrangements

Tripping arrangements for large generator units require particularly careful consideration. With modern high capacity generating units both turbines and generators are designed to a comparatively smaller frame size per MVA than earlier units, and in consequence, the relative inertia of the principal components is much smaller. This may result in greater risk of damage and introduces additional control problems under conditions of heavy load rejection.

For these reasons the complete tripping of a modern generator unit is carried out only for internal fault conditions, and for all external faults the generator back-up protection devices are arranged to trip the h.v. circuit breaker only, any speed rise being dealt with by the governor equipment.

For very large units it is considered necessary to minimise the risk of a set running away in the event of the turbine emergency stop and governing valves failing to close when the protection operates. An interlock is therefore included to prevent the generator circuit breaker from being opened until the steam supply to the turbine has been cut off. This interlock is applied only to those protection circuits for which a significant increase in the damage caused by the fault is unlikely to result from delaying the opening of the generator circuit breaker until cut off of the steam has been detected.

12.7.4   Generator transformer overfluxing protection

It is necessary to safeguard generator step-up transformers against the risk of damage that may be caused if they are operated at flux density levels significantly greater than their design maximum value (typically 1·9 T). Such conditions may occur when a unit is on load, but are more likely to arise when it is on open circuit under automatic voltage regulator (a.v.r.) or manual excitation control, particularly when running up to, or down from, synchronous speed.

It follows from the fundamental transformer equation $E = 4.44\ (BA)fT$ that $B = k.E/fT$, that is flux density B is directly proportional to induced voltage E and inversely proportional to frequency f and turns T, so that disproportional variations in these quantities may give rise to core overfluxing. If the core flux density increases to a point above saturation level, the flux will no longer be contained within the core and so will extend into other (unlaminated) parts of the transformer and give rise to eddy current circulation.

Depending on the quantity of flux, the dimensions of the metal path and its physical properties, losses would be generated which may be manifested in four ways:

(*a*)   a large increase in magnetising current
(*b*)   an increase in winding temperature
(*c*)   an increase in transformer noise and vibration
(*d*)   overheating of non-laminated metal parts affected by the stray fluxes.

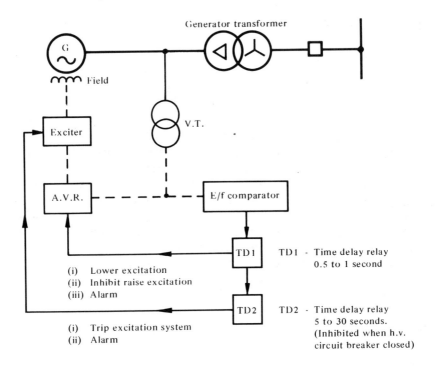

Fig. 12.7C   *Generator transformer overfluxing protection*

Since other protection devices do not afford complete protection against all of these conditions, overfluxing protection is provided either as an integral feature of the a.v.r. equipment itself, or as separate relay system (Fig. 12.7C). In both systems the action of the overfluxing protection is to initiate a reduction of excitation by normal excitation control and, if that should fail to produce the necessary correction, to proceed after a short time delay (typically 5-7s) to trip the generator.

12.8   Transformer feeder protection

The transformer feeder results from the need for economy in switchgear, the transformer being connected directly to the feeder without an intervening switch. It is used mainly to provide a bulk supply from a major switching station. A second case is that of interconnecting two low voltage systems by means of an h.v. line, each end of which is directly connected to a transformer.

The problems of transformer feeder protection are usually similar to those encountered in the protection of transformers and feeders as separate units. Some simplification in the feeder protection is often possible by virtue of the impedance of the transformer windings, and a high-speed protection is therefore obtainable over the whole feeder length using distance or high set overcurrent relay principles. The application of such schemes is dependent, however upon maximum and minimum fault levels, feeder and transformer impedance, etc. and must be carefully considered at the design stage.

The complete isolation of the transformer and feeder for a fault on either almost invariably requires the use of intertripping or fault throwing.

12.8.1 Overall protection for feeder and transformer

It is possible to protect the feeder and transformer in one zone of protection using a differential system. This necessitates pilot wires, but has the advantage that current transformers are not required in the transformer bushings. The fault setting of such schemes makes adequate protection of the transformer windings very difficult, and this together with the long operating time (due to the need to stabilise the relay against magnetising inrush conditions by means of time delay) limits the application of this type of scheme to the smaller transformer circuits. In all cases it is desirable to utilise separate high-speed earth fault protection.

The general principle of overall differential protection providing protection against phase faults is shown in Fig. 12.8.1A. The summation transformers do not incorporate an earth-fault winding since earth-fault balance is not required. An earth fault on the delta side will not result in the appearance of zero-sequence current on the star side and vice versa. In order to avoid blind spots for phase faults on the star side (which gives a 2:1:1 current distribution on the delta side) the two sections of the summation transformer have an unequal number of turns.

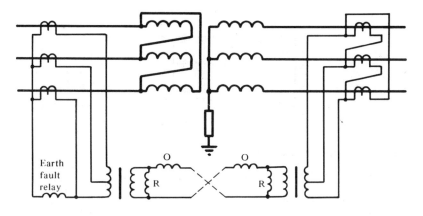

Fig. 12.8.1A *Voltage balance system for delta/star transformer*

A separate relay system is required to give satisfactory earth-fault protection, and a typical arrangement of phase fault differential protection with instantaneous restricted earth-fault protection is shown in Fig. 12.8.1B. On the earthed star side the relay is energised from a core balance transformer which has primary windings energised from line and neutral c.t.s. In the case of the delta winding the earth-fault relay is connected in the residual c.t. circuit.

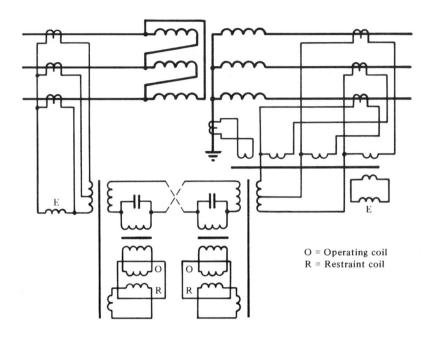

O = Operating coil
R = Restraint coil

Fig. 12.8.1B   *Overall Solkor protection for transformer feeder using two pilot wires Differential phase-fault protection with separate earth-fault protection (A Reyrolle & Co. Ltd.)*

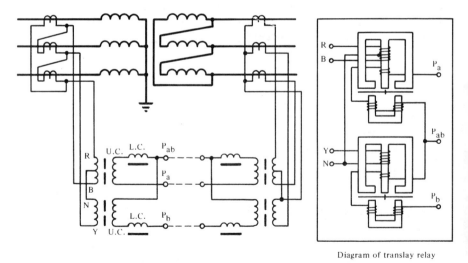

Diagram of translay relay

U.C. = Relay Upper Coil
L.C. = Relay Lower Coil

Fig. 12.8.1C   *Translay phase and earth-fault differential protection for a delta/star transformer using three pilot wires. (GEC Measurements Ltd.)*

Fig. 12.8.1C shows a typical overall differential protection scheme giving both phase and earth-fault protection to a transformer feeder. In this case two separate relay elements are used at each end of the line. One relay element is energised from R and B current and the second from the Y phase current and this arrangement avoids a blind spot under 2:1:1 fault conditions (see Chapter 8). The interconnection between the relays at the two ends requires the use of three pilot wires as shown.

Both types of scheme are suitable for use with 7/·029 pilot circuits up to about 15 miles in length and have fault settings in the range of 60-200%.

The separate earth-fault protection arrangement of Fig. 12.8.1B can have a low fault setting with high speed of operation, and it is often possible to protect the whole of the delta winding and a considerable portion, say 90%, of the star winding under solid earthing conditions. Some difficulty may be experienced if the earth-fault setting on the delta side of the power transformer has to be high to prevent operation by residual capacitance current effects under external fault conditions; this is described more fully in the general consideration of earth-fault protection.

12.8.2   Separate protection for feeder and transformer

Schemes employing separate protection for feeder and transformer are frequently used.

Unit feeder protection systems
The choice is between pilot wire protection systems using privately owned or rented GPO pilot circuits, and carrier current protection usually of the phase comparison type. In either case the transformer protection is conventional and will embody all the features discussed in Section 12.5.

Current transformers are required in the transformer bushings for the separate zones of feeder and transformer protection. Intertripping is also required. The use of separate unit schemes of feeder protection permits high speed tripping at both feeder ends, and such methods will often be used over transformer interconnector circuits, where fault power infeed may occur at both ends.

(*a*)   *Pilot wire feeder protection with separate transformer protection:* Pilot wires may be either rented or privately owned and the protection scheme employed will comprise any of the standard arrangements described in Chapter 8. Severe magnetising inrush suppressors, or equivalent stabilising means, may be necessary.

Post Office pilot wire systems are applicable only to two ended feeders and not to teed (three-ended) feeders for which distance or high-set overcurrent protection would normally be used.

(*b*)   *Carrier current protection with separate transformer protection:* Phase comparison carrier protection is often applied to longer transformer interconnector circuits, this being identical in every way to the standard schemes described in Chapter 8. Teed circuits cannot usually be protected by this method.

Non-unit feeder protection systems
The high impedance of the transformer will often permit the application of a high speed non-unit scheme of feeder protection. Of these types two are in general use, distance protection and high set overcurrent protection. The latter is the most economical form of protection possible for feeder transformer circuits and has all the attendant advantages of simplicity etc. It requires careful application and must be thoroughly investigated at the design stage.

Distance protection is particularly suitable for the protection of teed transformer feeders. In general, however, it tends to be more expensive than pilot wire systems for the shorter transformer feeder circuits.

(c)   *Distance protection with separate transformer protection:* A single zone distance protection will give high speed phase fault protection to the whole feeder, the setting reach normally being chosen to extend to the 'middle' of the transformer, that is feeder impedance +50% of transformer impedance; earth-fault protection can invariably be provided by means of an instantaneous relay which may in certain instances be required to embody a directional feature.

The distance relay must be carefully chosen to restrict the effect of the 'blind spot' on close up faults inherent in all directional relays. This blind spot can be avoided completely by the use of an impedance measuring relay with overcurrent starting feature, Fig. 12.8.2A; this arrangement being applicable as long as the remote l.v. fault infeed to a fault behind the relay does not exceed the overcurrent starting relay setting.

Where a high remote infeed may occur, a directional distance scheme is required, and the use of the polarised Mho relay offers the simplest solution for phase fault protection since it combines the functions of direction and distance measurement (see Fig. 12.8.2B). A memory action feature is invariably provided which reduces the effects of 'close up' faults but is not proof against 'switched on' faults.

A simple nondirectional-earth fault relay can be arranged to provide high speed protection in many cases, particularly where a phase current check feature is incorporated as described in the next section. The use of a directional earth-fault relay with a definite current setting will provide high-speed earth-fault protection covering all exigencies, and this is usually provided with the distance protection scheme.

(d)   *High-set instantaneous overcurrent and instantaneous earth-fault protection:* Overcurrent protection of the i.d.m.t. type will normally be fitted to one or both ends of the transformer feeders, either as a main or back-up protection feature. In many instances an additional overcurrent relay of the high set instantaneous type may be fitted, its current setting being chosen such that the relay operates for faults on the line but is inoperative for faults through the transformer.

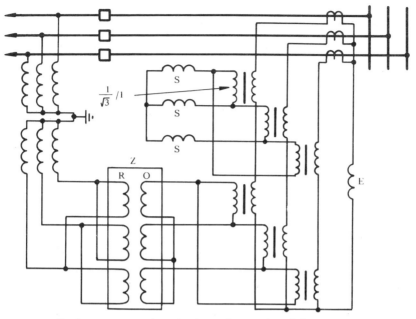

S = Overcurrent starting relay (controls operation of Z).
Z = Impedance measuring relay. (Operating coils normally
    short-circuited by contacts on S)
E = Earth fault relay (contacts in series with S to trip).
R.O. = Impedance relay operating and restraint coils

Fig. 12.8.2A   *Single zone impedance protection for transformer feeder with overcurrent starting*

The simple arrangement of Fig. 12.8.2C is suitable for application to relatively low MVA rating (high impedance) transformers connected to a high MVA (low impedance) source. The range of application of the simple scheme can be extended by using the modified relay connections of Fig. 12.8.2D using delta connected auxiliary current transformers so that the relay currents are similar under three-phase and two-phase fault conditions.

Fundamentally the problem is that the relay must operate for a fault at the h.v. terminals of the transformer under minimum plant conditions (fault at F_1 in Figs. 12.8.2C and D), and yet remain inoperative for a three-phase fault on the l.v. side of the transformer under conditions of maximum offset (fault at F_2). For the relay connections shown in Fig. 12.8.2D three phase fault conditions need only be considered, and the effect of the d.c. component in the fault current can be neglected if a transient free relay is used; such a relay is unresponsive to current levels than 90% of its setting (see Chapter 6).

The earth-fault relay must remain inoperative for all external faults, either on the local busbar (at F_3) or on the remote side of the transformer at F_2. This latter requirement is usually easy to fulfil, since most transformers are delta connected

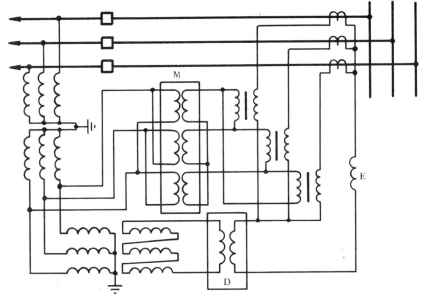

D = Directional earth fault relay
E = Earth fault relay (controlled by contacts on D.)
M = Polarised Mho relay

Fig. 12.8.2B   *Single zone Mho protection for transformer feeder with directional earth-fault relay*

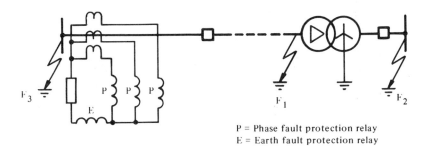

P = Phase fault protection relay
E = Earth fault protection relay

Fig. 12.8.2C   *High-set overcurrent and earth-fault protection for transformer feeder*

on one side and do not, therefore, transform zero sequence currents. The zero sequence infeed from the transformer star winding for a busbar fault at F_3 will tend to operate the residually connected relay E_1 (Fig. 12.8.2D), but will not operate relay E_2 because of the effect of the delta winding in eliminating zero sequence currents from the relay. The combination of relays E_1 and E_2 will therefore ensure that the relay is inoperative for all external fault conditions (assuming no remote infeed).

The residually connected earth-fault relays must be provided with the correct value of stabilising resistor to ensure that relay operation does not occur due to c.t. saturation under transient conditions.

This type of scheme is useful for the protection of important circuits feeding industrial loads where simplicity and economy of equipment is all important.

As a general rule, this scheme can be applied successfully to transformer feeders of up to 45 MVA rating and frequently to 60 and 90 MVA transformers when conditions are favourable. The lower ohmic impedances of the larger units sometimes precludes a successful design where large variations in source infeed are possible.

In generating stations also where stations transformers are banked, it is usual to apply separate differential protection to each transformer using c.t.s in the transformer h.v. bushings. The instantaneous overcurrent feature is arranged to protect the h.v. connections between circuit breaker and transformer.

Instantaneous earth-fault protection for the transformer l.v. winding is of course conventional practice in power transformer protection.

In the case of instantaneous feeder earth-fault protection some care is necessary in the choice of relay setting. For example, when the feeder is connected to the unearthed winding of a power transformer a large residual capacitance current may

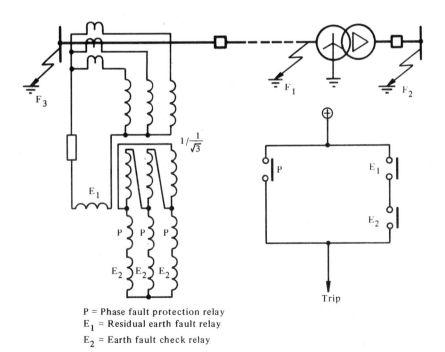

P = Phase fault protection relay
E₁ = Residual earth fault relay
E₂ = Earth fault check relay

Fig. 12.8.2D *High-set overcurrent and earth-fault protection for transformer feeder using delta connected auxiliary c.t.s and earth-fault check feature*

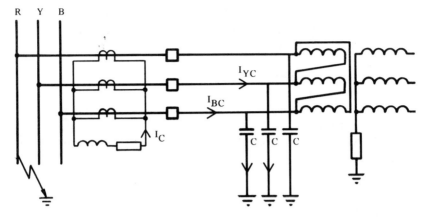

$$I_C = I_{BC} + I_{YC} = 3 \times \text{normal charging current/phase}$$

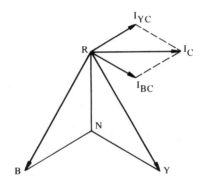

Fig. 12.8.2E   *Showing the effect of residual capacitance current on an earth-fault relay under external earth-fault conditions*

flow in the feeder under external earth-fault conditions. Fig. 12.8.2E shows the way in which this current appears in the relay circuit, and it is usual for the relay setting to be at least twice the residual capacitance current value.

12.8.3   Intertripping

Intertripping (the tripping of remote circuit breakers) is an essential requirement for transformer feeders to ensure complete isolation under internal fault conditions. The more common conditions requiring intertripping are:

(*a*)   Buchholz relay operation for a transformer winding fault which may produce insufficient current to operate the remote protection. It will trip the local breaker directly but the remote breaker will require intertripping.

(*b*)   Earth faults on a feeder connected to a delta or unearthed star winding which will normally trip the feeder circuit breaker only. The fault will remain alive from

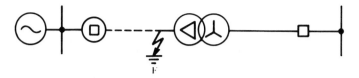

(a) Unearthed system after clearance from one end

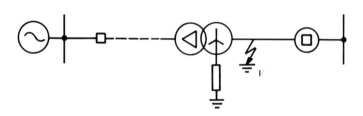

(b) Low fault current infeed l.v. earth fault with
resistance earthing

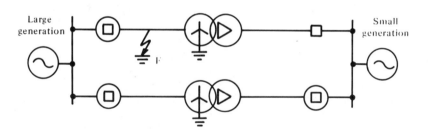

(c) Low fault current infeed (due to parallel line being
out of service)

Fig. 12.8.3A *Conditions requiring intertripping*

the l.v. side of the transformer and the condition will give rise to transient over
voltage due to intermittent arcing at the point of fault (Fig. 12.8.3A). Intertripping
is required here to disconnect the fault from the remaining end.

(c)   Where the fault current infeed is limited due to resistance earthing or high
source impedance (Fig. 12.8.3A(*b*) and (*c*)). The fault current magnitude may not
be sufficient to trip both ends of the feeder, and intertripping is again required.

The various methods commonly used for intertripping are described in Chapter 8. These may be summarised as:

(*a*)   The use of receive relays over private pilot circuits. Surge-proofing of the intertripping may be required.

(*b*)   The use of coded or frequency shift signalling over rented GPO or carrier channels.

(*c*)   Short-circuiting the stabilising signal of a unit protection scheme from transformer protection; this is applicable for higher fault levels.

A fourth method of achieving remote tripping, particularly applicable to transformer feeders, is the use of fault throwing switches. This is suitable for the clearance of transformer faults and comprises an automatic switch of special design connected between one phase and earth on the feeder side of the transformer. Operation of the transformer protection will trip the local circuit breaker and operate the fault throwing switch, which applies a single phase-to-earth fault at the transformer terminals. This fault is detected by the line protection at the remote end, which trips its circuit breaker. The arrangement is shown in Fig. 12.8.3B.

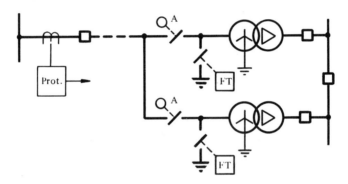

Fig. 12.8.3B   *Application of fault throwing switches showing automatic disconnectors*

Where intertripping is required only for transformer faults, either fault throwing, or pilot, or carrier systems are applicable. Fault throwing has advantages where automatic isolation followed by autoreclosing is envisaged, because it permits positive interlocking between the fault throwing switch and automatic isolator, and reacts directly upon the power system without placing reliance on pilot circuits.

Where intertripping is required to cover low fault infeed conditions, a pilot scheme is essential if high speed operation is required. The use of directional overcurrent relays on the l.v. side of the power transformer will often provide selective clearance but more slowly. As previously mentioned, however, a biased directional relay is required where the transformer may be required to import or export under difficult system conditions.

Pilot or carrier intertripping is invariably used for important interconnectors and fault throwing for bulk supply transformer feeders.

12.8.4 Neutral displacement protection

Where a delta or unearthed star winding is connected to a transformer feeder it is essential to ensure that this unearthed winding cannot remain energised under system earth-fault conditions. This condition will result in danger to life and possible hazard to the sound phases due to intermittent arcing via system earth capacitance.

Initiation of tripping may be by means of a neutral displacement relay arranged to detect residual voltage to earth at the transformer using either voltage transformer or coupling capacitors. Typical arrangements are shown in Fig. 12.8.4A. The relay will operate for external as well as internal feeder faults and must, therefore, be provided with a time delay to ensure discrimination.

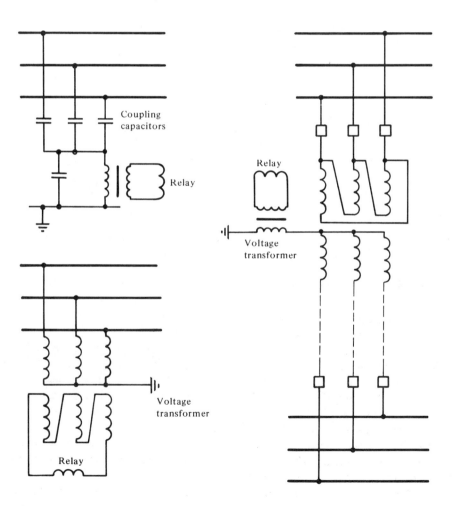

Fig. 12.8.4A   *Neutral displacement schemes*

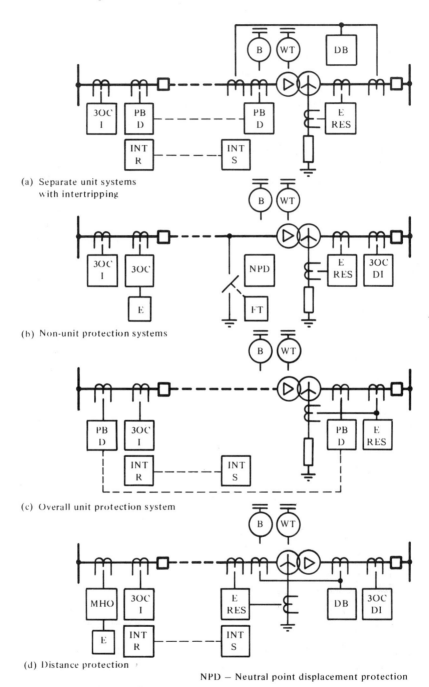

(a) Separate unit systems with intertripping

(b) Non-unit protection systems

(c) Overall unit protection system

(d) Distance protection

NPD — Neutral point displacement protection

Fig. 12.8.6A   *Typical schemes for transformer feeder protection*

12.8.5   Directional overcurrent protection

The application of directional overcurrent protection to transformer circuits was described in Section 12.5.5 which illustrated the use of the $(90°-45°)$ arrangements for the relay voltage circuits. This, of course, applies equally to transformer feeders as well as to transformers.

Directional overcurrent protection is applied extensively to parallel transformer feeder circuits where there is no normal infeed from the l.v. busbars, but where an infeed of fault current can occur through the l.v. sides of the transformers for a fault on the feeder. The directional overcurrent protection is often used as back up to the intertripping equipment, since it is the only means whereby the transformer l.v. circuit breaker can be tripped in the event of a failure of intertripping equipment.

12.8.6   Typical protection arrangements for transformer feeders

Many variations are possible in the overall protection of transformer feeders, depending upon the transformer and its functional importance. Some typical arrangements are shown in Figs. 12.8.6A and 12.8.6B. As with all forms of protection application, the best scheme for a particular system arrangement is that giving the requisite performance for minimum cost. Transformer feeder applications depend to a great extent upon the power system parameters, that is maximum and minimum fault levels, line and transformer impedances, etc., and perhaps in more

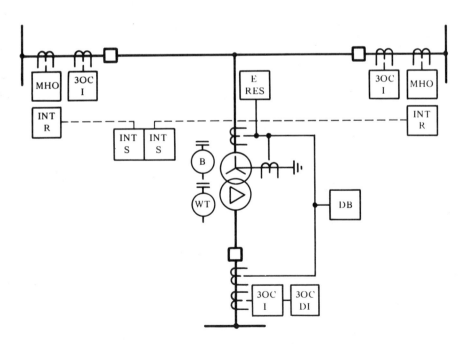

Fig. 12.8.6B   *Typical teed feeder transformer protection scheme*

than any other instance require a very careful investigation to ensure optimum design. It should be noted that in Figs. 12.8.6A and 12.8.6B directional overcurrent (OCD) and neutral displacement (ND) protection would only be employed where there are two or more transformer feeders in parallel.

12.9   Bibliography

Books

Protection relays application guide (GEC Measurements Ltd., 2nd edn. 1975)

Articles

'Developments in electrical protection of large generators' by J H Naylor and H D Nunney (Journées Internationales d'etude des centrales electriques modernes, AIM, Liège, October 1974)

'Some aspects of generator back-up protection in relation to synchronous-machine performance during h.v. system faults' by V Cook and J Rushton (*Proc. IEE,* July 1972)

'Protecting transformer circuits' by J Rushton and K T Yeates (*Electr. Times,* January 1962)

'Pole-slipping protection' by A Stalewski; J L H Goody and J A Downes (Second International conference on developments in power system protection, IEE, London, June 1980)

Chapter 13

Busbar protection

by L.C.W.Frerk

13.1   History of the development of busbar protection

Up to the mid 1930s, no widescale efforts had been made to protect busbars on a unit basis. Also there was reluctance in arranging one protective equipment to cause simultaneous tripping of a large number of circuits.

Before the British Grid System was built in the early 1930s, many undertakings ran isolated from adjacent ones, and so the power available for busbar faults was often relatively small, and damage due to these faults was generally not extensive.

By the late 1930s, the British Power Systems were extensively interconnected, with a consequent increase in fault power.

A number of busbar faults occurred about this time, but due to their relatively slow clearance from the system by overcurrent and earth-fault relays, considerable damage resulted, especially in indoor stations.

These faults led to efforts being made to produce busbar protection in such a form that it could be widely applied without itself being a further hazard to the system.

Construction of the British 275 kV supergrid system began in about 1953, by which time standard principles of busbar protection had been adopted for outdoor switchgear at the higher voltages. At this time the emphasis was placed on the avoidance of unwanted operations in order to give maximum security of supply. With the introduction of 400 kV substations in the 1960s, the transient stability of generators became the more important consideration and this led to a change of emphasis so that fast operating times and reliable operation would be obtained for a fault occurring within the protected zone, which in this case would be the busbars and switchgear.

13.2   General considerations

13.2.1   The basic philosophy of busbar protection

Busbar protection is that combination of c.t.s and relays which are used to detect faults occurring within the busbar zone of a busbar substation and which initiates tripping of all those circuit breakers, the opening of which is necessary to isolate these faults. In Fig. 13.2.1A which shows a double busbar substation with examples of typical circuits, the dotted line encloses the busbar zone but for simplicity c.t.s are not shown. Where unit protection is employed there may be one or more zones of busbar protection within the overall zone shown in Fig. 13.2.1A, the boundary of each being the circuit breakers (or the c.t.s thereof) connecting that zone to the transmission system, generators, transformers and to other zones of busbar protection. The circuit breakers themselves are included in the respective zones so that a fault within a circuit breaker causes operation of the busbar protection. This ensures interruption of all infeeds of fault current in the same way as for faults

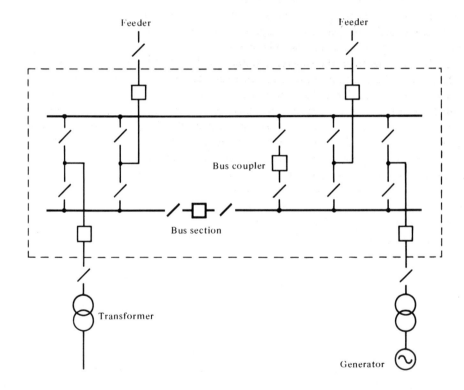

Fig. 13.2.1A   *A double busbar substation showing (dotted) the zone covered by busbar protection*

occurring on the busbars themselves or on bus selector disconnectors, busbar section disconnectors and the connections between these items.

Although the protection of other zones of switchgear, such as the corners of mesh substations, often uses similar principles they are not considered as busbar protection within the scope of this chapter.

13.2.2 Earth-fault protection versus phase and earth-fault protection

In some substations dividing walls, which may be part of the building structure for indoor switchgear, or steel plates separate the three phases one from another. In other designs of switchgear, each phase conductor is supported within an earthed tubular chamber. Such installations are commonly referred to as 'phase-segregated switchgear' and provided that the segregation is maintained throughout the busbar zone, it follows that all naturally occurring busbar faults must be between one or more phases and earth. This being the case, then, for lower voltage systems the whole installation need only be protected against earth faults. Three-phase faults on phase-segregated switchgear can, however, still occur if the busbars are energised in error with safety earths connected. In these circumstances the sum of the fault current in the three phases (which is the net current flowing to earth) would be small and unlikely to operate the relay(s) of an earth-fault protective system. It is for this reason that phase and earth-fault protection is applied to phase-segregated metalclad switchgear on the supergrid system. At lower voltages the choice will be influenced by the additional cost of the phase and earth-fault protective systems.

With open terminal switchgear it was originally considered adequate to protect against earth faults only, because experience has shown that most faults on busbars and switchgear had involved earth. The consequences of relying on back-up protection to clear the few phase faults that did occur were, however, sufficiently drastic to cause a change of policy and for many years now busbar protection responding to phase-to-phase faults as well as earth-faults has been regarded as essential. The only exceptions occur at those 33 kV, 11 kV and 6·6 kV substations where the justification for providing busbar protection is marginal and the simplest possible system is usually fitted.

Non-phase-segregated metalclad switchgear should, for obvious reasons, also be provided with busbar protection which will operate for phase faults and earth faults.

The method of achieving earth-fault only or phase- and earth-fault protection is described later on in this Chapter.

13.3 The clearance of busbar faults by non-unit circuit protection

13.3.1 Back-up overcurrent and earth-fault relays

For the reasons given in Chapter 8, faults cleared by back-up overcurrent and earth-fault protection will usually be nondiscriminative, causing unnecessary splitting of the system which may leave some sections with insufficient generation to meet the load, leading to widespread load shedding by voltage reduction and quite possibly the disconnection of some consumers.

Reliance on back-up protection to clear busbar faults is nowadays confined to radial systems at the lower distribution voltages of 11 kV and 6·6 kV where the economics are such that even the simplest form of dedicated busbar protection can rarely be justified. Where permitted by the substation configuration, some improvement in the security of supplies can be achieved by designing the protection so that, as a first step, relays operate to trip a limited number of circuit breakers so as to split the busbars into sections, each with its own infeed and as a second step to trip those infeeds still carrying fault current after a time-delay of, say, 0·4s. Where a more discriminative scheme is necessary it will usually be of the frame-earth type described in Section 13.4.2.

13.3.2 Distance protection

From Chapter 9 it was seen that feeders fitted with distance protection have a time characteristic as shown in Fig. 13.3A. This means that the distance protection fitted at end A of the feeder AB will, for a fault F on the busbars at B, open the circuit breaker at A in the Zone 2 time, which will be set between 0·4 and 1·0s.

Where all feeders connected to a busbar station are protected by 3-zone distance protection, this can, in some circumstances, provide a limited degree of busbar protection. If, however, some of the circuits connected to the busbars concerned are generators, one must consider how these would be tripped for a busbar fault. The only generator protective systems which operate for faults on the high-voltage circuit breaker or the remote side thereof are earth-fault and/or overcurrent and negative phase-sequence protection. These relays would all be unacceptably slow in clearing busbar faults and, due to the decrement of the generation contribution to the fault current, overcurrent and earth-fault relays may even fail to operate at all. Furthermore, the negative phase-sequence protection only operates for unbalanced faults. Therefore distance protection cannot be relied on to clear busbar faults where generation is connected to the same busbars.

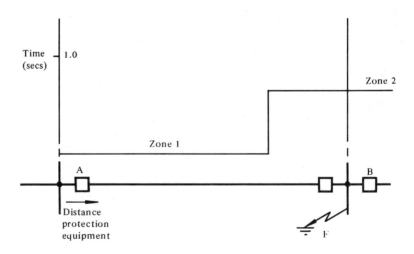

Fig. 13.3A *Characteristics of distance protection*

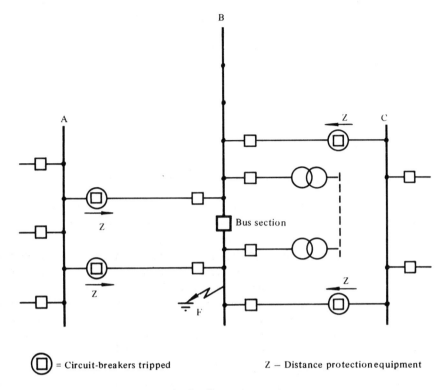

⬚ = Circuit-breakers tripped   Z — Distance protection equipment

Fig. 13.3B   *Limited busbar protection by distance protection*

Fig. 13.3B shows how the protection of busbars can be afforded by distance protection where the foregoing considerations do not apply. Here the infeed to fault F on busbar B from the four feeders is interrupted by the operation of their distance protection at the remote ends at substations A and C.

It is also to be noted that the whole of the busbars at station B are cleared by remote distance protection, although it is only necessary for the bus section, two feeder circuit breakers and one transformer circuit breaker to operate to clear fault F.

On a closely interconnected system such as the 132 kV British Grid, where there are a number of short feeders of insufficient length to permit protecting by distance protection, unit protection has to be used. Such unit protection remains stable for busbar faults, and so the back-up overcurrent relays, with their slow operating time, have to be relied upon to clear the fault.

Better discrimination may be possible by also fitting distance protection to bus coupler and section switches and possibly generators at large double busbar sub-stations, but perfect discrimination could still not be guaranteed under all circumstances.

From the foregoing, it is apparent that non-unit types of protection such as overcurrent, earth fault and distance cannot perform adequately for busbar faults on a large interconnected system. Consequently, unit forms have been developed to ensure short clearance times and correct discrimination for such faults. The only present day application for distance protection as a limited form of busbar protection is on distribution systems at 33 kV.

13.4   Unit systems of busbar protection for metalclad distribution switchgear

13.4.1   General considerations

The main requirements of unit protection when fitted to protect busbars are that it must:

(*a*)   Have a short operating time, especially where fault levels are high, in order to minimise damage to the switchgear and to assist system stability.

(*b*)   Be certain to operate on internal faults. Busbar faults are rare, especially so for indoor metal clad equipments, as they are less affected by atmospheric pollution etc. Only by very careful design and regular comprehensive routine testing of the busbar protection can the desired reliability be achieved.

(*c*)   Remain stable during all external faults. Since many more faults occur externally to busbars than internally, busbar protection is called upon to stabilise many more times than to operate. The maximum value of external fault current occurs when a fault is adjacent to the busbar and may be equal to the rupturing capacity of the switchgear. On the other hand, the current at which the busbar protection is required to operate on an internal fault may only be one fiftieth of this value. The protection in this instance is thus said to require a stability factor of at least 50.

(*d*)   Discriminate correctly, that is decide on which section of the busbars the fault has occurred, and then trip rapidly only those circuit breakers connected to that section. It is sometimes necessary to trip the remote ends of some circuits, but this depends on the location of the current transformers in the switchgear and is described in detail later.

(*e*)   Be immune from maloperation. Since busbar protection has to trip a large number of circuits, it is most important that it does not do so when there is not an actual fault on the busbar. Thus, besides requiring a high stability factor, as discussed in item (*c*) the equipment and circuitry should be as far as possible immune to the effect of faults in wiring, auxiliary switches and human errors. These additional precautions against maloperation are described in detail later.

This Section deals with frame-earth busbar protection which is commonly applied to metalclad switchgear at voltages up to 11 kV. At higher distribution voltages, the busbar protection uses the same principle as that for transmission substations dealt with in Section 13.5.

13.4.2 Frame earth systems

With metalclad switchgear, a very simple form of busbar earth-fault protection can be achieved by lightly insulating from earth all the metal framework. The framework is then connected to earth at only one point and a current transformer fitted over this connection. A typical physical arrangement is shown in Fig. 13.4.2A and the main cable gland in Figs. 13.4.2C and 13.4.2D. It is seen that there are two earth bars, which run the length of the switchboard. One is called the switchgear bonding bar and interconnects each cubicle or framework. Where the circuit breakers are withdrawable, e.g. truck type switchgear, the moving portion must also have a heavy current earth connection to the bonding bar to provide a path for any earth fault occurring within the circuit breaker itself. The second earth bar, known as the cable-sheath earth bar, is lightly insulated from the switchgear cubicle or framework and provides a direct earth connection for those cable sheaths which require to be earthed; this will not be used for every circuit because, for example, single-end or midpoint earthing may be specified. All cables with an earthed sheath, irrespective of the point of earthing, require an insulated cable gland to ensure that current from an earth fault within the switchboard can only flow to earth via the

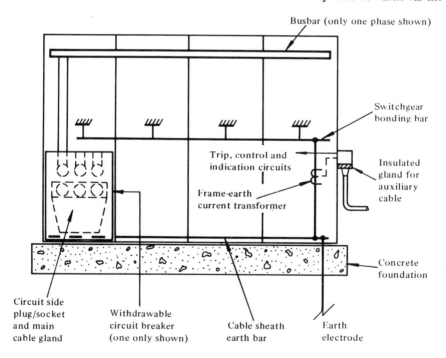

Fig. 13.4.2A *Cubicle switchgear arranged for frame-leakage protection*

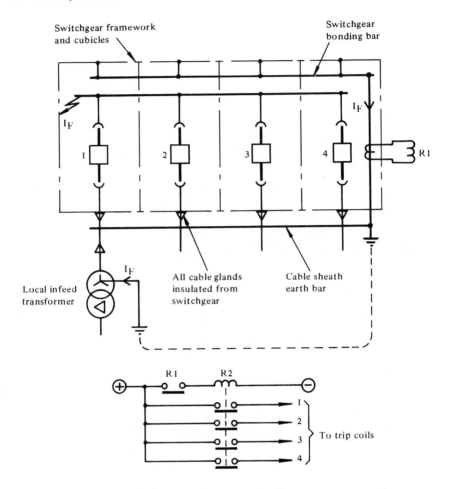

Fig. 13.4.2B *Frame-earth busbar protection without check*

switchgear bonding bar and frame earth-fault current transformer while, for cable faults, any current returning down the sheath flows directly to earth and not via the current transformer.

The bonding bar, earth bar, the interconnection between them and all the bonding connections referred to above must be adequate to carry the rated short-time current of the switchgear for the specified duration, which is usually three seconds.

Relay R1 fed from this c.t. would detect any fault to the metalwork of the switchgear as shown in Fig. 13.4.2B.

Relay R1 could then operate a multicontact d.c. repeat relay R2 to trip all the circuit breakers connected to the faulted busbar as shown.

Care has to be taken to ensure that the switchgear framework has no other earth connection than that through the current transformer. The usual concrete foundations used for switchgear are adequate for insulation from the general body of the ground provided the holding down bolts are clear of any reinforcing rods. Breaks must be made in any ventilating pipes or earthed conduits carrying secondary wiring, and both main and auxiliary cables must have insulated glands. A typical main cable gland with an insulated barrier is shown in Fig. 13.4.2C.

It is possible to check this gland insulation only by disconnecting the earth connections, since both sides of it are normally connected to earth. For reasons of safety, this would require an outage of the complete switchboard. A more elaborate gland which can readily be tested without breaking the main earth connections is shown in Fig. 13.4.2D. Here, the insulation is in two parts with a metal island layer between. Normally, this layer is joined to the main switchgear metalwork by a link connection. The cable gland is tested by opening this link and the insulation measured between the island layer and the cable sheath, and also between the island layer and the switchgear metalwork. If both insulated sections are sound, then the cable must be insulated from the switchgear metalwork.

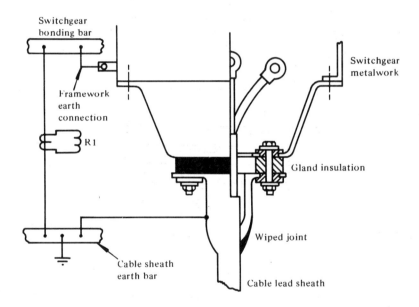

Fig. 13.4.2C *Simple insulated cable gland*

The elementary scheme of busbar protection shown in Fig. 13.4.2B suffers from the disadvantage that it may operate for spurious currents through the frame-earth or c.t., which, for example, could be produced by insulation faults on secondary circuit wiring on the switchgear. Also, inadvertent operation of relay R1 by, say, a mechanical blow would cause all the switches to trip. This limitation can be overcome by fitting an additional relay R3 which is called a check relay, as shown in Fig. 13.4.2E.

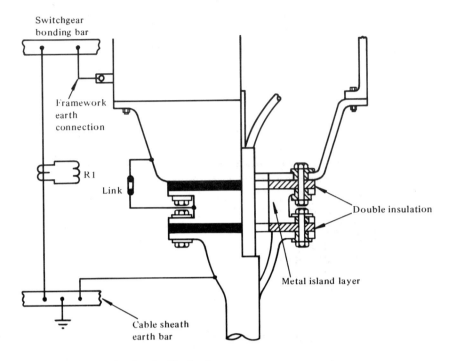

Switchgear
bonding bar

Framework
earth
connection

R1

Link

Double insulation

Metal island layer

Cable sheath
earth bar

Fig. 13.4.2D   *Double insulated cable gland*

If the infeed to the switchgear is from a local transformer then this relay R3 can be fed from a c.t. on the transformer neutral connection. Only an earth fault in the switchgear will cause operation of both R3 and R1.

If there are no suitable transformer neutrals at the station, then a core-balance c.t. fitted around the incoming cable could be used to supply R3. If more than one cable (or local transformer) were feeding the substation, c.t.s must be fitted around each cable (or neutral) and paralleled to ensure operation should one of the cables (or the transformers) be out of service.

(*a*)   *Single busbar switchboard with one section circuit breaker:* So far only a single section switchboard has been considered. If a section circuit breaker is included, then, when an earth occurs in one section, the busbar protection can be arranged to open only the bus section and feeder and transformer circuit breakers of that section to isolate completely the fault from the power system. To do this, the framework of the bus section circuit breaker must be insulated from the adjacent switchgear on both sides as shown in Fig. 13.4.2F. The three framework sections are then separately earthed, with a relay fed from a c.t. on each earth connection. The check relay R4 is shown in this case fed from a c.t. on the local transformer neutrals. The d.c. tripping circuits are so arranged that the inadvertent operation any of one a.c. or d.c. relay will not cause circuit breaker tripping.

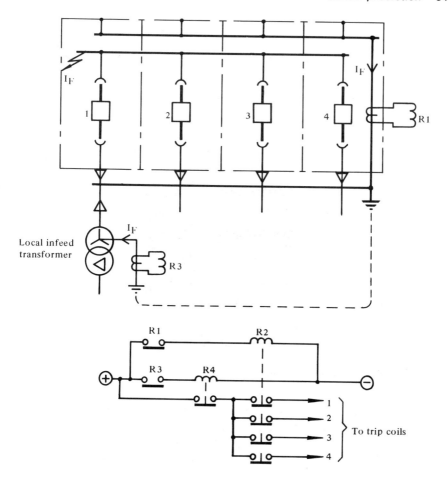

Fig. 13.4.2E *Frame-earth busbar protection with neutral check*

From these circuits it will be seen that the bus section circuit breaker always trips on a busbar fault, and that for the fault F_3 in the bus section itself, every circuit breaker connected to the busbars must be tripped. This is necessary because the relay R2 will operate for fault F_3 on the primary connection or contacts on the side connected to the L.H. busbars as well as for a fault in a similar position on the right-hand side, that is it cannot discriminate between the two, and so the whole switchboard is made dead.

(*b*) *Double busbars:* In the case of switchboards fitted with double busbars, because of the great difficulty of insulating between main and reserve busbar casings, it is not practical to discriminate between faults on one bar and the other. Therefore it is necessary to employ the same principle as for single busbars. It follows that the fault F_1 shown in Fig. 13.4.2G would trip all feeder switches

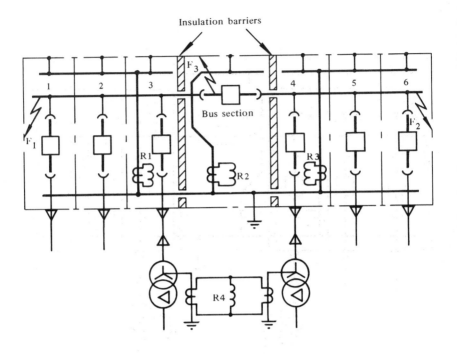

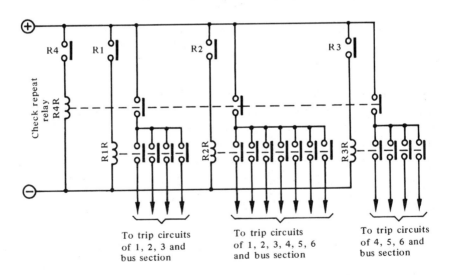

Fig. 13.4.2F   *Typical frame-earth protection for two sections of busbars*

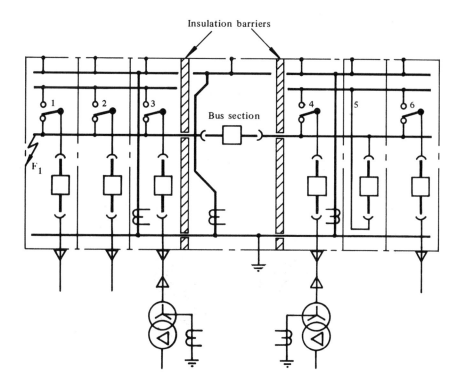

Fig. 13.4.2G *Frame-earth protection for double busbar switchboard*

selected to the left-hand side of the main bar, the bus section switch, and all feeders selected to the reserve bar. Auxiliary switches on the busbar selectors would be connected to achieve this.

(c) *Performance of frame-earth protection:* In Fig. 13.4.2E the frame earth-fault relay R1 and the neutral (or core-balance) check relay R3 are usually both attracted armature types and their operating times together with R2 do not usually exceed 80 ms. It is to be noted that the check relay will operate for earth faults both on the busbars and also for all external faults near to the station. If the installation is of sufficient importance, a fully discriminative check scheme can be achieved by fitting extra c.t.s to every feeder. This arrangement is described in detail in Section 13.5 and would respond only to faults at the substation.

13.5 Unit systems of busbar protection for transmission substations

13.5.1 General considerations

The requirements of unit protection as set out in Section 13.4.1 apply equally to busbar protection employed at the higher switchgear voltages including that on the supergrid system, where the unit feature is achieved by comparing the currents in each circuit connected to the protected busbar.

A number of systems were developed by protection relay manufacturers when the installation of unit busbar protection was found to be necessary. Most of these employed a bias feature to achieve the required stability and it was not uncommon to use a current summation technique to enable earth faults and phase faults to be detected by a single phase relay. However, as confidence in the high-impedance circulating current differential protection principle increased, it was used in the UK to the exclusion of other systems. Although some older substations are still equipped with one or other of the earlier designs, they are no longer fitted on new switchgear and are therefore not described here; readers requiring information thereon are referred to the first edition of this book and to the bibliography.

High-impedance circulating current differential protection was introduced in Chapter 4 dealing with protective transformers. The principle is of sufficient importance, however, to warrant a further explanation here, beginning from the basic principles of the circulating current system.

13.5.2   Current balance using circulating current principle

A very simple form of unit protection of a circuit can be achieved by comparing the currents entering it with those leaving, the circuit being healthy if they are equal, and faulty if they differ by more than a certain amount.

In order to understand the principle more easily, the application to a short single phase feeder carrying load current will first be considered, and Fig. 13.5.2A shows the two equal ratio c.t.s so connected to each other that their secondary currents flow in opposite directions in the relay R connected across them.

If the c.t.s were perfect, their secondary currents would be identical in both magnitude and phase angle, but as no two c.t.s perform absolutely alike, then let the two almost equal c.t. secondary currents caused by the load current be I_a and I_b.

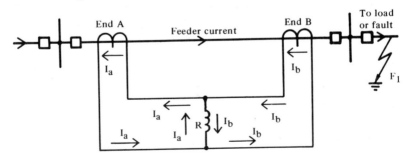

Relay current is phasor difference $(I_a - I_b)$ Amperes

Fig. 13.5.2A   *Circulating current protection (external fault)*

The instanteneous values of c.t. currents are shown during the period of time when the half-cycle of primary current is flowing from A to B. As these flow in opposite directions through the relay, the resulting relay current would be their difference $(I_a - I_b)$.

If a fault external to feeder AB were to occur at F_1 beyond end B of the feeder, the c.t. secondary currents I_a and I_b would flow exactly as for the load currents considered above, but they would be increased in value many times. For this fault at F_1, relay R must not operate and so the c.t. *difference* current $(I_a - I_b)$ flowing through the relay must not exceed the value of the current needed to operate the relay. This condition must remain satisfied up to the largest values of through current that can flow into any fault just beyond end A or end B.

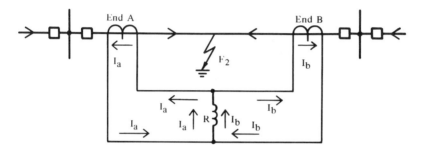

Relay current is phasor sum $(I_a + I_b)$ Amperes

Fig. 13.5.2B   *Circulating current protection (internal fault)*

Fig. 13.5.2B shows a distribution of instantaneous values of current when a fault occurs inside the protected circuit at F_2. Here it is seen that the relay now receives the *sum* of the c.t. secondary currents and the relay must be designed to operate rapidly for this value of current. If no infeed to the fault existed at end B then the relay current would be only I_a and this must also positively operate the relay down to the lowest value of fault current likely to exist on the primary system, that is during minimum plant conditions.

13.5.3   Connections for circulating current busbar protection

For busbar protection the application of the circulating current principle is shown in Fig. 13.5.3A for a busbar with four circuits connected to it. The c.t.s for this protection are shown fitted on the feeder side of the circuit breakers so that the protected zone includes all circuit breakers as well as the busbars.

The single phase system is still considered for simplicity, and the c.t.s are connected in parallel with the relay R. For the fault at F_1 on feeder D an assumed primary fault current distribution is shown, from which it will be seen that the summation of the c.t. secondary currents results in zero current in the relay R and therefore the busbar protection does not operate.

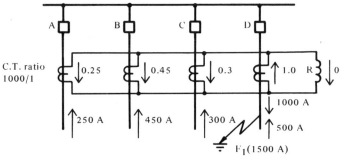

Relay current = 1.0 - 0.25 - 0.45 - 0.3 = 0A

Fig. 13.5.3A *Circulating current busbar protection stabilising on an external fault*

The fault in this case would be cleared by the feeder protection on circuit D.

If the fault were on the busbars as shown by F_2 in Fig. 13.5.3B then for the same primary fault current values as for the external fault, the relay current will now be 1·5 A and so it will operate to trip the circuit breakers A, B, C and D to isolate the fault.

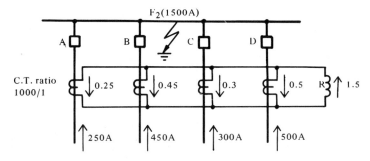

Relay current = 0.25 + 0.45 + 0.3 + 0.5 = 1.5A

Fig. 13.5.3B *Circulating current busbar protection operating on an internal fault*

(a) *Single busbar arrangement:* For simplicity, the application is first considered on a single-phase basis. In order to reduce the risk of wrong operation on through faults, the principle of having two independent lines of defence is used, as was done in the frame earth systems. These two separate forms of protection have both to operate before tripping can take place, and they are shown in Fig. 13.5.3C.

One group of c.t.s (a) (b) and (c) forms a circulating current system covering zone 1 and a similar group (d) (e) (f) covers zone 2: these are called discriminating zones. A third group of c.t.s made up of (g) (h) (j) (k) covers both zones 1 and 2, that is the whole of the busbars, and is used for a check system. Thus for a fault F in zone 1, the discriminating zone 1 relay R1 will operate together with the

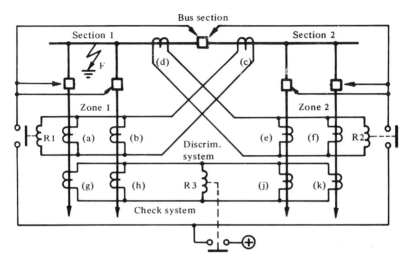

Fig. 13.5.3C *Circulating current duplicate line of defence busbar protection*

check system relay R3 to trip all circuit breakers in zone 1, together with the bus section circuit breaker.

To appreciate the purpose of employing a check system consider now the condition of a healthy system carrying normal load currents. If one of the leads to, say, c.t. (a) were to become open-circuited, then relay R1 would have a current flowing in it due to the lack of the c.t. current (a) balancing out those of c.t.s (b) and (c). This current in R1 may not be large enough to operate it, but when an external fault occurs the current could well be large enough to cause R1 to pick up. Tripping of zone 1 would, however, still be prevented by the fact that the check system relay R3 will not have operated.

The method of using separate check and discriminating systems also covers against the inadvertent operation of any one relay due, for example, to vibration, or operation by hand.

(b) Double busbar arrangement: Fig. 13.5.3D shows the arrangement required to cover duplicate busbars, a single phase system still being considered at this stage to help in more easily demonstrating the principles involved.

Here, four discriminating relays are required, one for each main and reserve section of busbars. If feeder A on the left-hand side of the drawing were selected to the reserve busbar, then the auxiliary switch operated by the selector would close, so selecting its discriminating c.t. to the reserve zone 1 discriminating system. If feeder B were selected to the main busbar, then the reserve zone 1 discriminating system would only have two c.t.s connected to it, namely those of feeder A and those of the bus coupler (b). Main zone 2 would only have two c.t.s selected to it, namely feeder B and the c.t. (c) of the bus section.

In order to make one of the two lines of defence immune from defects which might arise in auxiliary switches, none are fitted in the check system, which there-

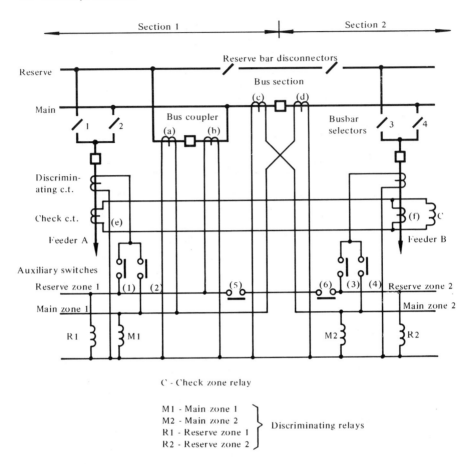

Fig. 13.5.3D   *Circulating current protection for double busbars (a.c. circuits)*

fore covers the whole substation and does not discriminate between busbar sections. Thus the check system has only the feeder c.t.s permanently connected to it; additional feeders would have their c.t.s added in parallel with these two.

The c.t.s in the bus section and bus coupler are permanently associated with the discriminating zones on the opposite side of their breakers to include the breaker in both zones on either side of it. This means that faults on bus couplers and sections cause the loss of two sections of busbar.

In the double busbar arrangement shown there are disconnectors 5 and 6 fitted in the reserve busbar, but no circuit breaker. Therefore, if the former are closed, their associated auxiliary switches (5) and (6) join the buswires of zones 1 and 3 together, and under these circumstances a fault on the reserve busbar would require all circuits selected on it to trip. This would result from the operation of R1, R2 and C.

The d.c. tripping circuits required for the a.c. scheme in Fig. 13.5.3D are shown in Fig. 13.5.3E. Further busbar selector auxiliary switches are required in these circuits to ensure that only the circuits selected to a particular zone are tripped. Since both the bus coupler and bus section must be tripped from two zones they need two tripping relays.

The check relay contact is connected in the common negative lead of the individual tripping relays, whilst the discriminating relay contacts are in the positive lead. This ensures that no tripping would occur if a positive supply were inadvertently applied to the wiring of any trip relay, as, for example, at point P on feeder A in Fig. 13.5.3E. This could happen because the leads to the disconnector auxiliary switches may be of considerable length and pass through several junction boxes.

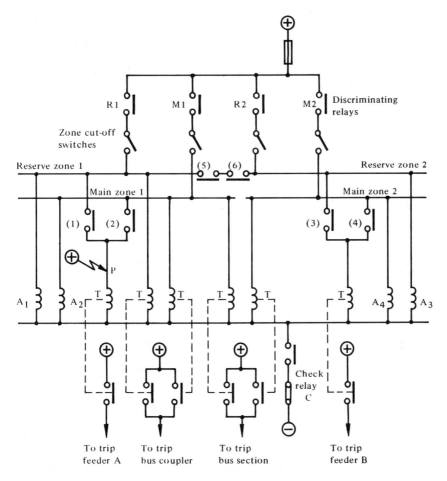

A_1, A_2, A_3, A_4 — Zone defective alarm relays
T — Individual circuit tripping relays

Fig. 13.5.3E *Circulating current protection for double busbars (d.c.. circuits); individual circuit-tripping relays*

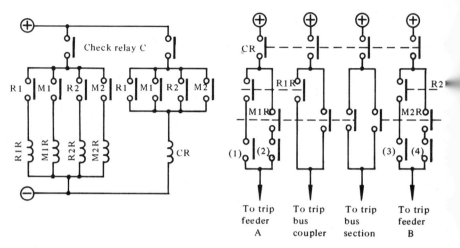

Fig. 13.5.3F   *Circulating current protection for double busbars (d.c. circuits); multicontact tripping relays*

The individual circuit-tripping relays arrangement shown in Fig. 13.5.3E has the advantage that regular proving tests of circuit tripping can readily include proving the tripping from the busbar protection relay T. With the alternative arrangement of multicontact tripping relays shown in Fig. 13.5.3.F, careful consideration has to be given before operating such relays, in order to ensure that during 'trip testing' only the desired circuit is tripped.

(*c*)   *Protection for earth faults:* If only earth-fault protection of the busbars is required, then the c.t.s can be connected as shown in Fig. 13.5.3G where it will be seen that only one relay element is required since the c.t.s of all phases are paralleled together.

If the outgoing circuits are cables (either three core or three single cores), an alternative arrangement of c.t.s is to fit a single core-balance c.t. on each circuit, as shown in Fig. 13.5.3G.

With this form of earth fault protection, as with frame earth-fault protection described earlier, the check feature may be by a relay fed from the sum of the currents in the neutrals of the local transformers connected to the busbars. The disadvantage of this arrangement however, is that this relay will operate for external earth faults. Also, the relay will not operate if there is no neutral current due to the local transformers being out-of-service. The most reliable check arrangement is current balance as shown in Fig. 13.5.3C.

(*d*)   *Protection for phase and earth faults:* Fig. 13.5.3H shows the principle of such a current balance system which is, in effect, three separate systems, each covering one phase and joined together at the star point of each set of c.t.s to save in multicores. For simplicity, part (a) shows only two primary circuits connected to the three-phase busbars. For the blue to yellow busbar fault F shown, both blue

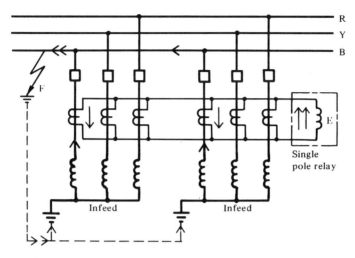

(a) Earth-fault protection using residually connected c.t.s

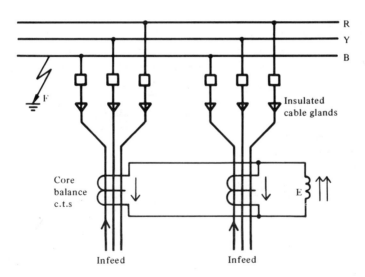

(b) Earth-fault protection using core balance c.t.s

Fig. 13.5.3G *Protection for earth faults*

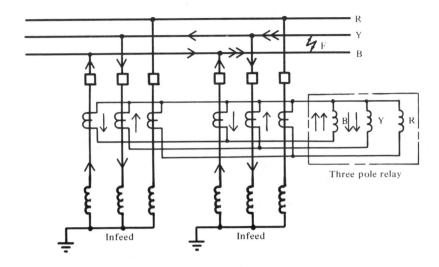

(a) Phase-to-phase fault. Current distribution

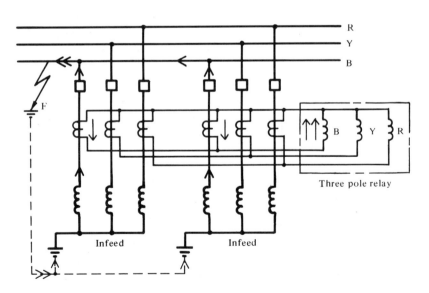

(b) Earth fault. Current distribution

Fig. 13.5.3H   *Combined phase and earth-fault protection*

and yellow relays will operate. In the event of a blue phase-to-earth fault, as shown at F in part (b) of Fig. 13.5.3H then only the blue element will operate.

13.5.4 The influence of c.t. performance on through-fault stability

The circulating current principle can be extended for application to various substation configurations with multiple sections of single or double busbar switchgear, but before doing this a practical limitation to the system described so far must be eliminated. There would be no problem with such a system if the output of the current transformers was a faithful reproduction of the primary current at all times. However, one must allow for the fact that fault current may, as explained in Chapter 4, contain a transient d.c. component current which can cause saturation of the current transformer cores and distortion of the secondary current, effects which can only be avoided by increasing the core size substantially. Since the c.t.s which are connected together to form a circulating current zone will each generally be carrying different magnitudes of current and hence different magnitudes of dc component, the degree of distortion will vary from one c.t. to another, with the result that (for an external fault) the secondary current will not sum to zero and there will be an unbalance (spill) current in the relay. If the magnitude of the spill current exceeds the relay setting for sufficient time, operation of the relay will occur and the protection will be unstable. Many early applications of circulating current protection used relays with a relatively short operating time and these occasionally operated incorrectly for an external fault. The relays were frequently of the attracted armature type of fairly low impedance with a nominal operating time of about 100 ms. At this time it was not clearly understood why the relay misbehaved in this way. It was found, however, that if a relay with a much longer operating time was used, for example an induction disc relay it did not-operate on external faults. It is now known that this was because it provided time for the dc component to decay and for steady state conditions to become established. Unfortunately, the long fault clearance times resulting from the use of such relays were found to be unacceptable and, for a time, biased systems were considered to be the only solution.

13.5.5 Basic principles of high-impedance circulating current busbar protection: stability

The requirements of high-impedance circulating current protection are, in principle, the same whether it is applied to a two-ended zone, such as a short interconnector, or to the multi-ended zones of busbar protection. The notable differences occur in the stability level and the increased complexity of busbar protection required to prevent the unwanted tripping of the several circuit breakers in one zone, e.g. due to the inadvertent operation of a single relay.

The disadvantages of circulating current protection using low impedance relays were described earlier, the main one being through fault instability due to c.t.

saturation. It was found that this could be overcome by the correct choice of c.t.s and relay circuit components, in what has become known as high-impedance circulating current protection.

Consider a system to protect a zone have only two circuits connected to it. The most onerous conditions for stability arise when:

(i)   Maximum fault current enters the zone through one circuit and leaves through the other to a fault just outside the zone, as shown in Fig. 13.5.5A.

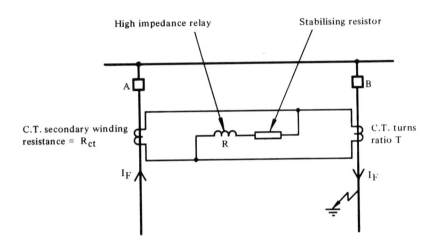

Fig. 13.5.5A   *High impedance scheme*

(ii)   One c.t., say that on circuit B, saturates completely due to assymmetry of the fault current, while the other c.t. does not enter saturation at all, and maintains its output as a faithful reproduction of the primary current.

In Chapter 4 the equivalent circuit of a c.t. was described and this can be used to illustrate the conditions existing in the system being considered, at which point it should be noted that the calculated performance of the protection can only be obtained with the desired reliability if the c.t.s are of the low reactance type as defined in BS 3938. This being the case, the primary and secondary leakage reactances can be omitted from the equivalent circuit, which is shown in Fig.13.5.5B. Because the c.t. on circuit B is saturated by the d.c. component of the primary current its magnetising branch may be assumed, pessimistically, to have zero impedance. Hence it is valid to insert the connection PQ. In the absence of a secondary e.m.f., the c.t. on feeder B will behave as a resistor having a value equal to the resistance of the secondary winding.

The equivalent circuit can be further simplified to that shown in Fig. 13.5.5C by

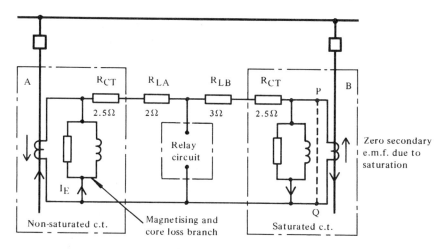

Fig. 13.5.5B   *Equivalent circuit of high-impedance scheme*

making the following assumptions:

(*a*)   For the c.t. on circuit A, the impedance of the magnetising branch and the resistance of the core loss branch are high relative to the other paths through which the secondary current can flow (i.e. the c.t. is performing almost perfectly).

(*b*)   Since, in general, all c.t.s installed for the busbar protection of a given substation will be identical, their secondary winding will have the same resistance, shown in the equivalent circuit as R_{ct}.

The secondary current from the c.t. on circuit A will divide between the relay circuit and the secondary winding of the c.t. on circuit B. If, as we shall subsequently find to be the case, the relay circuit resistance is high compared with the loop comprising the saturated c.t. and its connections, the latter can be considered to carry the whole of the current. The resultant voltage drop appears across XY and therefore across the relay circuit and this must be insufficient to operate the relay if

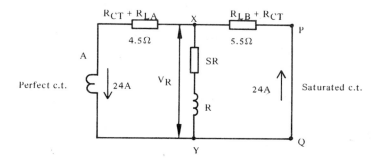

Fig. 13.5.5C   *Simplified equivalent circuit*

the protection is to remain stable. The lead burdens will nearly always differ due to variations in the distance from the relay to each three-phase of c.t.s and are shown as R_{LA} and R_{LB}.

A similar calculation must be made assuming that the c.t. on circuit A saturates and that on B behaves as a perfect c.t. Whichever voltage is the higher is referred to as the stability voltage of the system. (In this instance, for the values of resistance given in Fig. 13.5.5C, the former will be higher).

The relay circuit is shown as the relay operating coil, R, and a series resistor, SR. If the relay is of the current-operated type with adjustable settings, its resistance must be ascertained for the setting to be employed. The selection of the current setting is discussed in Section 13.5.6. Almost invariably, the product of setting current and the corresponding resistance is less than the stability voltage referred to above and the value of the resistor SR is calculated so that the product of the relay setting current and the sum of relay resistance and stabilising resistor (SR) is equal to, or slightly greater than, the stability voltage V_S. It is apparent from this how the stabilising resistor became so-called.

Summarising the stability calculation, the stability voltage must be determined from:

$$V_S = I_F T(R_L + R_{ct}) \qquad\qquad 13.5.1$$

and, for relays with current calibration,

$$I_S (R_R + R_{SR}) \geqslant V_S \qquad\qquad 13.5.2$$

while, for relays calibrated in voltage:

$$\text{setting} \geqslant V_S \qquad\qquad 13.5.3$$

where:

$I_F =$	fault current in primary amps
$I_S =$	setting of relay in amps
$R_{ct} =$	secondary winding resistance of c.t. at 75°C
$R_L = R_{LA}, R_{LB} =$	resistance of leads between relay and the c.t. of circuits A or B (total for the loop)
$R_R =$	resistance of relay coil
$R_{SR} =$	resistance of stabilising resistor

$$T = \qquad\qquad \text{turns ratio of c.t.}$$

$$V_S = \qquad\qquad \text{stability voltage}$$

Let us take, as an example, the circuit of Fig. 13.5.5B with resistances as shown, a c.t. ratio of 1/2000 turns and a maximum fault current of 50 kA.

Substituting in eqn. 13.5.1 to obtain the stability voltage, firstly assuming saturation of the c.t. of circuit A:

$$V_S = \frac{50000}{2000} (2 + 2 \cdot 5)$$

$$= 112 \cdot 5 \text{ V}$$

and then for saturation of the c.t. of circuit B:

$$V_S = \frac{50000}{2000} (3 + 2 \cdot 5)$$

$$= 137 \cdot 5 \text{ V}$$

If the relay to be used is of a type calibrated in current and having a burden at setting of 0·5 VA we could select one having a setting range of 20 to 80% of 1 A and use the 0·5 A tap, at which the impedance is:

$$\frac{VA}{I_S{}^2} = \frac{0 \cdot 5}{0 \cdot 5^2} = 2 \ \Omega$$

Unless the relay has a low power factor, this may be taken on the coil resistance R_R; otherwise the resistive component, R_R should be determined.
Rearranging eqn. 13.5.3 to give R_{SR},

$$R_{SR} \geqslant \frac{V_S}{I_S} - R_R$$

$$\geqslant \frac{137 \cdot 5}{0 \cdot 5} - 2$$

$$\geqslant 273 \ \Omega$$

Alternatively, a setting range of 10-40% of 0·5 A could have been chosen and the calculation based on the use of the 20% (0·1 A) tap, in which case the stabilising resistor should have a minimum value of $(1375 - R_R) \ \Omega$.

If a relay calibrated in voltage were used in this application, it would merely be necessary to select a setting equal to, or greater than, 137·5 V. One design of such a relay has settings in 25 V steps from 25-175 V, and in this case the 150 V setting would be used.

13.5.6 Basic principles of high-impedance circulating current busbar protection: operation

One of the main requirements to ensure reliable and fast operation of this type of protection on internal faults is that all current transformers must have a knee-point voltage which is at least twice the setting voltage of the relay circuit. For the example just considered, therefore, the c.t.s should have a knee-point voltage of at least 275 V (or 300 V in the case where the relay is set to 150 V).

The maximum internal fault current will usually be the same as that for the stability condition and if we look at the current flowing in the secondary circuit (as shown in Fig. 13.5.6A) it is seen that the c.t. attempts to drive 25 A through the relay circuit. Since, in one solution to the previous example, the resistance of the relay circuit was 1375 Ω (and could be higher for a voltage calibrated relay) it would appear that the voltage across the relay circuit could be 34·4 kV or more. Due to the limitation imposed by its core entering saturation on each half-cycle, no practical c.t. could produce a voltage of this value but it could produce spikes of very high voltage around the instants of zero flux as explained in the chapter on c.t.s and v.t.s.

A formula due to Mathews (see Bibliography) gives a reasonable approximation to the peak voltage produced under these conditions:

$$V_{pk} = 2\sqrt{2V_f\,V_k}$$ 13.5.4

where:

V_{pk} is the peak value of the distorted voltage waveform

V_f is the r.m.s. value of the voltage that would appear if the c.t. did not saturate

V_k is the knee-point voltage of the c.t.

For example, V_f is the voltage of 34·4 kV already referred to and V_k is say 275 V, just meeting the requirement of twice the setting voltage.

Hence,

$$V_{pk} = 8·7 \text{ kV}$$

To protect the c.t.s, the secondary wiring and the relay from damage due to such a high voltage, a nonlinear resistor is connected across points XY as shown in Fig. 13.5.6A if the peak voltage would exceed 3 kV. This resistor is of the type which reduces in value as the voltage across it increases and is selected with characteristics which limit the voltage to between 1 kV and 2 kV. The nonlinear resistors used for this purpose contain a large proportion of silicon carbide or similar material manufactured as discs. The properties of the material, coupled with the dimensions, give the required characteristics.

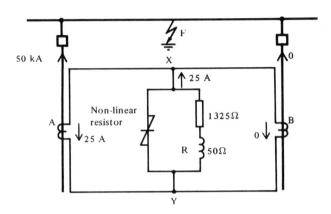

Fig. 13.5.6A *Connection of voltage-limiting device*

The voltage is applied between the two circular faces of the disc by connections which ensure contact with the material over the whole of each area.

The resistor current and applied voltage are related by the following expression:

$$V = kI^\beta \qquad\qquad 13.5.5$$

where β varies from 0·2 to 0·25 and k is controlled by the dimensions.

For nonlinear resistors used for high-impedance protection, k usually has a value between 200 and 1000. Because the manufacturing process is such that there are large tolerance on both β and k, it is an advantage to specify the limits of voltage at the maximum current and also the maximum value of β.

The relationship in eqn. 13.5.5 only applies to instantaneous values of current and voltage and therefore if the current is sinusoidal the voltage waveform will not be. For this and a number of other reasons (thermal rating, for example) calculations for the selection of suitable nonlinear resistors for busbar protection should be supported by the results of tests on a typical installation.

A necessary part of the design of high-impedance circulating current protection is the calculation of the fault setting, sometimes referred to as primary operating current (p.o.c.).

An internal fault, whose magnitude is just sufficient to cause operation of the relay, will result in a voltage between X and Y (Fig. 13.5.6A) equal to the setting voltage of the relay circuit. The currents which, at this voltage, pass through each component and all the c.t. magnetising and core loss branches will, when added together and referred through the ideal c.t., equal the fault setting in primary amps. The relevant components and parts of the c.t. equivalent circuits are shown in Fig. 13.5.6B and it will be seen that an additional resistor, R_{SH}, has been added in parallel with the relay circuit. This shunt setting resistor is fitted when it is required to raise the fault setting above that which would otherwise obtain. Reasons for doing this are given in Section 13.6.10.

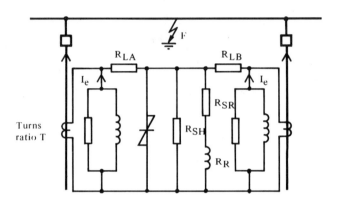

Fig. 13.5.6B   *Equivalent circuit for internal fault condition*

The primary fault setting is calculated from:

$$I_F = (nI_e + rI_R + I_{SR} + I_{NLR} + I_{SH}) \div T \qquad\qquad 13.5.6$$

where:

$n =$ number of c.t.s in parallel

$I_e =$ exciting current of each c.t. at relay circuit setting voltage

$I_R =$ relay current at setting

$I_{NLR} =$ current in nonlinear resistor at relay circuit setting voltage

$I_{SH} =$ shunt setting resistor current at relay circuit setting voltage

$I_{SR} =$ supervision relay current at main relay setting voltage

$$r = \quad \text{number of relays in parallel}$$

$$T = \quad \text{current transformer turns ratio.}$$

If the relays have a range of current settings, it is frequently possible to avoid the need for a shunt setting resistor by selecting the relay setting to give the required fault setting. Where, however, there is a variable number of relays in service depending on the running arrangements of the substation, for example for busbar protection discriminating zones, it is usual to select as low a relay current setting as possible in order that the fault setting does not vary too widely and to fit a shunt setting resistor.

It is usual to assume that:

(i) I_e is in phase with the resistive currents
(ii) I_{NLR} is sinusoidal with a peak value calculated from eqn. 13.5.5.

These assumptions simplify the calculation and tend to give a slightly pessimistic result, that is a higher setting than will be found by injecting current through one c.t. and increasing the current until the relay operation. The calculated setting is adequate for most purposes. The c.t. exciting current is usually obtained from the manufacturer's estimated curve but can be obtained from test certificates or measurements made on site.

13.5.7   Extension of the basic principles to busbar protection

The basic principles just described are applicable to busbar protection with few changes.

In the stability calculation, there is a larger number of c.t.s to consider and the lead resistance between the relay and each c.t. in turn must be considered in order to find the circuit which gives the highest stability voltage. If the c.t.s do not all have the same secondary resistance, this should also be taken into account; this occurs chiefly when a substation is extended with a different design of switchgear or separately mounted post-type c.t.s. Modern practice is to connect the c.t.s by buswire rings as will be described later and the resistance between relay and c.t. must take account of the parallel paths formed by the two routes provided by the ring.

When calculating the fault setting there will also be a larger number of c.t.s in parallel corresponding in general to the number of circuits connected to a given zone. Also, as can be seen from Fig. 13.5.9A, the number of c.t.s in parallel at double busbar substations can depend on the number of circuits selected to a given busbar. With busbar protection in particular, it is now common practice to fit more than one relay per zone and the current passed by the additional relays must be included when calculating the fault setting. For the reasons given in Section 13.6.10, control over the fault setting is also required and once the relay type has been decided and the c.t.s designed, this is achieved mainly by the selection of the value for the shunt resistor.

13.5.8   Types of high-impedance relays

A common form of relay used is the attracted armature type whose current setting may be around 30 mA, and it has a relatively high stabilising resistor connected in series with it to give it the voltage setting determined by the stability requirements. Its operating time will be less than 60 ms at twice the setting current.

Another form of attracted armature relay circuit incorporates a capacitor in series with the operating coil, which renders the relay insensitive to any d.c. voltage which may be present during the first few cycles of fault current. The relay is given the required voltage setting by the addition of linear and nonlinear resistors, and its circuit is shown in Fig. 13.5.8A. The use of the latter ensures high operating speeds at small increments above the setting voltage, since the current rises more rapidly than the voltage. With this relay it is not necessary to take into account the possibility of almost twice the calculated sinusoidal a.c. current flowing during the first few cycles.

Developed from this is a similar relay in which the nonlinear resistors are replaced by ohmic resistors.

Because of the distorted waveform of the current through the relay during stability and operation, only certain relays are suitable for high-impedance circulating current protection. For this reason, relays should be selected from types which have been tested in conjunction with typical c.t.s to demonstrate that they give the performance predicted by calculation. In these tests the current or the lead burden will have been increased until the system becomes unstable, showing that there is a factor of safety in the calculations varying, for typical relays, from 1·4 to 2. From the earlier calculation of stabilising resistor value, or relay voltage setting, it appeared that the relay would be just on the point of operating for a fault of maximum severity and with the most adverse of other conditions. However, because of the pessimistic assumptions made in the calculation, this factor of safety ensures that the required stability is achieved without introducing other factors to increase the setting voltage above the value given by eqn. 13.5.1.

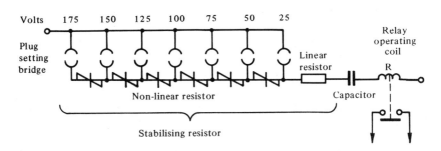

Fig. 13.5.8A   *Relay with capacitor and nonlinear stabilising resistors*

13.5.9 Practical high-impedance installations

For the reasons already given, most of the high-impedance schemes which have been installed are of the phase and earth-fault type, employing three-pole relays instead of the single-pole relays which would be required for earth-fault only schemes. The three-pole relay scheme has the additional advantage of enabling lower earth-fault settings to be achieved for the same size of switchboard.

The early installations employed only one relay for each check and discriminating zone, as shown in Fig. 13.5.9A. The disadvantage of busbar protection schemes employing relays controlling the tripping of more than one circuit breaker was that the protection tended to be taken out of service more often than was necessary, because of the fear of causing maltripping while testing. It is now recognised that the consequence of a busbar fault, when the busbar protection is not in service, can be considerably more serious than that of a possible maloperation while testing. It was from the desire to reduce the risks of maloperation to a minimum and to eliminate the difficulties associated with taking the busbar protection out of service for normal commissioning and maintenance purposes that the scheme of Fig.13.5.9B was developed for 400 kV substations. Maintenance of this type of installation, employing separate a.c. relays for each circuit breaker, is very much easier than it is with installations employing only one relay per zone, and can be carried out with the protection in service. The absence of auxiliary switches in the d.c. circuits results in a simpler scheme and therefore one which is less likely to fail to operate when required to do so. The scheme is designed in accordance with the principles described in Section 13.5.5 and 13.5.6, and although there are now several relays in parallel per zone a satisfactory fault setting can still be obtained by using relays with a low current at setting so that the total current required for their operation is still low.

Since individual relay rooms are provided at British 400 kV double busbar substations using open-terminal switchgear, that is to say one room adjacent to each circuit breaker, the *per circuit* high-impedance relays and the associated trip relays are accommodated therein. It will be seen that bus section and bus coupler switches require three high-impedance relays, namely one for the check zone, and two for discriminating zones. Each relay room is equipped with a 110 V battery and this supplies the local relays.

Since the introduction of this system with its *per circuit* relays, the need to achieve reliable, fast clearance of busbar faults has assumed even greater importance. Although relay failures have been small in number, it was considered necessary to cater for such a situation by connecting to the a.c. buswires per zone relays, the contacts of which are connected to d.c. buswires (now known as back-trip buswires) in order to trip each circuit breaker selected to the faulty zone so providing a second independent tripping route for each circuit breaker.

A simplified diagram, Fig. 13.5.9C shows how the *per zone* relays are incorporated with separate trip relays and with the use of three tripping batteries, i.e. '1' and '2' in the relay rooms of circuits 1 and 2, respectively, and 'STN', the station common battery. Apart from the c.t.s and their associated bus-wiring there is

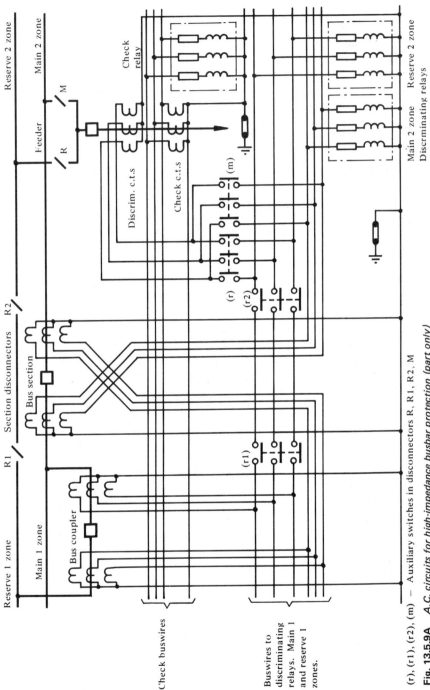

(r), (r1), (r2), (m) — Auxiliary switches in disconnectors R, R1, R2, M

Fig. 13.5.9A *A.C. circuits for high-impedance busbar protection (part only)*

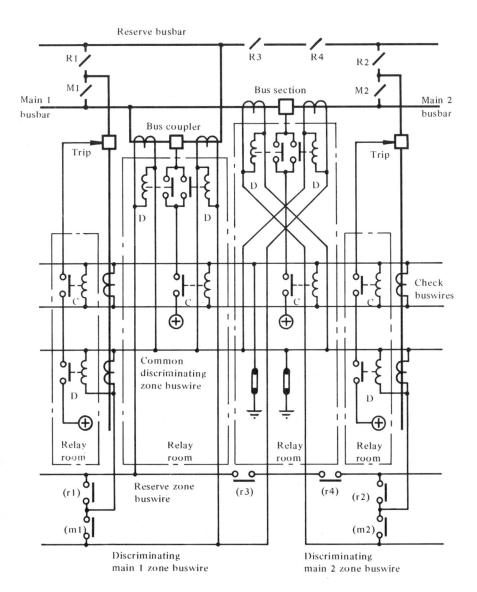

Reserve busbar

R 1

M 1

Main 1
busbar

Trip

Bus coupler

D   D

R 3   R 4

Bus section

D   D

R 2

M 2

Trip

Main 2
busbar

C   C   C   C

Check
buswires

Common
discriminating
zone buswire

D   D

Relay
room

Relay
room

Relay
room

Relay
room

(r1)   Reserve zone   (r3)   (r4)   (r2)
buswire

(m1)   (m2)

Discriminating
main 1 zone buswire

Discriminating
main 2 zone buswire

Note: (1) All c.t.s are 1/2000 turns ratio
        (2) Relays are high impedance type shunted by
            non—linear resistors (not shown)

Fig. 13.5.9B *Simplified a.c. and d.c. circuits of busbar protection for a 400 kV substation
with individual relay rooms*

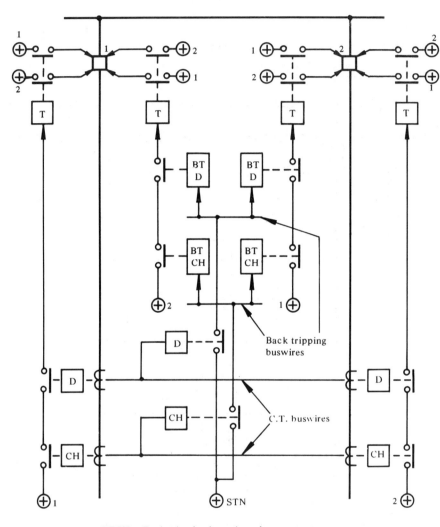

BTCH — Back trip check receive relay
BTD — Back trip discriminating receive relay
CH — Check zone high impedance relay
D — Discriminating zone high impedance relay
T — Tripping relay

Fig. 13.5.9C *Simplified arrangement of MkII 400 kV busbar protection*

duplication of the fault-detecting and trip-processing arrangements. Even the failure of one of the d.c. supplies could not, by itself, be the cause of a circuit breaker not tripping when required to do so for a busbar fault. This reliability is aided considerably by the existence of duplicate trip coils — a standard feature of 400 kV circuit breakers. The back-trip discriminating relays would be connected to the buswires via auxiliary switches on the bus selector disconnectors, but these have been omitted in this diagram to illustrate the basic principle more clearly.

The arrangement in Fig. 13.5.9C has, in England and Wales, become known as Mk II 400 kV busbar protection and that in Fig. 13.5.9B as Mk I.

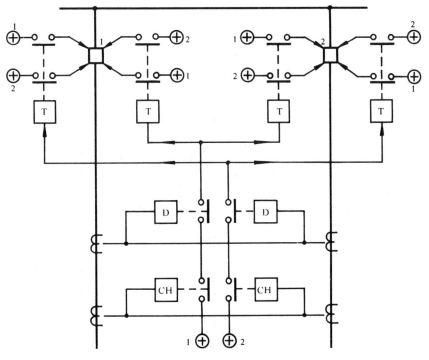

CH — Check zone high impedance relay
D   — Discriminating zone high impedance relay
T   — Tripping relay

Fig. 13.5.9D   *Simplified arrangement of MkII 275 kV busbar protection*

A large part of the 275 kV system was complete before the principle of *per circuit* high-impedance relays was adopted for 400 kV busbar protection so that, although similar arguments applied, the practice of depending on *per circuit* relays had become well established. This factor, coupled with the exclusive use of common relay rooms led to the required improvements being achieved by duplication of the high-impedance relays and the busbar protection trip relays. Since the

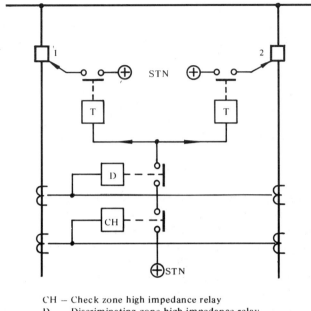

CH – Check zone high impedance relay
D   – Discriminating zone high impedance relay
T   – Tripping relay

Fig. 13.5.9E   *Simplified arrangement of Mk.I 132 kV busbar protection*

station batteries have been very reliable, this single source of d.c. was considered adequate but duplicate supplies have been derived, where practicable, from the battery distribution board via separately cabled and fused ring mains or radial feeders. The simplified diagram of Mk II 275 kV busbar protection is shown in Fig. 13.5.9D.

At 132 kV the measures requiring duplication of relays and associated circuits are not justified and the simplified diagram of Fig. 13.5.9E shows a typical arrangement.

13.6   Practical considerations

13.6.1   Factors affecting the position of c.t.s in busbars

Although it is common for one or more bus section circuit breakers to be installed in the main busbar, provision for sectionalisation of the reserve busbar is, with a few exceptions, by means of disconnectors.

To obtain correct performance of busbar protection, it is necessary to consider at the outset where the c.t.s are to be located. Previous references to the zones of busbar protection have implied that there is only one check zone. For the present this assumption will be maintained. Check zone c.t.s are only required in outgoing or incoming circuits since the summation of the currents in all such circuits will show whether or not there is a fault within the overall busbar zone shown in Fig. 13.2.1A. Bus section and bus coupler circuit breakers do not have check zone c.t.s since the circuit breakers are only carrying current between discriminating zones within a given switchboard. This is shown in Fig. 13.5.9A, from which it is also seen that the discriminating c.t.s are situated on the side of the circuit breaker remote from the zone to which their secondary winding is connected. This ensures that the fault of F_1 shown in Fig. 13.6.1A, anywhere between the circuit breaker contacts and the c.t.s on the Main 1 side of the circuit breaker, would be detected as within the Main 1 Zone and result in the tripping of all circuit breakers selected to the Main 1 Busbar. A fault in the position just mentioned would also be detected by the Main 2 Zone, perhaps unnecessarily since opening the bus section circuit breaker may clear the infeed from the Main 2 Zone. If, however, the fault is within the circuit breaker itself, it might not be interrupted when the circuit breaker opened and the tripping of all circuit breakers selected to Main 2 Busbar would be essential to the interruption of the fault. Similar arguments apply for tripping both of these sections for a fault at F_2. This overlapping of the discriminating zone c.t.s at a bus section (or bus coupler) circuit breaker is therefore necessary for the rapid clearance of such faults, not withstanding the fact that the provision of c.t.s on both sides of bus section and bus coupler circuit breakers is, with some types of switchgear, an expensive item.

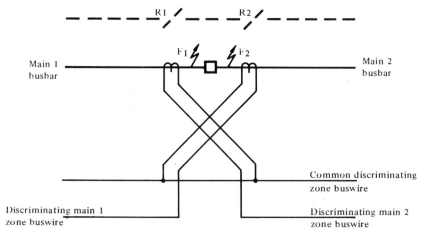

Fig. 13.6.1A *Discriminating main zone connections at a bus section*

It will be noted from Fig. 13.6.1B that c.t.s are not required in the reserve busbar between the Reserve 1 and Reserve 2 Zones when these are only separated by disconnectors. In the absence of a circuit breaker between disconnectors R3 and R4 it is necessary, when these are both closed, to connect the Reserve 1 Zone and Reserve 2 Zone buswires through auxiliary switches on R1 and R2. In the absence of such a connection, a fault at F_1 shown in Fig. 13.6.1B would result in instability of both reserve zones since the current flowing through R3 and R4 would not appear as a secondary current in the buswires and therefore each zone would be unbalanced by the corresponding amount, which would flow through the high-impedance relays and any parallel paths. If only one of the disconnectors is closed,

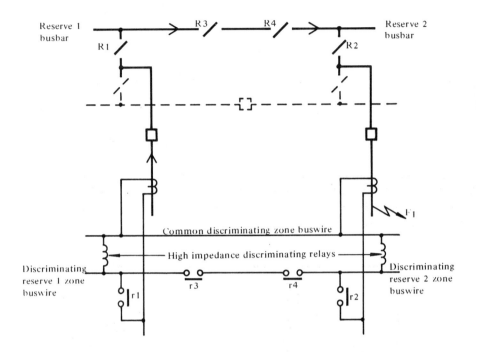

Note: Disconnectors R1, R2, R3 and R4 closed

Fig. 13.6.1B   *Discriminating reserve zone connections at a bus section*

say R3, the section of busbar between R3 and R4 becomes part of the associated discriminating zone.

13.6.2   Effect of c.t. location in outgoing circuits

The position where the current transformers for the circuit and the busbar protection are fitted on outgoing circuits varies according to the type of the switchgear.

(a)   C.t.s overlapping the circuit breaker: Fig. 13.6.2A(a) shows the arrangement of c.t.s fitted on both sides of the circuit breaker which is common in outdoor bulk oil types and metalclad SF_6 insulated switchgear. The performance of the protection will now be considered for the faults F_1 to F_4.

A fault at F_1 is a busbar fault which should be cleared by the busbar protection. Fault F_2 is a circuit fault and should be cleared by the circuit protection. F_3 is a busbar fault but because of its position would cause both busbar and circuit protection to operate and the fault will be cleared, although the circuit breaker at the remote end of the circuit may also be tripped. Although F_4 is a circuit fault, it may be detected by both circuit and busbar protection depending on their relative operating times. Thus, circuit breakers selected to the busbar may be opened unnecessarily for a circuit fault. This disadvantage is acceptable in view of the low incidence of such faults.

(*b*)   *C.t.s on the circuit side of the circuit breaker:* Fig. 13.6.2A(b) shows the most common arrangement of current transformer location for airblast switchgear and other designs employing post type c.t.s. Faults F_1 and F_2 should be correctly cleared as before, but F_3 will only cause operation of the busbar protection, because the fault is outside the circuit protection zone. Thus, the fault may remain fed from the remote end of the circuit. Arrangements must, therefore, be made to cause the circuit breaker at the remote end to trip in these circumstances.

(i)   Direct tripping of the remote circuit breaker(s) without introducing any time delay is the fastest of the available alternatives but, for feeder circuits, depends on the existence of intertripping equipment which, on some circuits, would not otherwise be required.

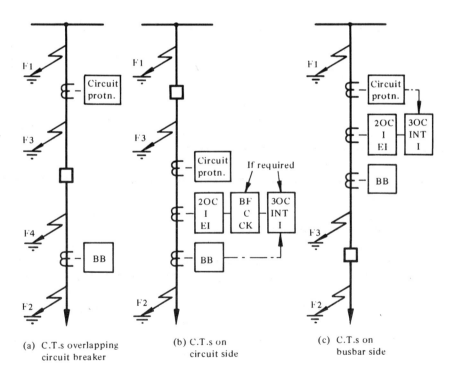

(a) C.T.s overlapping
       circuit breaker

(b) C.T.s on
      circuit side

(c) C.T.s on
       busbar side

Fig. 13.6.2A   *Effect of c.t. location on intertripping requirements*

(ii)   Each feeder circuit can be fitted with a time-lag relay set at about 100 ms, this being started by operation of the busbar protection having its contacts connected to unstabilise unit protection or to accelerate or unblock distance protection. This gives a measure of discrimination in that only the circuit on which the fault exists will have its remote end circuit breaker tripped.

(iii)   If circuit breaker fail protection is installed, it would be connected so that it is initiated by the busbar protection trip relay as well as by the circuit-protection trip relays. Circuit breaker fail protection is described later in Section 13.7, here it is sufficient to state that any fault current infed to Fault F_3 from the remote end would, provided the initiation signal has been received, maintain a current check relay in the operated position. If this condition still persists after a predetermined time the circuit breakers at the remote end of the circuit would be tripped by unstabilising unit protection or by accelerating or unblocking distance protection. It should be noted that there is no failure of the circuit breaker in the situation just described but the features of the circuit breaker fail protection are being used to advantage.

(iv)   An additional relay called an interlocked overcurrent relay can be fitted to detect any power infed at F_3 after the circuit breaker has opened. When circuit breaker fail protection is not fitted, i.e. at 132 kV and lower voltages, this method can be applied to feeders having unit protection and to generators and transformers. This relay can be either a three-pole, or a single pole with summation winding, induction-disc overcurrent type having an extremely inverse time characteristic with an operating time of about 0·3s. Its lower magnet circuit is only completed while the busbar protection keeps operated, and so if the fault persists at F_3 after the circuit breaker opens, the busbar protection will remain operated, so permitting the interlocked overcurrent relay to function and send an intertripping or unstabilising signal to the remote end of the circuit.

(v)   Where grid transformers feed busbars associated with metalclad switchgear, the busbar protection covering these busbars is arranged to trip directly both the h.v. and the l.v. circuit breakers of the transformer so eliminating any prolonged infeed to a fault at F_3.

Two grid transformers feeding different sections or voltages of busbars may be banked on a common h.v. circuit breaker. In this case the low voltage busbar protection would first trip only the grid transformer l.v. circuit breaker associated with the faulty busbar. If the fault were at F_3, then the stage 2 of the standby earth-fault protection or stage 2 of the overcurrent protection would later operate to trip the other transformer l.v. and the common h.v. circuit breakers.

(vi)   If the remote ends of the feeders connected to the busbars are fitted with distance protection, the infeed to the fault at F_3 will be cleared by the operation of the distance protection on the faulty feeder in second zone time (0·4-1·0 s) and no special arrangements are needed for 132 kV and low voltage switchgear.

(c)   C.t.s on the busbar side of the circuit breaker: In Fig. 13.6.2A(c) the faults at F_1 and F_2 will be correctly cleared. A fault at F_3 will cause the circuit protection to trip the circuit breaker, but the fault will remain fed from the busbars. The busbar protection will not operate as F_3 is outside its zone. Again, an interlocked overcurrent relay is used, but in this case, since it is the circuit protection which remains operated for the fault at F_3, it is this protection which is used to initiate operation of the interlocked overcurrent relay. If F_3 persists for about 0·3s, the interlocked overcurrent relay then operates the tripping relays of the protection of the section of busbar to which the circuit is selected.

13.6.3   Multiple check zones

Until now we have considered busbar protection systems with a single check zone, an arrangement having the advantage of relative simplicity and economy. At the larger stations, however, there may be strong reasons for departing from the concept of a single check zone and using instead two or more check zones. One consideration is that the total number of circuits may be such that it is not practicable to obtain a suitable primary fault setting from a single check zone covering the whole substation because of the number of c.t.s and, if applicable, per circuit relays in parallel. Furthermore, the provision of more than one check zone leads to greater security of the busbar protection during construction, commissioning and maintenance and may be specified for this reason alone.

At substations where only bus section circuit breakers or permanent breaks are provided to sectionalise the main and the reserve busbars, the splitting of check zones is a simple matter, only requiring the addition of check zone c.t.s either side of the bus section circuit breakers. The overlapping zones that this creates are shown in Fig. 13.6.3A. However, where there is neither a circuit breaker nor a permanent break (as is the case with the reserve busbar at the majority of double-busbar switching stations) it is necessary, in order to sectionalise the check zone, to adhere to the following rules:

(i)   The check-zone demarcation points shall in all cases coincide with discriminating zone demarcation points.

(ii)   Discriminating and check-zone currents shall each be measured by separate c.t.s at the demarcation points so as to satisfy the reasons mentioned earlier for providing two or more check zones.

(iii)   There shall be no auxiliary switches in the c.t. circuits of the check zone.

(iv)   With both of the section disconnectors open in the absence of a circuit breaker (or with the single disconnector open if only one is fitted) a fault on any part of one busbar must result in the immediate tripping of all circuit breakers

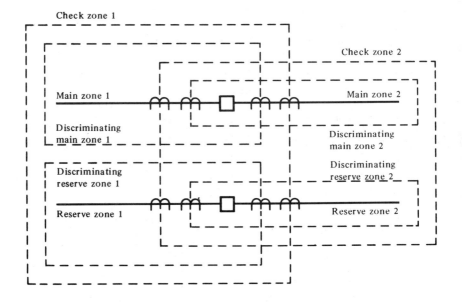

Fig. 13.6.3A   *C.T. arrangements wth section switches in both busbars*

selected to that busbar but must not result in the operation of the protection or in the tripping of circuit breakers associated with the adjacent busbar.

(v)   If both (or the single) section disconnector(s) referred to in (iv) are closed, a fault on any part of one busbar must result in the immediate tripping of all circuit breakers selected to that section of busbar and to the section connected by the disconnector(s) in question.

(vi)   On installations having duplicate section disconnectors, when one section disconnector is closed and the other open, a fault on any part of one busbar, including that part connected to it by the closed disconnector, must result in the immediate tripping of all circuit breakers connected to the faulted busbar, but must not result in the operation of protection or in the tripping of circuit breakers associated with the healthy section of the busbar.

An arrangement which meets all these requirements for the case of a single section disconnector is shown in Fig. 13.6.3B. The main busbars and bus selector disconnectors have been omitted for clarity. A fault occurring at F_1 with the disconnector open is within check zone 2 and discriminating zone R2; c.t.s on circuits through which current flows to the fault will energise the check zone 2 and discriminating reserve 2 zone a.c. buswires, operating the *per zone* and *per circuit* relays connected thereto, so tripping all circuits connected to the reserve zone. Neither check zone 1 nor discriminating reserve 1 zone a.c. relays will operate for this fault whether the section disconnector is open or closed, but in the latter case circuits connected to

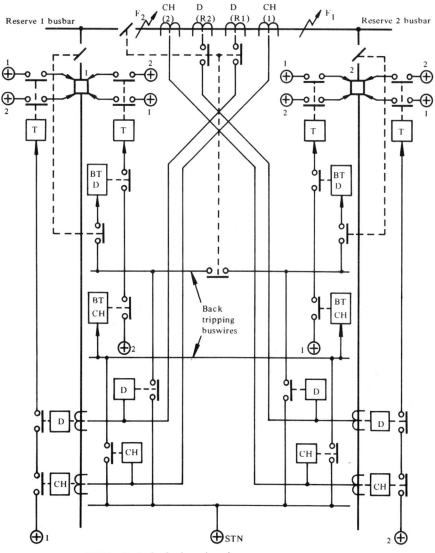

BTCH — Backtrip check receive relay
BTD — Back trip discriminating receive relay
CH — Check zone high impedance relay
D — Discriminating zone high impedance relay
T — Tripping relay

Fig. 13.6.3B   *Simplified arrangement of Mk.II 400 kV busbar protection with two check zones and a single reserve section disconnector*

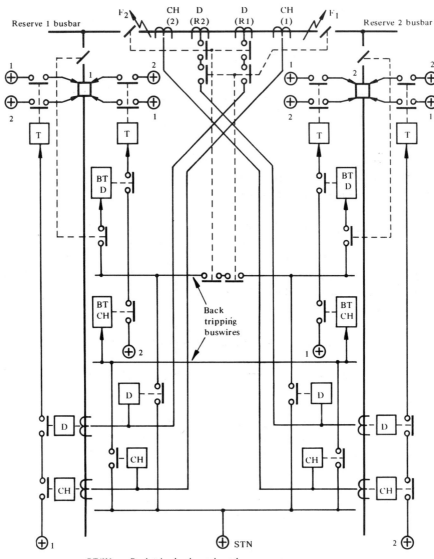

BTCH – Back trip check receive relay
BTD   – Back trip discriminating receive relay
CH   – Check zone high impedance relay
D   – Discriminating zone high impedance relay
T   – Tripping relay

Fig. 13.6.3C *Simplified arrangement of Mk.II 400 kV busbar protection with two check zones and duplicate reserve section disconnectors*

reserve 1 busbar will be tripped from the zone 2 *per zone* relays via the back-tripping system.

If we now consider the fault to be at F_2, again with the section disconnector open, the check 1 zone relays will operate but check 2 zone will be stable. Since the discriminating zone c.t.s in the busbar are disconnected by the disconnector switch their output will not be available to stabilise the reserve 2 zone and so its *per zone* and *per circuit* relays will operate. The back-trip receive relays of Section 2 will be operated by the *per zone* relays of check 1 zone and discriminating reserve 2 zone. A fault in this position with the disconnector closed would be detected by check 1 zone and discriminating reserve 1 zone which would result in the direct tripping of circuit breakers in Section 1 while those of Section 2 would be opened via the back-tripping system.

If two disconnectors are installed between sections of busbar, the c.t. secondaries must be connected as shown in Fig. 13.6.3C. With the left-hand section disconnector open and the right-hand one closed, a fault at F_2 would be cleared in the same way as has just been described for F_2 in Fig. 13.6.3B. Conversely, a fault at F_1, with the left-hand section disconnector closed and the right-hand one open, would be cleared in a similar manner, but with the back-trip receive relays of Section 1 operated by the *per zone* relays of the check 1 zone and the discriminating reserve 2 zone.

With both disconnectors closed, a fault in either position would be detected by the check and discriminating zones within which it has occurred, resulting in the direct tripping of circuits selected to the corresponding section of busbar, while those of the adjacent section would have their circuit breakers opened via the back-tripping system.

13.6.4 Busbar selector auxiliary switches

In a limited number of busbar installations it is not possible to carry out on-load transfers of a circuit from, say, the main busbar to the reserve. In this case it is necessary to have auxiliary switches fitted in only one of the busbar selectors (say the main busbar), and they are connected so that when a circuit is not selected to the main busbar, it is assumed that it is selected to the reserve, Fig. 13.6.4A shows this. With the more usual on-load selection possible with outdoor switchgear, the condition of both selectors simultaneously closed must be allowed for, and so auxiliary switch contacts are fitted in each busbar selector, as shown in Fig. 13.5.9A.

The relative times of opening and closing of busbar selector contacts to their auxiliary switches is important. When closing a busbar selector, its auxiliary switch must close before the main contacts close or pre-arc. When opening the selector, the primary contacts must all open before the auxiliary contacts open. The need for this can be seen in Fig. 13.6.4B where an on-load changeover of a feeder is being made from the main to the reserve busbars. Let the current distribution in the primary and secondary circuits be as shown and assume that the c.t. ratio is unity.

In Fig. 13.6.4B, the current of three units is entering the main busbar from feeder A, passing through the bus coupler and leaving the reserve busbar via feeder B. The c.t. secondary currents circulate as shown in Fig. 13.6.4B(a) and both main and reserve busbar discriminating relays remain unoperated. If now the contacts of the reserve busbar selector of feeder A close before its auxiliary switches, then a

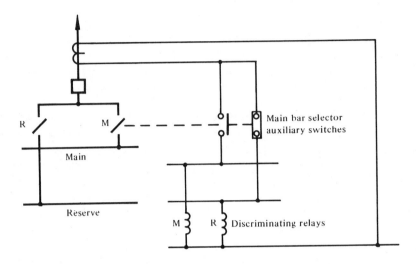

Fig. 13.6.4A   *C.T. selection by only one busbar selector*

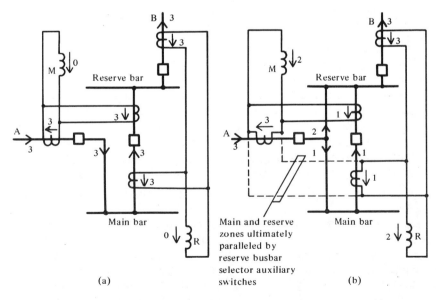

Fig. 13.6.4B   *Instability due to reserve busbar disconnector contacts closing before auxiliary switches*

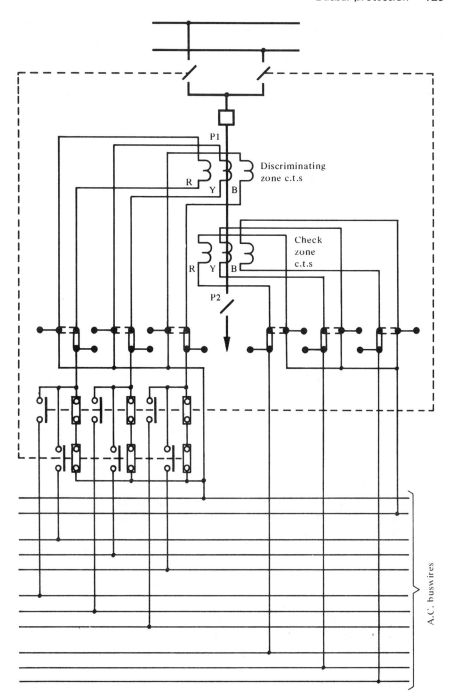

Fig. 13.6.4C   *Busbar selector auxiliary switch connections*

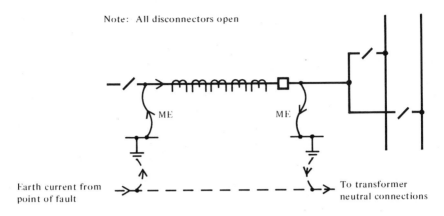

ME - Fixed or portable maintenance earth

Fig. 13.6.4D   *Possible fault current path through c.t.s. of earthed circuit breaker*

current distribution, as shown in the Fig. 13.6.4B(b) causing instability may arise before the auxiliary switches parallel both main and reserve discriminating zones, as shown by the dotted lines.

By consideration of similar current distribution during opening a busbar selector, it can be seen that instability will again occur if the auxiliary switches do not open after the main contacts, that is, auxiliary switches must make early and break late.

Measures must be taken to ensure that, with both busbar selectors for a given circuit open, the c.t. secondary connections are not left open-circuited. Where *per circuit* high-impedance relays are fitted these would still be connected to the c.t.s as can be seen from Fig. 13.5.9B. In other cases auxiliary switches must be connected to short-circuit the discriminating c.t.s as shown in Fig. 13.6.4C. If they were left open-circuited there is the risk of damage to the insulation of the secondary winding due to, say, maintenance earths on either side allowing current in the substation earth mat to be diverted through the c.t. primary winding during a fault elsewhere in the substation, or even externally to it, as shown in Fig. 13.6.4D.

13.6.5   C.T. test links

To enable c.t. secondary currents to be readily measured without disturbing any secondary wiring, c.t. test links are fitted in every set of discriminating and check c.t.s. These can be seen in Fig. 13.6.4C. They also have a changeover position whereby the c.t.s are disconnected from the scheme wiring and short-circuited, and this position may be used when a feeder is out of service and having current injected through its c.t.s for test purposes, as it permits the busbar protection to safely remain in service to cover all the live busbars.

13.6.6 Precautions against maloperation of busbar protection

As described earlier, the use of duplicate lines of defence, requiring the simultaneous operation of separate discriminating and check systems before tripping takes place, is one of the most important methods of avoiding maloperation of busbar protection. Whereas maloperation of the protection for an individual circuit normally results in the wrong tripping of one or two circuit breakers, maloperation of busbar protection may completely shut down a whole section of busbar. Also, busbar protection d.c. circuits are arranged so that the inadvertent operation of any one relay will, at the most, only trip a single circuit breaker.

Reliability of busbar protection is improved by avoiding the use of auxiliary switches in the check system. Where they occur in the discriminating system British practice follows one of the following alternatives:

(a)   When disconnector auxiliary switches have been specifically approved for switching current transformer circuits, single contacts are used throughout.

(b)   When the auxiliary switches have not received such approval, two silver-plated switches connected in parallel are used where contacts are open when the disconnector is open and one silver-plated switch is used where contacts are closed when the disconnector is open.

Further precautions can be taken by fitting relays to constantly supervise the integrity of the c.t. circuits. The present method is to fit a sensitive supervision relay S in parallel with the main protection relay E. The system primary load currents will cause an out-of-balance c.t. secondary current if any connection or c.t. becomes faulty. This method depends on there being sufficiently high load current in the primary circuit which has the defective c.t. (or wiring) to operate relay S.

With this in mind, it is usual to specify that the primary operating current of the supervision relay lies between 1 and 5% of the rated current of the switchgear; for discriminating zones this current will vary with the number of circuits selected to the zone (because of the number of c.t.s connected to the relay a.c. circuit) but the minimum and maximum values should be within the foregoing limits. Circuits with a low full load current relative to other circuits in the same zone present a problem since the normal load current may, in the event of an open circuit in one of its c.t. secondary circuits, be insufficient to operate the supervision relay. The only action that can be taken in such circumstances is to set the supervision relay to give as low a primary setting as possible within the limits mentioned previously.

Inevitably there will be situations where, for part of the time, the supervision relay would not operate on the occurrence of an open circuit in the secondary circuit of one of the c.t.s because the current flowing at the time is below the primary setting. The risk of instability due to such an open circuit remaining undetected is accepted in view of the low incidence of open circuits in the c.t. secondary wiring coupled with the coincident low probability of a busbar fault.

The operation of the supervision relay starts a time lag relay which after, say, 3–5s brings up an alarm that the particular discriminating or check zone is defective. Originally an auxiliary relay, which operated after the time delay, was arranged to switch out this defective zone by short-circuiting the c.t. bus wiring and interrupting the d.c. supplies. The supervision relay would always have operated for a busbar fault, and the time lag was provided to ensure that operation of the protection would not be interfered with.

A reassessment of the priorities led, with the advent of the 400 kV system, to the abandonment of buswire shorting. Retaining the busbar protection in service so that it will operate for a genuine busbar fault is now considered essential. The incorrect operation of the relays in the faulty zone on the occurrence of a fault external to that zone, should one happen before the open-circuit connection is located and repaired, presents a tolerable risk particularly since it would require the complementary zone (check or discriminating, as appropriate) to become unstable before circuit breakers were tripped. The absence of buswire short-circuiting relays does require special consideration of the rating of relays and associated components as explained in Section 13.6.10.

13.6.7. Tripping and alarm circuit arrangements

The tripping sequences of the d.c. relays in busbar protection installations are arranged such that the operation of any relay in error, or by vibration, does not cause more than one circuit to trip. Figs. 13.5.3E and F show the two most common arrangements. The arrangement comprising one tripping relay per circuit, as shown in Fig. 13.5.3E, permits the trip circuit selection to be achieved in the relay operating coil circuit instead of in the actual circuit breaker trip coil circuit as is done in the multi-contact tripping relay method shown in Fig. 13.5.3F. In large substations with circuit breaker trip coil currents of 30A or more, the voltage drops in the leads may well prohibit the use of multicontact tripping relays. Trip testing from busbar protection can also be more safely carried out from schemes using individual tripping relays.

Whenever practicable, the d.c. wiring for busbar protection should be segregated from other wiring to reduce the possibility of multiple inadvertent tripping.

Fig. 13.6.7A shows one possible arrangement of d.c. isolating links fitted in the contact circuits of the individual tripping relays on the busbar protection panel. The advantage of the duplication of links, as shown in the figure, is that when it is desired to make every wire dead in the busbar protection panel, as, for instance, when making alterations or extensions to the panel, the links are removed at every circuit relay panel. Similarly, the links are removed at the busbar protection panel if it is desired to make the relay panel wiring dead. If secondary injection is being carried out to prove the busbar protection relays, it is necessary to remove the links only at the busbar protection panel. To prove the final trip testing of the circuits, the links are then replaced one pair at a time.

With the increased complexity of protection on circuits at the higher system voltages, coupled with the use of duplicate trip coils, the number of links for all purposes has tended to become unacceptably high, both from consideration of the space required and the appreciation by the field engineer of the purpose of them. As a result other arrangements will frequently be found such as the fitting of links or disconnecting points in only one wire of a pair of trip relay contact connections.

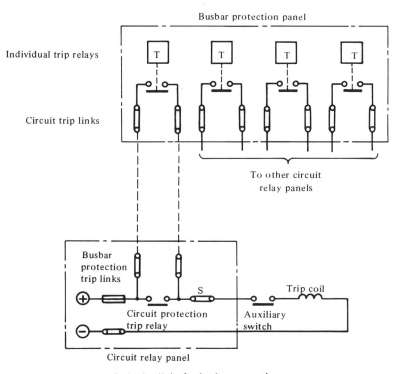

Fig. 13.6.7A *Arrangement of tripping links for busbar protection*

A disconnecting point is usually an integral part of a relay panel terminal block, such as a removable plug connecting the two wires to a given way.

As described earlier, a 'busbar protection defective' alarm is given after a time delay of 3-5 s when a sensitive supervision relay operates for a fault in the c.t. circuits, leads, buswiring etc. The operation of intermediate manually reset d.c. relays, if any, can also be arranged to give an alarm.

The d.c. supplies for busbar protection can be monitored by a normally energised protection supply supervision relay which gives a 'protection supply fail' alarm when it drops off.

On the occurrence of a busbar fault an indication is given showing exactly which zone of busbar protection has operated, this being achieved by contacts of the d.c. repeat relay of the check relay in series with contacts of the d.c. repeat relay of the appropriate zone discriminating relay.

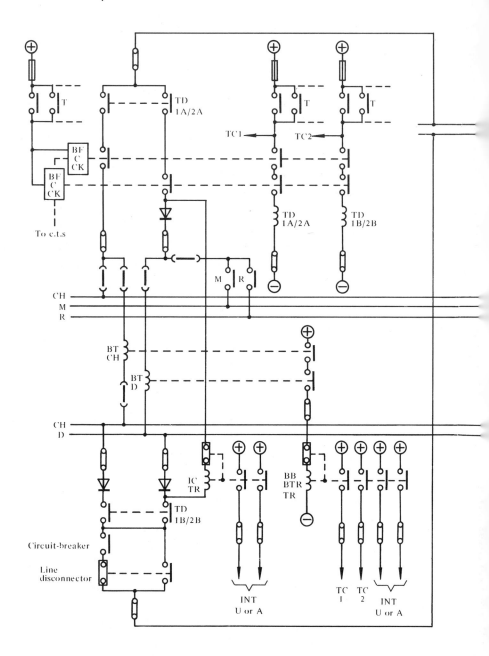

Fig. 13.6.8A *Circuit diagram of back-tripping, busbar protection and circuit breaker fail protection (feeder circuit)*

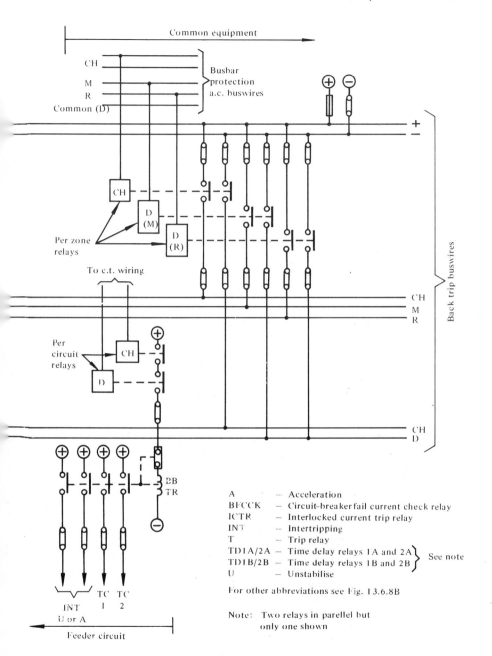

A   — Acceleration
BFCCK   — Circuit-breaker fail current check relay
ICTR   — Interlocked current trip relay
INT   — Intertripping
T   — Trip relay
TD1A/2A — Time delay relays 1A and 2A ⎫ See note
TD1B/2B — Time delay relays 1B and 2B ⎬
U   — Unstabilise

For other abbreviations see Fig. 13.6.8B

Note: Two relays in parellel but
          only one shown

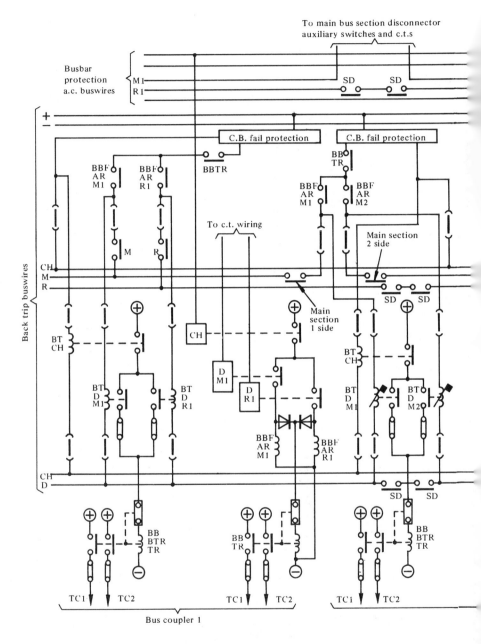

Fig. 13.6.8B   *Circuit diagram of back tripping and per circuit busbar protection relays for bus coupler 1 and bus section 1-2 (400 kV)*

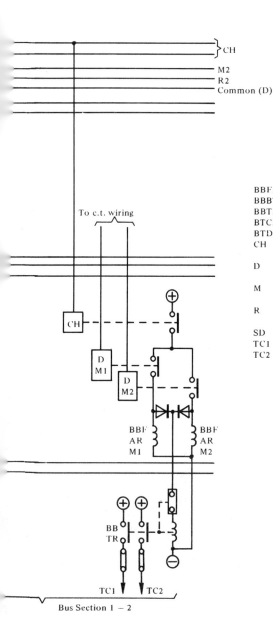

Bus Section 1 — 2

BBFAR   — Busbar fault auxiliary relay
BBBTRTR —   Busbar back trip receive trip relay
BBTR   — Busbar trip relay
BTCH   — Back trip check receive relay
BTD   — Back trip discriminating receive relay
CH   — Check zone (buswire or
              high impedance relay)
D   — Discriminating zone (buswire or
              high impedance relay)
M   — Main zone (buswire, auxiliary
              switch or high impedance relay)
R   — Reserve zone (buswire, auxiliary
              switch or high impedance relay)
SD   — Section disconnector (reserve)
TC1   — Trip coil 1
TC2   — Trip coil 2

13.6.8 Back-tripping

Where *per circuit* high-impedance relays are used, as at 400 kV substations, there is, at a first glance, no need for d.c. buswires since each circuit breaker in a discriminating zone containing a busbar fault, would receive a trip signal initiated by its *per circuit* relay.

However, a facility known as back-tripping is required to fulfil the following functions:

(i)   To trip all circuit breakers which must be opened to clear a busbar fault detected by the imgh-impedance *per zone* check and *per zone* discriminating relays as a safeguard against the failure of a *per circuit* relay.

(ii)   On the occurrence of a fault in a section of the reserve busbar at a substation with more than one check zone, to trip the circuit breakers of adjacent sections when the section disconnectors are closed.

(iii)   To trip all circuit breakers connected to the section of busbars to which is connected a generator circuit breaker of the pressurised head air-blast type in the event of a sudden loss of air pressure.   This is to guard against the consequences of an unwanted reclosure or internal flashover of the circuit breaker which could cause reconnection of the generator out of synchronism.

(iv)   Where circuit breaker fail protection is fitted, to trip all the local circuit breakers necessary to disconnect a circuit breaker which has failed to clear a fault which has been detected by the appropriate protection.

A standard back-tripping system has been developed for the British 400 kV double busbar substations. It is designed to effect the high-speed tripping of all circuit breakers selected to a particular busbar and to adjacent busbars through busbar selector disconnectors or busbar section disconnectors.

The back-tripping facility comprises a discriminating system and a check system arranged so that both systems must maloperate before incorrect circuit breaker tripping due to secondary equipment defects can occur. Both back-tripping systems have double-pole switched initiation in order that the back-trip receive relays do not have to meet the more difficult requirements applying to trip relays.

One back-tripping system discriminates between sections of busbar, employing auxiliary switches on busbar section disconnectors for this purpose, and is known as the discriminating system. The other back-tripping system is known as the check system.

Receipt of back-tripping by the discriminating relays associated with individual circuit breakers is qualified by auxiliary switches on the appropriate busbar selector disconnectors in order that the required circuit breakers, and no others, are tripped.

The basic connections of the back-tripping facility are shown in Fig. 13.6.8A and Fig. 13.6.8B.

13.6.9 Test facilities

Because of the importance of busbar protection, some installations have built-in testing facilities. Current can be injected into the secondary circuits to simulate in-zone faults, and in a few installations external faults can also be simulated. Fig. 13.6.9A shows an arrangement in which instruments are built-in so that the whole testing procedure can be carried out by first switching-out by the 'protection

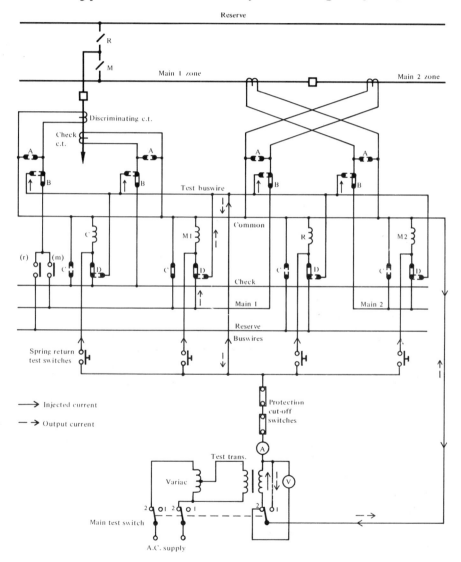

Fig. 13.6.9A   *Built-in test facilities for high-impedance busbar protection*

cut-off" (p.c.o.) switches and then switching on the test supplies, the latter being interlocked through the p.c.o. switch 'off' contacts. There is either a separate cut-off switch for each discriminating zone or a single switch for cutting-off the whole installation. Usually, indicating lamps on the busbar protection panel operated by the p.c.o. switches show whether the protection is in or out of service, and in large substations remote indications are also given in the control room.

With the main test switch in position 2 and all the protection cut-off switches open, an output from the test transformer can be injected to check each discriminating and check zone relay in turn by operating the appropriate test switch, the setting current and voltage being noted on the instruments A and V. By opening link D, the settings of individual relays can be checked. When on load the relay spill current is read on the ammeter A by changing over the main test switch to position 1 and link D to the dotted position. The current from the buswire under test, M1 in this case, then flows to the test buswire, through the ammeter to return to the common wire as shown by the dotted arrows. The output from the c.t.s can be similarly read by changing over link B. Before the link selections, described above, can be carried out, it is necessary for the shorting links A and C to be closed and opened again as appropriate, to avoid open-circuiting.

To obtain the magnetisation characteristics of any c.t. the main test switch is turned to position 2 and link B changed to its dotted position. In this case the primary circuit must be off load.

Other facilities to help trip testing are described in the section covering tripping circuit arrangements.

13.6.10   Fault settings

(a)   *Earth faults:* With a resistance earthed system, the fault current will be controlled by the value and number of neutral resistors in service. If possible one neutral earthing resistor circuit should be connected to each section of the busbars. The earth-fault setting of the busbar protection should be from 10-30 per cent of the smallest expected fault current, to ensure high speed relay operation.

If it is not possible to obtain such a low relay setting, then limitations may have to be placed on the system operating conditions, whereby the requisite number of neutral resistors are maintained in service.

With systems having solid multiple earthing, such as the 132 and 275 kV grid systems, the earth-fault current is comparable to the phase fault value, and so earth-fault settings are usually not difficult.

(b)   *Phase faults:* The value of the current which flows for two- and three-phase busbar faults depends on the number of infeeds to the busbar and the amount of generating plant running. The lowest value may be when the majority of the generating plant is shut down during the night, but lower values of current may arise if the only infeed to the busbar is a single long feeder. It may not always be possible to obtain a setting to meet this latter condition but that may well be an acceptable risk if it is known that it is a situation that will occur very rarely. Otherwise, back-up protection will have to be provided to clear such a fault if it is not part of the protection already required.

In general, the *overall* fault setting should be between 10 and 50% of the minimum fault current available, a range which caters for long term changes as the power system develops and for short term changes due to switching and the generation capacity required at any particular time. The *overall* fault setting is determined by the highest of the individual check and discriminating zone fault settings.

For uniformity of application and to avoid certain problems which will be referred to shortly, the fault settings of individual protection zones should normally meet the following requirements, always bearing in mind the foregoing comments so that only exceptionally will the setting exceed 50% of the minimum fault current available from the circuit providing the lowest infeed:

(*a*) The fault setting of the check zone and the minimum fault setting of the individual discriminating zones shall normally be equal to approximately 50% of the full load current rating of the associated busbar.

(*b*) The maximum fault setting of the individual discriminating zones shall not normally exceed the full load rating of the associated busbar.

(*c*) When two or more sections of busbar are connected together via section disconnectors, the corresponding discriminating zone buswires are parallel connected through the bus section disconnector auxiliary switches. Where the combined discriminating zone thus formed would otherwise give rise to a fault setting in excess of the full load current rating of the associated busbar, the minimum fault setting of the individual discriminating zones shall be reduced below the value specified in (*a*) above.

Reference has been made to the reduction in primary fault setting that can result from adopting more than one check zone. A point that must be borne in mind is that at those substations where the reserve busbar contains no permanent breaks, the reserve discriminating zone (if there is only one for the station) or the combined reserve discriminating zones (where there are section disconnectors and these are closed) can also be high. In fact, if all circuits are selected to the reserve busbar, there will usually be more c.t.s in parallel than would be connected to a single overall check zone because there will be bus coupler c.t.s connected to the reserve discriminating zones but not to the check zone, resulting in the former having a slightly higher primary setting than the latter. Although this would appear to detract from the advantages of employing more than one check zone, it will nearly always be the case that, with all circuits selected to the reserve busbar, the fault level will exceed the maximum primary fault setting of the (combined) reserve discriminating zones by an adequate margin. With fewer circuits selected to the reserve busbar, the fault level will be lower but so will the setting. This is in contrast to the check zone where the setting is constant and therefore must be less than 50% of the minimum fault infeed to any one busbar section.

The abandonement of buswire short-circuiting mentioned earlier imposes limitations on the fault setting and current rating of secondary equipment. The secondary current flowing in the relay circuit with an open-circuit current transformer secondary connection is related to the primary current and therefore can correspond to full load. The relay(s), series and shunt resistors including nonlinear resistors must therefore be rated to carry this current continuously since it may be an appreciable time before the faulty connections can be located and repaired; if the fault setting is half the rated current of the largest circuit these components must withstand twice the setting voltage continuously. This can usually be achieved but, since the power dissipated by the resistors for the condition considered will be very large, adequate ventilation must be provided. Where the fault setting is less than half the rated current of the largest circuit or of the busbars, whichever is the greater, the solution is more difficult and the installation must be designed with all these constraints taken into account.

Ideally, the fault setting of busbar protection should be greater than the full load current of the largest circuit, so that if a.c.t. becomes open-circuited no relay operation would occur. This is not always possible with resistance earthed systems. The sensitive supervision relays fitted to detect open-circuited c.t.s usually have a setting of 1-5% of the switchgear rated current.

In the high-impedance circulating current scheme of busbar protection, because the relays require only 10-30 mA, the idle c.t. magnetisation current decides the fault setting of the scheme. Thus, for schemes covering only earth faults, where each circuit's c.t.s are paralleled, the fault setting will be approximately three times higher than that of a scheme covering both phase and earth faults, since in this case only one third of the c.t.s are paralleled on to a relay element, as it now only covers one phase.

13.6.11   Stability limits

Busbar protection schemes are designed to remain stable on external close-up two- and three-phase faults up to the rated current breaking capacity of the switchgear being protected. For earth faults on multiple solidly earthed systems, at very large substations, the earth-fault current may be even larger than for phase faults, and due allowance must be made for this. On resistance earthed systems, particularly where liquid earthing resistors are fitted, allowance must be made for the possibility of their flashing over, so permitting much larger earth-fault currents to flow.

13.7   Circuit breaker fail protection

13.7.1   Principle of operation

This protection was first introduced onto the British Supergrid System in the mid

1970s. Its purpose is to deal with the situation in which a circuit breaker fails to interrupt the current which it is carrying in spite of the operation of a trip relay. Among the possible reasons are:

(i) Failure of the trip command to reach the circuit breaker trip coil. This is an unlikely cause where duplicate trip coils are fitted and Mark II standards of d.c. circuitry are employed to ensure tripping in the event of the failure of any single device or supply.

(ii) Failure of the circuit breaker mechanism due to an electrical or mechanical fault.

(iii) Failure of the circuit breaker current interruption device due to a defect or the inadvertent operation of the circuit breaker outside its limits of performance.

The policy of providing two fault-detecting systems is applied to feeder protection and, where possible, plant protection. The arrangements are such that, as far as is practicable no single secondary electrical failure should result in an uncleared system fault. In general, duplication ceases at the circuit breaker trip coils. The possibility that a circuit breaker may fail to perform its function, when instructed to do so, is higher than for the protection and trip circuits. This is due to the fact that mechanical, pneumatic or hydraulic tripping mechanisms and interruptors can not be duplicated for practical and economic reasons. The available methods of system back-up protection are generally inadequate to deal with the situation which would exist due to the failure of such components and therefore circuit breaker fail protection has been developed for this purpose.

The basic principle of this protection is the measurement of the duration of fault current from the instant at which any one trip relay operates to trip the circuit breaker. If, at the end of a preselected time delay, current is still flowing, it is considered that the circuit breaker has failed to trip and the tripping of all other circuit breakers connected to the connections on both sides of the circuit breaker will be initiated. At double busbar substations this is effected by means of the back-tripping system, while at mesh and other types of substation, circuit-breaker fail d.c. tripping circuits must be provided.

Circuit breaker fail protection is fitted to each circuit breaker and comprises two current check relays and four timer elements (two at mesh substations).

A simplified circuit diagram for circuit breaker fail protection is shown in Fig. 13.7.1A from which certain duplicated relay elements have been omitted for simplicity as have the back-trip check buswires and associated receive relay.

Detection of the circuit breaker fail condition is governed by the current check relays, which are static instantaneous overcurrent relays; these are only permitted to operate following operation of one or more of the circuit trip relays and hence coincidentally with the energisation of the associated circuit breaker trip coils. Although the c.t. secondary current passes through the relay whenever primary current is flowing, the relay only operates on the application of the auxiliary d.c. supply.

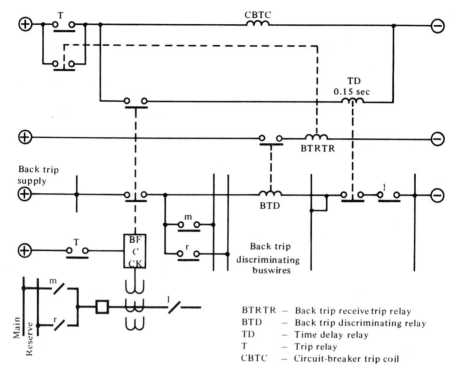

Fig. 13.7.1A   *Simplified diagram of breaker fail protection for a 400 kV double busbar substation*

Assuming that the circuit breaker has failed to clear a fault following operation of a trip relay, the following sequence of events will occur:

The d.c. circuit of the current check relay will be energised, and if the secondary current is in excess of the setting, the relay contacts will close, in turn energising the time delay relay from the d.c. supply to the trip coil.

At the expiration of the time delay, the current check relay is still energised by the uninterrupted fault current. Positive and negative supplies are connected to the back-trip discriminating buswires associated with the busbar to which the failed circuit breaker is selected. Energisation of these buswires trips all other circuits connected to the same busbar. Receipt of back-tripping signals by individual circuit breakers is effected via the same busbar selector disconnector auxiliary switches as would be used by that circuit for back-trip initiation.

13.7.2   Precautions against maloperation

At a double busbar substation where circuit breaker fail protection operates into the back-tripping system the consequences of an incorrect operation are comparable with a maloperation of busbar protection. The following precautions are therefore adopted to achieve a high security against such incidents:

(i) Two current check relays are employed and both must operate before the time delay relays are energised and both must remain operated for the back-trip buswires to be energised.

(ii) Two time delay relays must operate before the back-trip buswires are energised.

These points are shown in the diagram of the d.c. connections for a feeder circuit in Fig. 13.6.8A.

13.7.3 Current check relay settings

The setting for the current check relay must be selected so that positive operation is ensured for faults which occur at the electrical extremity of the protected circuit at minimum plant conditions.

Ideally, in order to obtain minimum operating times for circuit breaker fail protection, the current check relay setting should be above the resistor current of the circuit breaker (where resistors are fitted), so that the relay resets as soon as the main arc is extinguished. This shortens the time allowed to elapse before the decision is made that the circuit breaker has failed. The disadvantage of this policy is that one possible failure mode of some designs of circuit breaker is that in which the main contacts interrupt the fault current but the resistor contacts do not break the resistor current, which continues to flow causing the resistors to burn out. Such damage to the circuit breaker is a hazard to the system since it may lead to an internal flashover to earth (either as a busbar fault or circuit fault or both) and even if this does not occur the circuit breaker will be unlikely to interrupt subsequent faults satisfactorily. Therefore, it is preferable that the current check relay setting is not more than two-thirds of the resistor current (to provide a margin for reliable operation) even though this entails the adoption of timer settings giving longer overall operating times.

Another factor must be considered in the case of circuit breakers which switch generators. In such installations, the relay setting must be low enough to cater for the situation in which the circuit breaker fails to trip following the detection of a boiler, turbine or other nonelectrical fault condition. The resultant current drawn from the transmission system is small in the period immediately following circuit breaker failure when there is no steam input and the excitation has been suppressed. The setting should be sufficiently below this current (which varies with machine size and design) to ensure relay operation.

13.7.4 Circuit breaker fail timer settings

The setting applied to the time delay relays is governed by the following factors:

(*a*) The minimum circuit breaker trip operating time either to main arc extinc-

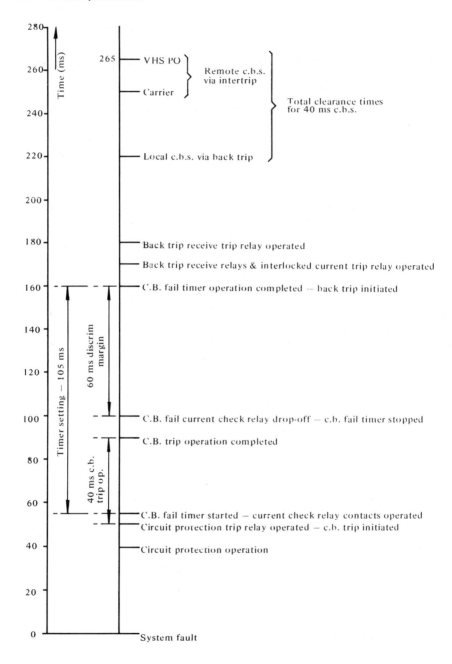

Fig. 13.7.4A   *Time sequence for circuit breaker fail protection — 400 kV with two-cycle circuit breaker*

tion or resistor contact separation, depending on the criterion adopted for setting the current check relay. This time must be that applicable under maximum short-circuit conditions at normal trip coil voltage and, where applicable, normal air pressure.

(*b*) The minimum allowable margin of time necessary to ensure discrimination between the correct circuit breaker tripping operation and initiation of back-tripping (or equivalent action at mesh substations etc.) due allowance being made for the scatter of operating times of relays and circuit breakers.

(*c*) The maximum fault clearance time acceptable from local back-up protection (in this case the circuit breaker fail protection). A common figure at the present time is 300 ms. Fig. 13.7.4A shows a typical operating time sequence for the circuit breaker fail protection and the resultant local back-trip and remote intertrip functions. A discriminating margin of 60 ms is typical and has been allowed in this case, resulting in a time setting of 105 ms when, as here, the nominal operating time of the circuit breaker is 40 ms.

The time delay relay setting is derived from the following constituent times:

(i) The minimum circuit breaker trip operating time (either to main arc extinction or to resistor contact separation as discussed earlier) for the particular type of circuit breaker, plus

(ii) the current check relay maximum drop-off time for the particular relay type (assumed as 10 ms for the purpose of Fig. 13.7.4A), plus

(iii) a discriminating margin of 60 ms to allow for scatter in circuit breaker and relay operating times, less

(iv) The current check relay minimum pick-up time for the particular relay type (assumed as 5 ms for the purpose of Fig. 13.7.4A).

Should the estimated fault clearance time be in excess of the allowable maximum, a reduction in the discriminating time margin may be accepted provided due consideration is given to the possible variation in the operating times of the circuit breaker and associated protective relays.

13.8 Terminology

The separate functions of busbar protection, circuit breaker fail protection and back-tripping have been described. While, in many installations all three will exist and will be closely related both in terms of accommodation and electrical connections, care is required to avoid the use of loose descriptions which ignore the separate duties performed by each of these facilities.

13.9   Bibliography

Books

The protective gear handbook by F E Wellman (Pitman, 1968)
Protective relays: their theory and practice (Vol.1) by A R Van C Warrington (Chapman & Hall, 1962)
Protective current transformers and circuits by P Mathews (Chapman & Hall, 1955)
Protective relays application guide (GEC Measurements, 1975)

Articles

'Busbar protection' by I A Reid, (*Electr. Rev.* June 1957)
'Instantaneous balanced current protection' by J Rushton and F E Wellman (*Metrovick Gazette,* May/June 1951)
'Busbar protection' by F L Hamilton (*Reyrolle Rev.* Spring/Summer 1958)
'Recent developments in busbar protection' by H D Nunney (IEE Colloquium Digest No. 1968/19, p. 69)

Chapter 14

Protection of motors, reactors, boosters and capacitors

by P.M.Dolby

14.1 Introduction

This chapter deals with the general characteristics of motors, reactors, boosters and capacitors, with the application of such plant to a closely interconnected power system and with the selection and application of suitable automatic protective equipment for the plant concerned. To specify adequate protection it is necessary to have an appreciation of the way in which the plant is constructed, its characteristics and how it is incorporated in the system, and so a significant proportion of the chapter is devoted to these aspects.

The main function of automatic protection is the detection of a fault condition, and, through the opening of the appropriate circuit breakers, the disconnection of the faulty item of plant from the remainder of the system. Coupled with this is the need to limit to an absolute minimum the damage caused to the affected equipment. Whilst discrimination is, without doubt, the most important requirement of any protective system, the need for rapid operation is frequently a consideration of almost equal importance, bearing in mind the need to minimise damage, to safeguard system stability and to reduce as much as possible the risk to life and limb.

14.2 Motors

14.2.1 Characteristics of d.c. and a.c. motors

D.C. Motors

D.C. motors are classified as series, shunt or compound motors depending upon the way in which the field winding is connected with respect to the armature winding, that is the method of excitation used (see Fig. 14.2.1A). The characteristics of the motor are determined by the method of excitation.

In a d.c. motor the armature current I_a adjusts itself to produce a torque balance, so that the torque developed is equal to the total opposing torque, this opposing torque consisting of the sum of the torque losses of the rotating armature and the

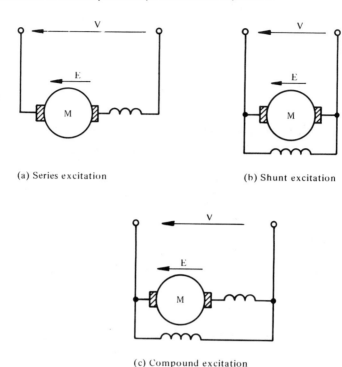

(a) Series excitation

(b) Shunt excitation

(c) Compound excitation

Fig. 14.2.1A   *Methods of exciting d.c. motors*

torque of the load. Developed torque, as the name implies, is the torque delivered to the shaft and available to do useful work.

If the flux Φ is sensibly constant, as with the shunt motor, I_a will vary as the torque T. If Φ varies with I_a, as with the series and compound motors, the relationship between I_a and the torque is no longer linear.

The equation for the back e.m.f. induced in a d.c. armature winding is

$$E = CN\Phi$$

where N is the speed, Φ is the field flux and C is a constant for the particular machine concerned. The back e.m.f., however, is also given by

$$E = V - I_a(R_a + R_{sf}) - V_b$$

where V is the supply voltage, usually assumed constant, R_a is the armature resistance, R_{sf} is the resistance of any series field winding and V_b is the brush voltage-drop, usually of the order of two or three volts.

Since the voltage-drop in the armature circuit including any series field circuit is usually quite small (at least for normal values of I_a), the back e.m.f. is sensibly constant and hence the product of N and Φ is also reasonably constant.

The developed torque is proportional to the product of the flux Φ and the armature current I_a.

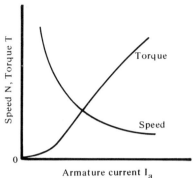

Fig. 14.2.1B *Speed and torque characteristics of a d.c. series motor*

(a) The series motor. In the series motor, the flux Φ is produced by the armature current I_a, the speed and torque characteristics of the motor, plotted as functions of the armature current, being as shown in Fig. 14.2.1B. It will be seen that when I_a and therefore Φ, is small, the speed of the motor is very high. At low values of I_a, Φ is directly proportional to I_a and the torque increases as the square of the armature current. At higher values of I_a the effects of saturation and armature reaction cause Φ to become relatively constant, the torque then increases proportionally with the armature current. At still higher values of I_a, the pronounced effect of armature reaction results in an actual reduction in Φ for an increase in I_a, with the consequence that the torque then increases at a lower rate than the armature current.

Because of its very high speed at low loads, it is important that a series motor should never be started without load. For the same reason, a motor of this type should not be used if there is a possibility of the entire load being lost while running.

(b) The shunt motor: In the shunt motor, the flux Φ is produced by the current I_f in the shunt-field winding, the current I_f being sensibly constant for a constant supply voltage V. The speed and torque characteristics of the motor are shown in Fig. 14.2.1C, the motor having a slightly drooping speed/current characteristic. Assuming constant terminal voltage, an increase in I_a will result in increases in armature reaction and total voltage-drop, and since these latter two quantities have opposite effects on the motor speed, they will tend to cancel each other to give an almost constant speed characteristic. In the normal case, the voltage-drop effect predominates so that the speed current characteristic has the gently drooping form shown.

It will be noted that the torque varies almost linearly with armature current, except at the higher values of armature current where the effects of armature reaction cause a reduction in Φ.

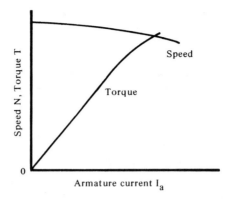

Fig. 14.2.1C *Speed and torque characteristics of a d.c. shunt motor*

A method of controlling a shunt motor is shown diagrammatically in Fig. 14.2.1D from which it will be seen that one end of the field winding is connected direct to the supply and the other end connected via a field rheostat. When it is required to increase the speed of the motor this is achieved by weakening the field by increasing the amount of resistance connected to it.

An alternative method of controlling a shunt motor is to employ a variable resistance in series with the armature. The resistance must, of course, be suitable for continuous energisation, but the method is not a particularly satisfactory one because of the relatively heavy losses in the resistance.

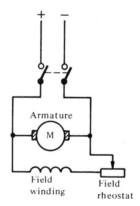

Fig. 14.2.1D *Simple method of speed control of a d.c. shunt motor*

(c)   The compound motor: Fig. 14.2.1A shows that the compound motor is provided with both a series and a shunt winding and that the characteristics of the motor depend chiefly upon the relative strengths of the m.m.f.s produced by the two field windings. If the series winding is connected so that it produces an .m.m.f. in the same direction as the shunt winding the motor is known as a cumulatively compounded motor; if the connection is such that the series winding m.m.f. opposes that of the shunt winding the motor is known as a differentially compounded motor. The cumulatively compounded motor may be connected in 'short-shunt' or in 'long-shunt' as in Fig. 14.2.1E.

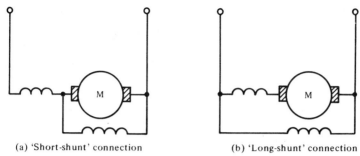

(a) 'Short-shunt' connection   (b) 'Long-shunt' connection

Fig. 14.2.1E *Alternative connections of a cumulative compound motor*

By adjusting the series field of the differentially compounded motor so that the speed at full-load is equal to the speed at no-load then the speed at any intermediate load will be approximately constant. This is not as advantageous as it may seem since there is a tendency for this type of motor to start up the wrong way. This is possible because of the initial rush of current through the series field and armature, the shunt field taking rather longer to build up than the series field. When both fields are fully established there may be only a relatively small nett field, and hence torque, to drive the motor.

Another disadvantage is that if overloaded, the resulting decrease in flux will tend to force up the speed so that the motor is overloaded still more. If the current reaches a critical value the motor will begin to race in much the same way as a series motor deprived of load. Thus the differentially compounded motor should be used only in circumstances where there is no likelihood of overloading.

In the cumulatively compounded motor an increase in the load applied produces an increase in flux and a corresponding decrease in speed, although the constant flux produced by the shunt winding prevents this decrease being as rapid as in the plain series motor. Thus its speed/torque characteristic will be approximately as shown in Fig. 14.2.1F, its position relative to the characteristics of the series and

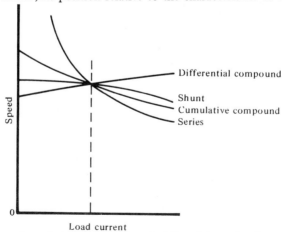

Fig. 14.2.1F *Comparison of speed/current characteristics of d.c. series, shunt and compound motors*

shunt motors depending upon the number of turns on the series winding. An advantage of the cumulatively compounded motor is that the speed falls when a sudden, heavy load is applied, thus helping to offset the burden of the increase in load.

(d)   Comparison of series, shunt and compound motors: A comparison of speed/ current and torque/current characteristics of the series, shunt and compound motors is shown in Figs. 14.2.1F and 14.2.1G. It will be seen from Fig. 14.2.1G

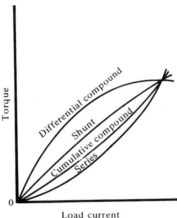

Fig. 14.2.1G   *Comparison of torque/current characteristics of d.c. series, shunt and compound motors*

that the shunt motor characteristic lies between those of the differentially and cumulatively compounded machines. The significant difference in characteristics obtained by connecting the series winding of the compound motor either to assist or to oppose the shunt winding should also be noted.

A summary of the characteristics of the three types of motor is given below.

Series motor:	(i)	High starting torque varying as the square of the current at low current values.
	(ii)	High speed at low values of load.
	(iii)	Decrease in speed as torque increases.
Shunt motor:	(i)	Practically constant speed from no-load to full load.
	(ii)	Practically constant flux and therefore torque proportional to the armature current.
Compound motor: Differential		
	(i)	Approximately constant speed from no-load to full-load.
	(ii)	Overloading tends to cause rapid increase in speed. Application of motor is strictly limited.

Cumulative
(i)   Steeper decrease in speed with increasing torque than in the shunt motor.
(ii) Speed/current and torque/current characteristics lie between those of the series and shunt motors.

A.C. motors

Polyphase induction motors: Induction motors fall into two distinct categories, namely the squirrel cage motor and the wound rotor, or slip-ring, motor. As the name implies, both operate on the induction principle, only the primary stator winding being connected to the supply.

The squirrel cage motor is often identified with its inherently poor starting qualities, but it will be seen later that measures are taken to improve its performance in this respect. In a squirrel cage motor the rotor conductors are copper rods laid in slots in the rotor core and riveted or brazed to a short-circuiting ring at each end, giving the appearance of a cage. The absence of slip-rings ensures that sparking will not occur and the cage construction gives a cheap and very robust motor. Its disadvantages are low starting torque, high starting current and difficulty in providing an easy means of control.

The slip-ring motor has a 'wound' rotor, that is a group of coils forming the windings is carried on the rotor itself. This makes it more expensive than the squirrel cage motor, but it has the advantage that it develops the same starting torque as a comparable squirrel cage motor with a considerably lower starting current. Unlike the squirrel cage rotor, the total resistance of the wound motor is not fixed but can be varied by adjustment of the external resistors connected in the rotor circuit during starting. An incidental advantage of the wound rotor is that much of the heat generated during starting is dissipated in the resistors. Smooth acceleration is achieved if the resistance can be reduced in small steps from the 'all in' to the 'all out' condition.

(a)   The squirrel cage motor: Fig. 14.2.1H shows the torque/speed curves of a squirrel cage motor. During starting the developed torque follows the upper curve until the motor attains a speed at which the developed torque is equal to the load torque. The motor will reach its rated speed if the load torque is not in excess of the developed torque.

The torque is proportional to the terminal voltage squared, and although for some drives the squirrel cage motor can be connected direct-to-line, it is often necessary to reduce the terminal voltage at starting as a means of reducing the starting current and the voltage drop in the connections. This is particularly applicable when only a small starting torque is necessary since the effect is to reduce the starting torque available. The methods used include the insertion of

(i)   series resistors or reactors;
(ii)   autotransformers;
(iii) star-delta switching.

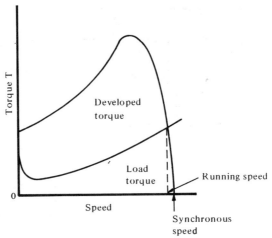

Fig. 14.2.1H   *Torque/speed characteristics of a squirrel cage induction motor*

(i)   Series resistor or reactor: By using this method the voltage applied to the motor at starting is reduced by the simple expedient of introducing a series resistor or reactor in the supply to the motor, the resistor or reactor being short-circuited as soon as the motor has reached its normal running speed. The starting current is thus reduced in proportion to the terminal voltage. The starting torque, however, is reduced as the square of the terminal voltage, so that the use of a series resistor or reactor to drop the voltage by 20% will have the effect of reducing the starting current by 20%, the starting torque being thereby reduced to $(0·8)^2 \times 100\%$, that is 64% of the full voltage value.

(ii)   Autotransformer: In this case (see Fig. 14.2.1I) the line current is equal to the transformer primary current and the motor current to the transformer secondary current. Similarly, the line voltage is equal to the transformer primary voltage and the motor voltage to the transformer secondary voltage. Thus

$$\frac{\text{line current}}{\text{motor current}} = \frac{\text{motor voltage}}{\text{line voltage}}$$

If, for example, the transformer secondary voltage is 80% of the line voltage, so that the motor current is 80% of the full voltage value, then the line current is $0·8 \times 0·8 \times 100\%$, that is 64% of the motor current at full voltage. As with the series resistor or reactor method, an 80% voltage value gives a motor torque of 64% of the full voltage value.

(iii)   Star-delta switching: By means of a three-pole changeover switch the stator windings are star-connected during the initial starting period and delta-connected when the motor has run up to speed. In this way the voltage per phase at starting is reduced to $1/\sqrt{3}$, that is 58% of the supply voltage, and is restored to full supply voltage for normal running. Switching from star to delta should be carried out at a speed corresponding to full-load torque to avoid an abrupt change in torque as the

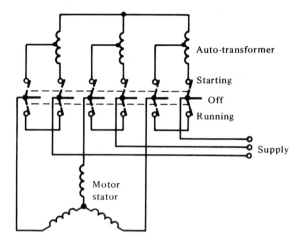

Fig. 14.2.1I   *Autotransformer starting of a squirrel cage motor*

delta connection is made. This difficulty can be avoided by maintaining the circuit through a resistor during the transition from star to delta connection.

(b)   The wound-rotor motor: The total value of the rotor resistance of a wound-rotor motor consists of the fixed resistance of the rotor winding plus the added external resistance which is variable.

As the load torque changes so does the ratio of the total rotor resistance r_t to the slip s.   To overcome the load torque, the appropriate values of secondary current and flux, which together determine the motor torque, must be produced and the motor's ability to achieve this is governed by the ratio r/s.   The slip, for a given value of torque, is proportional to the total rotor resistance.   It will be seen that for each value of external rotor resistance a speed/torque curve can be drawn, and a set of typical curves is shown in Fig. 14.2.1J.   Curve (a) represents the condition when the external resistance is zero and curves (b) and (c) the conditions with different values of external resistance connected.

By maintaining the ratio r/s constant, or nearly so, by a step by step reduction of the external resistance the torque of the wound-rotor motor can be kept reasonably constant during the running-up period.

This contrasts with a squirrel cage motor in which the rotor resistance is fixed and therefore only one speed/torque characteristic is obtainable.

Single-phase induction motors: There are many types of single-phase induction motor and a representative selection will be considered here.   The majority of such motors have rotors of the squirrel cage type.

Unlike the polyphase induction motor, the single-phase version has no starting torque and starting is achieved by the introduction of an auxiliary starting winding in the stator to produce a rotating field (as with the split-phase motor), or by using

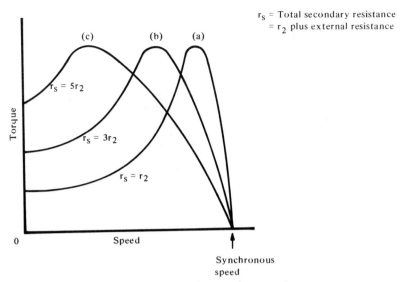

r_s = Total secondary resistance
= r_2 plus external resistance

Fig. 14.2.1J   *Torque/speed characteristics of a wound-rotor motor*

a commutator and brushes on the rotor (as, for example, with the repulsion-induction motor).

(a)   Rotating field method: To obtain a rotating field, the axis of the starting winding must be displaced in space with respect to the main stator winding, and the currents in the two windings must be out of phase.   The first requirement is satisfied by placing the starting winding in empty or partly filled slots of the main winding and the second by the choice of suitable resistance and reactance values for the two windings, or by the addition of resistance, reactance or capacitance in series with the starting winding.   Some typical applications are given below.

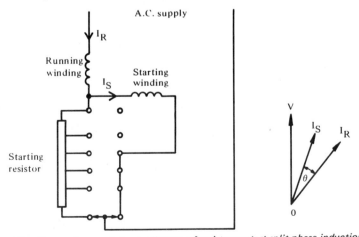

Fig. 14.2.1K   *Connections and phasor diagram of resistance-start split-phase induction motor*

In the split-phase motor, the resistance and reactance values of the two windings are usually such that an angle of approximately 30° between the two currents is obtained. To increase this angle and so produce a stronger rotating field, and consequently a larger starting torque, a resistor is inserted in parallel with the starting winding (usually categorised as a resistance-start split-phase motor as shown in Fig. 14.2.1K). Again an increase in angle is achieved by using a reactor (reactance-start split-phase motor). A further increase in the angle, making the current in the starting winding lead the terminal voltage, is obtained by using a capacitor in place of the resistor (capacitor-start split-phase motor, as shown in Fig. 14.2.1L). To prevent overheating of the starting winding it is necessary in all these cases to disconnect it as the motor approaches synchronous speed and this is done automatically by a centrifugal switch on the rotor.

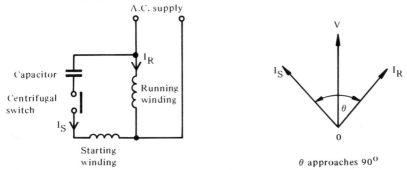

Fig. 14.2.1L   *Connections and phasor diagram of capacitance-start split-phase induction motor*

(b) Commutator method: This method of starting is used for the repulsion induction motor which is a form of induction motor with commutator and brushes and with an additional squirrel cage winding in the rotor. This type of motor may have constant-speed or variable-speed characteristics depending upon the design of the windings. It differs from the plain a.c. series motor in that no current is led into the armature, the brushes being short-circuited.

If the brush axis is perpendicular to the main flux, as shown in Fig. 14.2.1M(*a*), the e.m.f.s induced in the two halves of the winding will cancel each other out, and the armature will not carry any induced current nor produce any torque.

If the brush axis is in the same direction as the main flux then a current will be induced in the armature. The four parts of this current will in turn produce four torques which, as shown by the arrows in Fig. 14.2.1M(*b*), will cancel one another out.

If now the brush axis is inclined at an angle to the direction of the main flux, then torques T_1 and T_2 are produced, as shown in Fig. 14.2.1M(*c*). Thus resultant torque $T = 2(T_2 - T_1)$ and it can be shown that T is a maximum when the angle ϕ between the brush axis and the horizontal axis of the armature is 45°.

Three-phase commutator motors

The Schrage motor; Of several types of three-phase commutator motor, the rotor

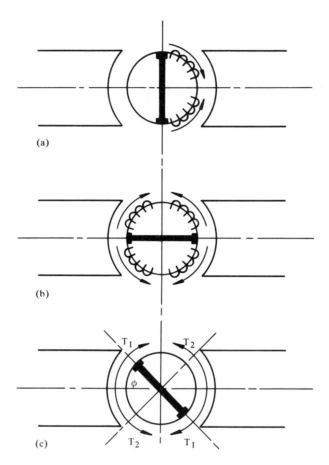

Fig. 14.2.1M *Effect of different brush positions on the action of a repulsion motor*

excited shunt commutator motor (the Schrage motor) is by far the most commonly used, and this section will be limited to a discussion of the salient features of such a motor.

The outstanding feature of the Schrage motor is that the commutator allows good speed control and power factor correction to be obtained in the one machine. The speed of an induction motor can be controlled by impressing on its secondary (stator) winding a voltage in the same direction and of the same frequency, that is the slip frequency, as the e.m.f. induced in this winding by the rotating flux. Selection of the correct phase and magnitude of the impressed voltage gives control of the speed above and below synchronous speed. The three-phase shunt commutator motor, or Schrage motor, is in effect a combined three-phase rotor excited induction motor and a three-phase commutator machine, as shown in Fig. 14.2.1N.

Of the two rotor windings, one is connected to the slip-rings and the other to the commutator segments. The stator winding consists of three separate phase windings each connected to a pair of brushes which can be moved individually in either

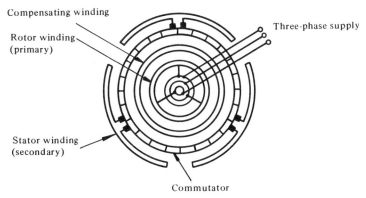

Fig. 14.2.1N *Connections of the three-phase Schrage motor*

direction round the commutator. The commutator voltage varies as the angular distance between the brushes of each pair, being greatest when the distance is 180 electrical degrees, and decreasing to zero when they are both on the same commutator segment, thus short-circuiting the stator winding. In Fig. 14.2.1P(*a*) the brushes are shown in this latter position and the machine will run as an ordinary induction motor. In Fig. 14.2.1P(*b*) the connections are such that the potential difference between brushes x and y will have a component in direct opposition to the e.m.f. induced in the stator, reducing the motor speed to a value below synchronous speed. By reversing the brushes, as shown in Fig. 14.2.1P(*c*), the commutator e.m.f. will have a component in phase with the rotor induced e.m.f., thus increasing the motor speed to a value above synchronous speed.

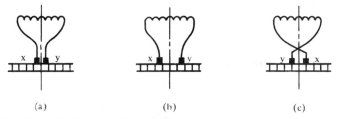

(a) (b) (c)

Fig. 14.2.1P *Alternative brush positions of Schrage motor*

The phase of the commutator e.m.f. between brushes is determined by the positions of the centre point of the brushes relative to the centre of the rotor winding, so that by moving the brush system as a whole round the commutator the phase of the e.m.f. injected into the secondary circuit will be varied relative to the rotor induced e.m.f.

Thus the angular separation of individual brush sets determines the speed variation above and below synchronous speed, the angular position of the brush system as a whole controlling the power factor of the motor.

From the typical speed/torque curves shown in Fig. 14.2.1Q it will be appreciated that the speed is reasonably constant up to approximately 100% torque, particularly at the higher speeds.

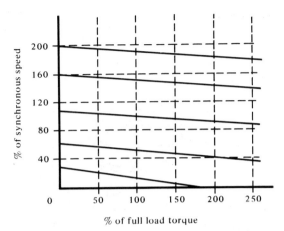

Fig. 14.2.1Q   *Typical speed/torque characteristics of a three-phase commutator motor*

14.2.2. Application of d.c. and a.c. motors

In choosing a motor for a given application, consideration must be given to the type of load it will drive, and from this the speed and torque requirements can be determined.   For loads such as cranes, hoists and electric traction, motors with speeds varying with the load are required and the d.c. series motor or the a.c. repulsion motor are most often used.   Fans, blowers and unloaded compressors demand low starting torque while pulverised fuel mills and loaded compressors start under load and demand high starting torque to break away from standstill.

Constant speed applications include motor-generator sets, concrete mixers and constant speed conveyors and in these an increase in load torque, for example the addition of coal to a conveyor, requires a proportionate increase in power output, the power output being proportional to the load torque. Of the motors dealt with in this chapter, the d.c. shunt motor and the induction motor would be suitable for such loads.

Variable speed applications may be classified as (i) constant torque, (ii) variable torque, (iii) constant power-output.

(i)   A good example of constant-torque application is the automatic machine tool where the output is directly proportional to the speed. The wound-rotor induction motor is the obvious choice for this application, but a d.c. shunt motor provided with means of speed adjustment by field control could be used.

(ii)   Fans and blowers are typical of the variable-torque application. With such loads the torque varies as the square of the speed, and a d.c. shunt motor provided with means of speed adjustment by field control would be suitable.

(iii)   Machine tools fall into the constant power-output category requiring, as they do, torque varying inversely with speed. Again, the d.c. shunt motor as for (i) and (ii) or the wound-rotor induction motor could be applied.

When fluctuations in speed with varying load have to be catered for a 'shunt' type of three-phase commutator motor is used. The best known of these, the Schrage motor described earlier, is used extensively in the speed-control systems for large three-phase induction motors providing power factor improvement at the same time. It is applied widely in the printing and textile industries and for driving some conveyor equipment.

14.2.3.   Motor control

It will be seen later that the type of protection used, in particular the protection against short-circuits in a motor or its connections, is to some extent dependent upon the type of switchgear used to control the motor. This falls into two classes:

(*a*)   a contactor, with high-breaking-capacity fuses providing the short-circuit protection; and

(*b*)   a circuit breaker, with short-circuit protection provided by instanteneous attracted-armature type relays.

In general, the choice of switchgear will depend upon the size of the motor, for example contactors and fuses for up to approximately 150 h.p. and circuit breakers for larger motors.

Control by contactor and fuses: A contactor consists of a moving contact operated by an electromagnet attracting an iron armature against the action of a spring. The pressing of the 'start' push button energises the electromagnet, thus completing the operating coil circuit. When the 'stop' button is pressed the coil circuit is opened, de-energising the electromagnet and allowing the moving contact to isolate the motor from the supply. Contactors may be of the air insulated or oil insulated type, the latter having the advantage that the motor current is broken in oil which generally permits a smaller overall size of the control unit.

Contactors can be used where the current to be interrupted is limited to approximately six times their rated current, the rated current being of the same order, or a little higher, than the normal full load of the motor. Direct-acting over-load trip devices may be incorporated in the contactor, protection against short-circuits being provided by fast operating high-breaking-capacity fuses. The fuses should blow at currents in excess of those which can be handled by the contactor but should not blow at currents within its capacity.

Since the contactor coil will hold the armature against the spring only when there is sufficient magnetic flux, any severe drop in or failure of the supply will result in the opening of the contactor. Thus an inherent 'no-volt' release feature is provided ensuring that the motor cannot re-start after a partial or complete failure of the supply.

When the contactor unit is small it is generally located adjacent to the machine being driven, so that control of the machine is facilitated. In such cases the 'start' and 'stop' push buttons are an integral part of the contactor. When the contactor is too large to be located close to the machine, local controls are provided at the machine.

Control by circuit breaker: Large motors are controlled by circuit breakers of either the air-break or oil-break type, which should be capable of interrupting the highest current which can flow under the most severe fault condition. Oil-break gear is seldom installed in generating stations chiefly because of the additional fire hazard when oil is present under fault conditions.

A circuit breaker may be arranged for hand closing, electromagnetic solenoid closing or spring closing. Hand closing is usually provided for small, infrequently operated circuit breakers, solenoid closing for those operated frequently or from a remote point, and spring closing for circuit breakers operated only occasionally and where hand operation is undesirable. Overload trip devices operating direct on to the tripping mechanism usually form an integral part of the circuit breaker.

14.2.4 Types of fault

In general it is necessary to protect a motor against abnormal running and fault conditions arising from:

(*a*) prolonged overloading as a result of the application of excessive mechanical load:

(*b*) single-phasing caused, for example, by the rupturing of a fuse or by the open circuiting of a connection in one phase of a three-phase motor. If one phase is open-circuited when the motor is running it will continue to run and provide power even though it is connected to what is, in effect, a single-phase supply. If the load on the motor is of the order of its rated output, the current drawn from the supply will be appreciably higher than the current for which the windings are designed and if the condition is allowed to persist, severe damage may be caused:

(*c*) short-circuits between phases or between phase and earth in the motor winding or its connections. Short-circuits may be caused by the chafing of connections, accidental shorting of the motor terminals or cable sealing ends or by cable faults:

(*d*) partial or complete collapse of voltage.

14.2.5 A.C. and d.c. motor protection

The protection of motor plant is based on the same essential considerations whether the motor is driven from an a.c. or a d.c. source. In some instances, for example, the thermal overload relay, a modified single-phase version is applied to the protection of d.c. motors. Any dangerous or potentially dangerous condition in either an a.c. or a d.c. motor, its control or connections, must be detected and action taken automatically to disconnect the affected equipment. Such conditions are classified broadly as low or falling supply voltage and overloading beyond a predetermined safe value for an excessive time. To these conditions must be added the open-circuiting of one phase of a three-phase a.c. motor and a short-circuit in either an a.c. or d.c. motor.

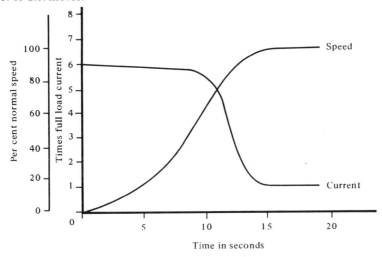

Fig. 14.2.5A *Typical starting characteristic for 'direct-on' started induction motor*

Many motors draw a starting current from the supply of several times their normal full-load current, and it is essential that the protection should be unresponsive to this starting surge provided that the motor current returns to its running value within the time determined by the design of the motor. On the other hand, the protection must not be given a setting greatly in excess of full load or it will be unable to safeguard the motor against overcurrent conditions. Figs. 14.2.5A and 14.2.5B show typical starting characteristics for an a.c. 'direct-on' induction motor and for a d.c. shunt-wound motor, respectively.

Thermal relays: The two opposing requirements referred to are met in a relay having an inherent time-lag characteristic, an example of which is shown in Fig. 14.2.5C. The essence of the thermal relay is the specially designed element which simulates as closely as it can the changing thermal conditions in the motor, allowing the motor to be retained in service up to the point beyond which damage would probably be caused. Essentially, the relay consists of three single-phase elements, each element comprising a heater and an associated bimetal actuated movement. The three bimetal spiral elements are mounted axially in line and respond to a rise in temperature of the heaters which in turn produces movement

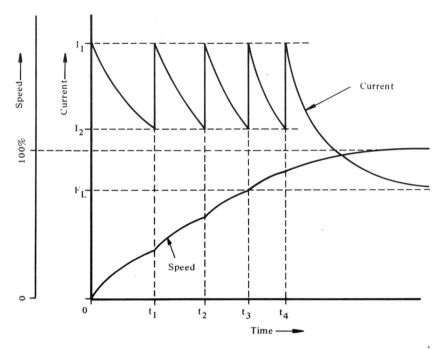

Fig. 14.2.5B   *Typical starting characteristic for a d.c. shunt-wound motor*

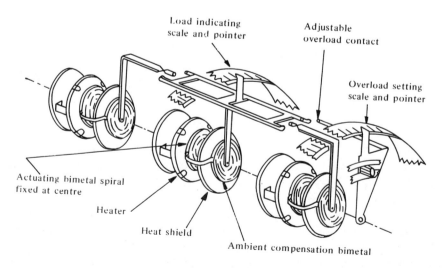

Fig. 14.2.5C   *Construction of typical thermal relay for motor protection*

of the contact assembly (Fig. 14.2.5D). A change in ambient temperature rotates the two outer ends of an element through the same angle without causing movement of the contact arm. Characteristic curves for a setting of 125% under 'starting from cold' and 'running' conditions are shown in Fig. 14.2.5E.

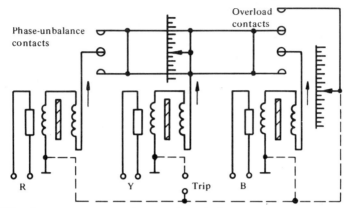

Fig. 14.2.5D   *Contact arrangement of typical thermal relay*

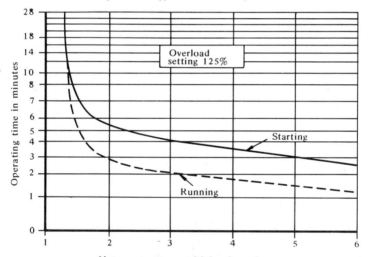

Motor current as multiple of rated current

Fig. 14.2.5E   *Characteristic of typical thermal relay for motor protection*

Single-phasing protection: This is necessary in view of the ability of a three-phase motor to continue to run with an open-circuit in one phase, although it may well suffer damage as a consequence. The advent of motors designed on a maximum continuous rating (m.c.r.) basis providing very limited continuous overload capacity, has emphasised the importance of protection against single-phase running. The single-phase feature is conveniently incorporated in the three-phase thermal simulating relay, the operating time-lag depending to some extent on the load being carried by the motor when the open-circuit occurs. With the motor on full load the operating time is usually 20 – 30 s with correspondingly longer times at smaller loads. The single-phasing contacts will close also if the out-of-balance between any two phase currents exceeds about 12% at full load.

Short-circuit protection: Protection against short circuits in the motor winding, or the connections to it, is often provided by incorporating in the thermal relay case separate high-set, instantaneous overcurrent or earth-fault elements or both. The attracted-armature type element operates against the action of a return spring and in one design rests against a leaf spring to reduce the effects of vibration and shock. In another design these effects are guarded against by using a statically pivoted beam, the armature being attached to one end of the beam and the moving contacts to the other end. Typical settings are 4 to 8 or 8 to 16 times full load for the instantaneous overcurrent elements and 0·2 to 0·4 times full load for the instantaneous earth-fault element. Three such overcurrent elements or two over-current and one earth-fault element can be incorporated in the standard three-phase thermal relay case.

It will be appreciated that when the motor supply is earthed via a resistor, the earth-fault current may be less than that needed to operate positively the over-current elements connected in the phases. In such cases it is necessary to employ the residually connected earth-fault element.

A frequent cause of single-phasing is a 'blown' fuse and care is needed in the choice of fuse ratings. During starting, the current approaches fusing current, causing the fuses to run hot for an appreciable time. This may give rise to oxidation and deterioration of the fuses and ultimately a fuse may blow during starting. The motor will continue to run with considerably increased current flowing in the other two phases which, if allowed to persist, will damage the windings.

The use of high-breaking-capacity fuses for short-circuit protection has the merit that the circuit is opened during the first quarter-cycle of fault current thus preventing the current from attaining its theoretical maximum or 'prospective' assymetrical peak value which would flow in the absence of the fuses. The current at which the fuse 'blows' is known as the 'cut-off current'. The fusing time may be extremely short, for example between 0·001 and 0·002 s compared with a minimum operating time of an overload trip of about 0·1s. Thus the fuse is well able to completely interrupt the fault current before the overload trip can operate.

Stalling relays: The stalling relay is designed for use in conjunction with the thermal overload and single-phasing relay. Basically the stalling relay consists of a control contactor and a thermal overload unit fitted in the same case. The thermal overload unit is energised via the contactor which closes only during the starting period or, if the motor stalls, while starting or running (see Fig. 14.2.5F). During a normal healthy start the contactor closes, switching the thermal unit into circuit, but the motor current falls to normal before the thermal unit operates and the contactor opens, de-energising the thermal unit. An optional extra feature is shown in Fig. 14.2.5G and consists of an auxiliary contactor having a 'twice-in'

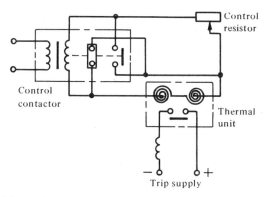

Fig. 14.2.5F *P and B type L1A stalling relay*

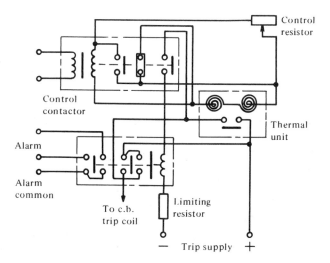

Fig. 14.2.5G *P and B type L1A stalling relay incorporating a 'twice-in' feature*

feature. This permits one attempted restart of a motor after a stall but is so constructed that it latches in on the second stall, thus preventing repeated attempts to restart a defective motor.

In one design the 'twice-in' feature consists of a shunt-connected attracted-armature relay with a follower-pin attached to the top of the armature, and moving in a labyrinth slot in a hinged metal plate (see Fig. 14.2.5H). As the armature moves in and out on successive stalls the pin works through the labyrinth slot, allowing the hinged plate to fall until, on the second stall, the pin is trapped at the end of the slot, thus latching the armature. Flags are incorporated to indicate the number of times the motor has stalled since the 'twice-in' feature was last reset. Resetting after two stalls is by hand only.

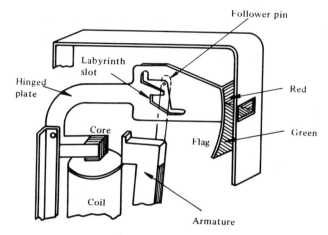

Fig. 14.2.5H　*Arrangement of mechanical 'twice-in' feature of type L1A stalling relay*

Electronic overload relay:　A modern alternative type of thermal relay, of solid-state design rather than of the bimetallic element design protects the motor against overload by deriving an a.c. input from, and related to, the motor supply current. This current transformer derived input is rectified, adjusted to an appropriate level by a current setting circuit and then applied to the overcurrent detection circuit. When the reference level is exceeded by the input the time-setting circuit, incorporating a resistor/capacitor network, followed by an amplification stage and closure of the tripping circuit, is triggered. The relay has a characteristic similar to that of a bimetallic element relay, i.e. an inverse-time characteristic such that higher levels of overload cause faster disconnection of the motor and lower levels are tolerated for longer periods. The block diagram of a relay of this type is shown in Fig. 14.2.5I.

Protection against an open circuit in one phase is provided by a separate circuit which detects the higher ripple content of the full-wave rectified current derived from the current transformers. After passing through a waveform and gating circuit into the power circuit it provides a signal for operation of the tripping circuit.

The more sophisticated versions of this relay may incorporate means to adjust the model characteristics so that an analogue closer to the actual temperature rise of a motor may be obtained. Outputs may be used for purposes other than tripping, e.g. regulating the motor load. The closer control provided by such devices is particularly useful in the protection of maximum continuous rating (m.c.r.) motors and others with an arduous duty cycle. Appropriate modelling will overcome the problems encountered when a motor is required to start against a stalled load, to 'inch' or to start and stop frequently.

Thermal trips and electromagnetic overload protection:　For the smaller size of motor with a full-load rating of up to approximately 25A it is usually adequate

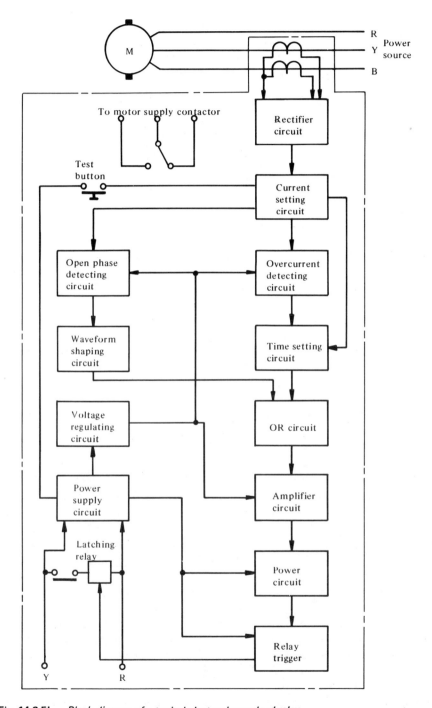

Fig. 14.2.5I   *Block diagram of a typical electronic overload relay*

technically, and attractive from an economic standpoint, to employ a simpler form of protection than the sophisticated thermal overload relay described at the beginning of this Section. Recourse is then made to either the thermal overload trip (in essence a much simplified form of the thermal overload relay) or the electromagnetic overload and associated time-lag device. The thermal trip is operated either directly or indirectly by the heating effect of the current on a thermal element and the electromagnetic trip is operated by the increase of magnetic flux with current.

(*a*)   *Thermal trips:*   In an early type of thermal trip a bimetal strip was used as the sensing element, the motor current passing directly through the element. As the thermal strip heated up it lifted and so raised, against spring tension, a horizontal trip rod positioned above it. If the overload condition persisted, further movement upwards of the rod, to a point predetermined by the setting, caused the mechanical trip to operate to open the associated contactor. A second rod, positioned so that the bimetal strip was between the two rods, followed the movement of the bimetal and upper rod until held by a stop of the same material and therefore having the same thermal characteristics as the thermal strip. Ambient temperature compensation was thus obtained, and the motor current at which the relay operated was substantially unaffected by temperature changes. These relays were applied to d.c., single-phase a.c. and three-phase a.c. motors. When used with the latter, inherent protection against single-phase running was obtained as any appreciable unbalance in the phase currents caused the two rods to move in opposite directions and so operate the tripping mechanism.

In a later version of this type of relay the bimetal elements do not carry current but are operated indirectly by heaters. In the case of small motors, the heaters are direct connected to carry the motor currents and are fed from current transformers when used with larger motors. Two slotted trip bars or slides are coupled together at one end and in normal, healthy conditions the two bars move together in a horizontal direction corresponding with the balanced deflection of the three bimetal thermal elements, as shown in Fig. 14.2.5I. After a predetermined amount

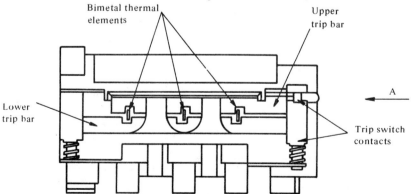

Fig. 14.2.5J   *Simple thermal overload and single-phasing preventor for motor protection (Electrical Apparatus Co.)*

of movement during an overload condition, one of the bars strikes a stop which prevents it following the other bar any further. Continued movement of the other bar under the action of the bimetal elements operates the mechanical trip to open the motor contactor. If one phase is open-circuited while the motor is running the thermal element in that phase will cool and deflect in the opposite direction to those still carrying current. These two elements will remain deflected and differential movement of the two bars will again cause the mechanical trip to operate. Part of the contact arrangement of this relay is shown in Fig. 14.2.5K.

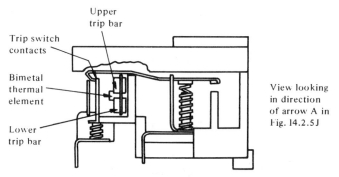

Fig. 14.2.5K *Contact arrangement of thermal overload and single-phasing preventor*

The simple thermal trip devices just described should not be confused with the much more sophisticated and comprehensive thermal relay described at the beginning of Section 14.2.5. The latter relay is used extensively for the protection of the larger three-phase a.c. motors driving power station auxiliaries, and a single-element version of that relay is available for use with single-phase a.c. motors and d.c. motors.

(*b*) *Electromagnetic trips:* These overload trips are instantaneous in operation and, in order to take advantage of the motor's permissible overload capacity, are usually employed with a time-lag device. The complete assembly consists of a series-wound coil surrounding a vertical iron plunger, to form a solenoid, and an associated time-lag in the form of an oil or silicone fluid filled dashpot or air vane. Their application thus depends on the current/time characteristic which can be obtained to ensure the necessary retarding action to prevent tripping on the occurrence of heavy overloads of short duration. The oil dashpot time-lag is the type most commonly used.

The required time-lag is obtained by adjustment of the rate at which oil is permitted to pass from the upper side to the lower side of the piston in Fig. 14.2.5L. Oil flow is governed by a small hole B in the rotatable plate C and a large hole D in the piston. Plate C has a number of holes graded in diameter and by changing the size of hole in use a range of time-lag settings between, for example, 10 and 30 s can be obtained. Overload current calibrations are marked on the outside of the plunger casing, the overload setting being changed by releasing the setting screw E

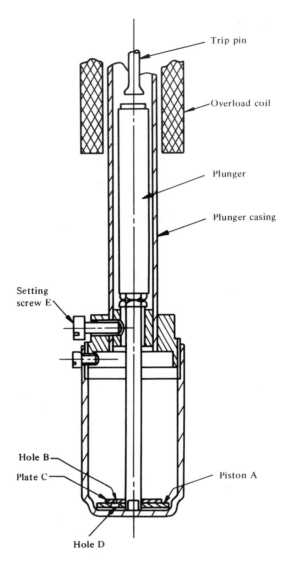

Fig. 14.2.5L   *Cross-section of a typical oil dashpot time-lag for an electromagnetic overload trip (Allen West & Co. Ltd.)*

and raising or lowering the dashpot to change the position of the plunger in relation to the magnetic field of the series overload coil.

A more sophisticated design of oil dashpot is available in which a restraining device, designed to operate on the occurrence of heavy transient or short duration overloads, prevents unnecessary tripping under such conditions. When a heavy overload occurs the sudden rush of oil causes a flap to close over the hole B. The heavy current causes the plunger to lift slightly, creating a vacuum beneath it, and when the current falls the plunger returns to its earlier position ejecting oil through hole B, forcing the flap off the hole. The piston is then able to function as a time-lag device under normal system conditions.

The restraining feature has applications with direct-on starters for squirrel cage motors and where motors may be subjected to severe peak loads of limited duration, enabling the overload trip to be given a normal setting without fear of operation under short-duration, heavy-current conditions.

When an overload condition has ceased or the trip pin has operated, the plunger and piston sink back to the bottom of the dashpot taking typically some 10 – 30 s to do so: in special designs this resetting time can be extended. This delay should be considered a necessary feature preventing the motor from being restarted immediately after the clearance of an overload condition. Even with the special designs it is not generally possible to extend the resetting time beyond 100 – 150 s.

As the reset position of the plunger is determined by the position of the dashpot, the further this is screwed down the more current is required through the solenoid to raise the plunger and operate the trip pin. Thus the position of the dashpot can be calibrated in terms of motor line current and if one such device is used in each line, three-phase protection can be provided.

Fig. 14.2.5M shows a typical current/time curve for a two-rate dashpot the function of which is to allow the device to clear a motor start condition but to operate as intended under overload conditions. Time/current curves vary depending

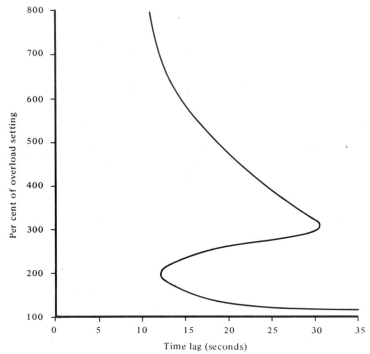

Fig. 14.2.5M *Typical current/time curve for an electromagnetic overload relay with a two-rate dashpot*

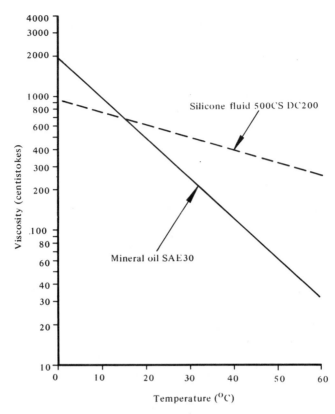

Fig. 14.2.5N   *Variation of the viscosity of the dashpot fluid with temperature*

upon the viscosity of the dampening fluid used to fill the dashpot. The viscosity of mineral oil decreases significantly with temperature (Fig. 14.2.5N) and a point may be reached when the timelag is unacceptably short. The use of silicone fluid instead of oil considerably improves the performance but the change of time delay with temperature will still have some significance (Fig. 14.2.5P).

To obtain optimum performance and take account of seasonal changes in the viscosity of the fluid the dashpot setting should, theoretically, be adjusted to take account of temperature changes between summer and winter working. This is obviously difficult to ensure in a large installation and the need for it has to be considered a limitation of the device.

It is not permissible for the dashpot to be filled with a fluid having a much higher viscosity than that for which it was designed in an attempt to prevent the device from tripping during starting: such an expedient would inevitably lead to much slower operation than is indicated by the published current/time curves and probably result in damage to the motor.

As the time delay is produced by utilising the effect of a piston moving in a viscous fluid, the operating current/time curve cannot match, except in a very

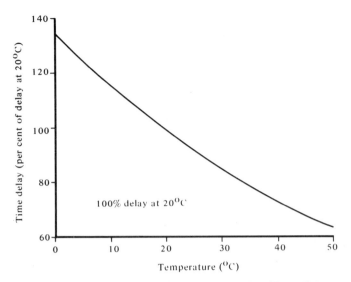

Fig. 14.2.5P   *Change in dashpot time delay with temperature using silicone fluid in the dashpot*

approximate manner, the heating and cooling characteristics of the motor and this limits the degree of protection which can be afforded the motor.

Comparison of magnetic and thermal protective devices

As described in the earlier parts of this Section, motor protection falls into two broad categories based on the detection of and response to either electromagnetic or thermal effects. Although simpler and essentially of one basic type the former clearly has a number of applications, but the range of thermal devices available is more readily matched to the motor characteristics and to the conditions which lead to motor failures. The performance comparison which follows will serve to illustrate and summarise the essential features of the two categories.

Electromagnetic trips:

(i)   These devices are relatively insensitive to small degrees of overload which, if sufficiently frequent and allowed to continue for extended periods, could shorten the life of the motor insulation. They cannot easily be set accurately enough for close protection which is a prime requirement for m.c.r. motors.

(ii)   The devices perform more effectively on medium to heavy overloads particularly the latter when currents approaching stalling level are reached and the required rapid operation under the conditions is achieved.

(iii) The current/time curve is not related to the actual conditions within the motor and the device therefore has no thermal memory.

(iv)   Under single-phasing conditions the performance is completely dependent upon the degree of overload which this effect produces in the two healthy lines. If the increase in line current is only small the operation of the device is doubtful.

(v)   Changes in the viscosity of the dampening fluid with temperature will cause variation in effective overload settings.

Thermal overload devices:

(i)   All types provide some degree of protection at all motor overloads: the more sophisticated relay types can be set more accurately and are thus better suited to the protection of m.c.r. motors.

(ii)   The relay types give a consistency of performance which is often as important as inherent accuracy and a running load scale can also be incorporated.

(iii)   As the operation of the devices is based on thermal effects the protection provided is better related to the needs of the motor than that given by the electromagnetic type: even so the thermal time constant of the relays is much shorter than that of the motors being protected.

(iv)   Single-phasing performance is good and with the more comprehensive types of relay, operation on small degrees of load unbalance is achieved.

(v)   Bimetallic devices and particularly relays with coiled bimetals have an appreciable resetting time. This is a desirable feature in that the motor has some time in which to cool down before a restart is possible. Even if the relay allows a restart, it will trip again if insufficient cooling has taken place.

Thermistors

The forerunner of this type of device as used in motor protection was the thermo-couple or thermostat embedded in the motor end-windings and applicable with equal facility to a.c. and d.c. machines. Commonly referred to as 'motor overheat protection' they provided protection against most motor internal conditions which give rise to excessive temperatures including sustained overload;   high, low or unbalanced voltages; locked rotor; blocked ventilator; and single-phase running of a polyphase a.c. motor.

The main advantage of this type of protection is that the temperature sensitive elements are located in the motor windings themselves and thus give an accurate measurement of temperature at the points where the overheating is likely to occur. This feature also allows a motor to be run nearer to the limit of maximum permissible temperature at times of necessity.

The modern version of this type of device is the thermistor (positive-temperature – coefficient resistor). Several such devices are embedded in and bonded to the enamel-covered wires forming the stator windings during manufacture and connections brought out to a solid-state control unit and interposing relay mounted separately for small motors and usually built into the motor terminal box of motors above 10 h.p. The relay is inoperative until the thermistors indicate that the winding temperature and the current flowing in any phase exceed their stipulated limits. High winding temperature and excessive current are thus needed before tripping takes place and tripping is avoided on starting and on the occurrence of thermal overloads of short duration.

The thermistor need be little larger than a match head with a correspondingly low thermal inertia. As these small sensors can tolerate only a few milliamperes the control unit includes an amplifier which, in conjunction with the relay (now frequently solid-state) would initiate tripping and, if required, an alarm. The unit is designed to fail to safety, i.e. to the tripping condition. The characteristics and testing requirements are laid down in BS 4999 which deals with the thermal protection of electric motors.

Thermistor characteristics are now amenable to close manufacturing control and any appropriate value of reference temperature may be selected from the nominal 110 – 160°C range of motor-trip reference temperatures. The use of positive-temperature-coefficient (p.t.c.) thermistors gives a resistance/temperature characteristic as shown in Fig. 14.2.5Q, from which it can be seen that over a relatively narrow critical-temperature range the resistance increases very rapidly. Typically, this increase is from about 100Ω to over 1000Ω over a temperature range of only about 20°C in the band between 100 and 200°C.

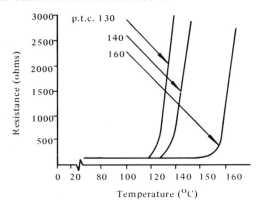

Fig. 15.2.5Q *Resistance/temperature characteristics of positive-temperature-coefficient thermistors for operating temperatures of 130°, 140° and 160°C*

The characteristics are stable and the steep rate-of-change of resistance continues well beyond the 1000Ω level. The characteristics are controllable during manufacture and the reference temperature (defined in BS 4999 as 'the nominal temperature of the thermally sensitive device at which it is required to cause the protection system to operate') can be selected to provide a warning or a tripping signal at any temperature required. In practice the required temperature will generally lie between the 110°C recommended in BS 4999 as the early warning reference for Class E windings and the 160°C trip reference for Class F insulation.

The application of thermistors has been extended certainly up to motors operating at 3·3 kV and they are now generally accepted as a useful, relatively inexpensive form of close protection of particular value for motors running at or near full output. A disadvantage is that they can only be installed at the manufacturing stage and later replacement is difficult. Their response time is rather slow so that there is a tendency for them to lag behind the temperature of the winding with the consequent risk that they may operate only after the insulation has been overheated.

A future development may be that a a unit incorporating direct thermal protection for attaching to a motor after manufacture thus moving towards the universal application of thermistor type devices.

Undervoltage protection: The chief reason for employing undervoltage protection of either a.c. or d.c. motors is to ensure that the motor circuit-breakers or contactors are tripped on a complete loss of supply, so that when the supply is restored it is not overloaded by the simultaneous starting of all the motors. This is particularly important with a.c. motors in a power station where the simultaneous starting of a large bank of motors would probably overload, and result in the tripping of the feeding transformer. It is necessary also to avoid danger to operators when the supply is restored without their prior knowledge and, for those motors which are not direct-on-line started, to prevent full voltage being applied to a stationary machine. Undervoltage protection may take the form of:

(*a*) a plain undervoltage release coil fitted with an oil-dashpot time-lag and operating direct on to the circuit-breaker trip bar or contactor mechanism;

(*b*) an undervoltage no-close relay with contacts interlocked with the motor starter and connected in the d.c. trip coil circuit, the time-lag being obtained by oil-dashpot;

(*c*) an undervoltage relay with an auxiliary time-lag relay; or

(*d*) a simple contactor with electrically held-in coil.

The releases or relays are of the single-pole type connected between the two poles of a d.c. supply or between two phases of a three-phase a.c. supply, the voltage and time-settings being variable. To reduce the risk of unwanted tripping of whole groups of motors, for example, on the occurrence of a fault on the transmission system, it is necessary to ensure that the relay will not operate when voltage depressions of short duration are experienced. A sufficiently low voltage setting and an adequate time-setting must therefore be applied to this protection to allow it to remain inoperative during transient disturbances. In practice this means that a voltage setting of about 50% and a time setting of several seconds may be required, the settings chosen being compatible with the characteristics of the associated plant. In the particular case of pulverised-fuel-boilers, special consideration should be given to the time setting of the undervoltage protection to guard against the risk of boiler explosion.

The electrically held-in contactor has an inherent undervoltage feature in that when the coil is energised the contactor closes but remains closed only as long as the coil remains energised. Face-plate type starters, particularly those used with the small d.c. motors, incorporate an undervoltage release coil in the starting box. The spring loaded moving-contact arm is held in the 'fully on' position by the electromagnetic coil which is energised when the control contactor is closed. If the voltage falls to a level at which the strength of the electromagnetic field is insufficient to hold the arm, the spring returns the contact arm to the 'off' position, disconnecting the motor from the supply.

14.3   Reactors

14.3.1   The place of reactors in a power system

The reactors which may be used in a power system can be generally classified into two main groups:

(*a*)   series reactors for short-circuit current limitation
(*b*)   shunt reactors for reactive compensation.

The purpose of the series reactor follows from the fact that the fault current which flows for a fault at any given point in a power system is determined by the impedance of the power system as seen from the point of fault. The maximum fault current can, therefore, be limited to an acceptable value by the provision of series reactors of appropriate value at suitable points in the power system. The provision of such fault-limiting reactors can avoid the necessity of providing larger or specially braced conductors or circuit breakers of higher rating, capable of withstanding the short-circuit currents which would otherwise occur. The use of series reactors may thus show appreciable advantages in capital cost and space requirements, a disadvantage being the increased regulation of the system, particularly when supplying low power-factor loads. However, this increased regulation can be compensated by the use of voltage regulators (see Section 14.4) where necessary.

The second type of reactor referred to, namely the shunt reactor, finds its application in the compensation of capacitive reactance, the lagging current taken by the shunt reactor being used to reduce or cancel the leading current taken by the shunt capacitive reactance of the system at the point concerned. Thus, shunt reactors are commonly used to compensate for the large capacitance currents which tend to be present in cable networks.

14.3.2   Types of reactor

Series reactors may be classified according to their construction:

    (*a*)   air-insulated, cast-in-concrete or concrete clad types, as in Fig. 14.3.2A, and

    (*b*)   oil-immersed, as in Fig. 14.3.2B.

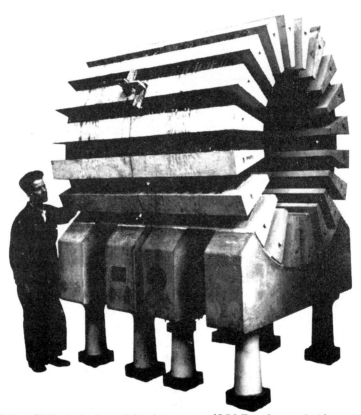

Fig. 14.3.2A   *50 Hz single-phase air insulator reactor (GEC Transformers Ltd.)*

They may be classified also according to their application, namely generator, busbar or feeder reactor.

Air-insulated reactor: In this type, the winding is wound on supports and then set in concrete so that the vertical and horizontal spacers are solid concrete, or the winding is clamped firmly between concrete end-rings. A cast-in-concrete reactor is inevitably bulky, and because of the strong magnetic field surrounding it, it must be sited well away from metal work and with adequate space for heat dissipation. The use of a tank is thus ruled out making it necessary to provide some other form of accommodation; this is often in the form of a special cell or chamber in, or

Fig. 14.3.2B   *50 Hz three-phase oil-immersed reactor (GEC Transformers Ltd.)*

adjoining, the main building. This type of reactor is used generally at voltages up to and including 33 kV.

Oil-immersed reactor (magnetically shielded):   In the oil-immersed reactor the difficulty of the external magnetic field is overcome by providing a laminated iron path around the coil through which the flux can pass easily and without significant losses. Thus there is no appreciable external field to cause heating of nearby steel-work or affect adjacent electrical measuring equipment. This type therefore lends itself to both indoor and outdoor service. The magnetic shield, as shown in Fig. 14.3.2C, consists of a 'bird cage' of iron laminations built up in the form of a barrel, the end clamping bars and the hoops around the body having insulated joints to prevent the formation of short-circuited turns in which the flux would otherwise set up a circulating current. The presence of the magnetic shield reduces the reluctance of the magnetic path causing the reactance under normal operating conditions to be, perhaps, 10 – 15% higher than under short circuit conditions.

Fig. 14.3.2C   *Coil assembly of 1980 kVAr, 11 kV, 50 Hz three-phase oil-immersed reactor (GEC Transformers Ltd.)*

During the short circuit, saturation of the iron occurs and the reactor behaves substantially the same as an air-cored reactor. However, the rating is based on the short circuit reactance, the increase in reactance at normal load currents being of no great importance.

Oil-immersed reactor (nonmagnetically shielded): The alternative of nonmagnetic shielding with copper, or sometimes aluminium, sheets bent to form a cylinder is often used. Typical shields are shown in Fig. 14.3.2D. The ampere-turns induced in the shield have the effect of reducing the reactance by an amount equal to the percentage of the coil ampere-turns induced in the shield. The larger the diameter of the shield the smaller will be the $I^2 R$ loss, but this advantage has to be weighed against the disadvantages of a larger tank and a greater volume of oil.

The circulating currents induced in the shield result in a counter m.m.f. which confines the flux to a path between the winding and the shield.

Fig. 14.3.2D   *Aluminium shields*

Since no iron is introduced into the flux path, the nonmagnetically shielded reactor can be considered as being of a constant ohmic reactance over very wide limits of current.

This is the important advantage of the copper-shielded reactor but against this is the relatively high loss in the shields when compared with the magnetically shielded type. Again, compared with the magnetically shielded reactor, the copper-shielded type gives a lower reactance for the same size of coil and requires a larger clearance between coil and shields, with the result that it is usually bigger than an equivalent reactor with magnetic shielding.

14.3.3   Reactor rating

The overcurrent factor of a reactor is defined as the ratio of the symmetrical r.m.s. through-fault current to the rated current. When this ratio is small the thermal rating of the reactor is determined by the normal throughput conditions, calculated usually as for a transformer but making allowances for more widely spaced conductors giving a less steep gradient between oil and winding temperatures and permitting the use of a somewhat higher current density.

When the overcurrent factor is large, the current density is determined by the short circuit conditions. There is no British Standard exclusive to reactors but B.S. 171:1970 should be used where it applies. It specifies that reactors shall be designed to withstand, without damage, the electromagnetic forces due to a current having a peak value equal to 2.55 times the r.m.s. value of the rated current multiplied by the overcurrent factor; and also the thermal effects corresponding to the specified overcurrent conditions. Table 13 of that Standard lays down the maximum current densities depending upon the duration of the overcurrent.

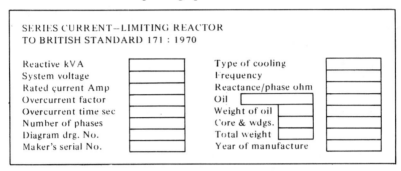

Fig. 14.3.3A   *Rating plate for series current-limiting reactor*

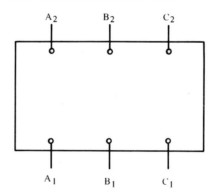

Fig. 14.3.3B   *Terminal marking plate for series current-limiting reactor*

A typical rating plate and terminal marking plate for a series current-limiting reactor are shown in Figs. 14.3.3A and 14.3.3B.

14.3.4   Reactor application

The most commonly used positions for the application of current-limiting reactors are in the generator connections to the circuit breaker, between adjacent sections of busbar, and in series with the feeders. Their effectiveness as regards the maintenance of busbar voltage and the safeguarding of switchgear under fault conditions is the dominant factor in deciding their location.

Generator reactors: Most modern generators are designed and built with sufficient inherent reactance to enable them to withstand a symmetrical short circuit across their terminals. This was not always so and in older stations it is not unusual to find a current-limiting reactor connected in series with each generator. The reactor limits the current which can flow to a generator fault from the other machines connected to the same section of busbar, and in doing so reduces the damage sustained by the faulty generator as well as effectively reducing the short circuit MVA to be handled by the switchgear. Thus the effect of the reactor is to confine the disturbance and provide relief to healthy apparatus and feeders. Generator reactors are effective whenever the machine is running and therefore involve a small but continuous energy loss under running conditions. Fig. 14.3.4A shows a typical arrangement.

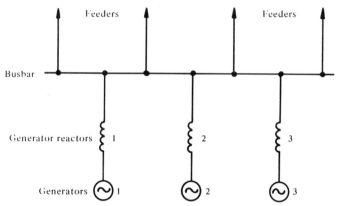

Fig. 14.3.4A *Connection of generator reactors*

Busbar reactors. (a) Series connected: A typical example of this method of connection is shown in Fig. 14.3.4B and it will be seen that the reactor is inserted directly in the busbar run. Preferably the connection of the feeders to the various sections of busbar should be such that at full load the current circulating between the sections is a minimum. Absolute balance between sections is unlikely to be obtained but if this ideal can be approached undesirable losses and voltage drops in the reactors will be kept to relatively insignificant values. They differ from

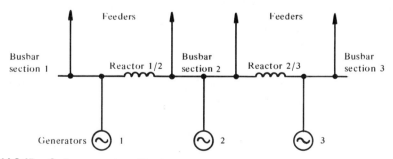

Fig. 14.3.4B *Series connection of busbar reactors*

generator reactors in that such units incur losses whenever the machine is connected to the system whether it is operating on light load or full load.

This method divides the station capacity into several sections so that nominally generator 1 supplies the load on busbar section 1, generator 2 the load on busbar section 2, and so on. When a feeder fault occurs, for example on one of the section 2 feeders, reactors 1/2 and 2/3 have the effect of limiting the current flowing to the fault from generators 1 and 3.

Busbar reactors. (b) Tie bar connected: Two methods are commonly adopted and may be classified as

(i)   the star connection, as illustrated by Fig. 14.3.4C and
(ii) the ring connection, as illustrated by Fig. 14.3.4D.

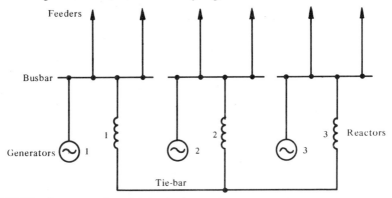

Fig. 14.3.4C   *Star connection of tie-bar busbar reactors*

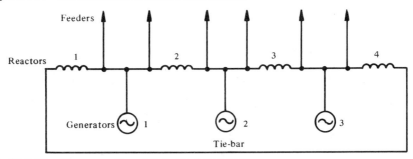

Fig. 14.3.4D   *Ring connection of tie-bar busbar reactors*

In (i) each section of busbar is connected via a reactor to a common star point, and if the feeders and generators are suitably arranged little or no current need flow through the reactors. If one section of busbar is out of service the other sections remain in parallel through the reactors. This method has the obvious disadvantage that an additional busbar, the tie-bar busbar, is required. It will be noted that there are two reactors in series between sections and the ohmic value of each reactor will thus be generally less than that of those required in the ring formation.

In (ii) the reactors are connected in series between sections of busbar and closed by a tie-bar to form a ring. The ring is broken when one section is out of service, and there will be considerable reactance between remaining sections resulting in poor voltage regulation. As in the star connection an additional busbar is required.

Feeder reactors: The function of the feeder reactor is to localise the voltage drop to the feeder on which the fault has occurred and also to enable smaller and cheaper feeder circuit breakers to be used. Compared with generator reactors, the advantages of connecting a reactor in series with each feeder are that a feeder fault will not seriously affect the busbar voltage with consequently less tendency for the generators to lose synchronism and the effect of the fault will be localised. The connection of feeder reactors is shown in Fig. 14.3.4E.

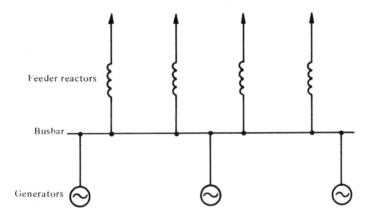

Fig. 14.3.4E   *Connection of feeder reactors*

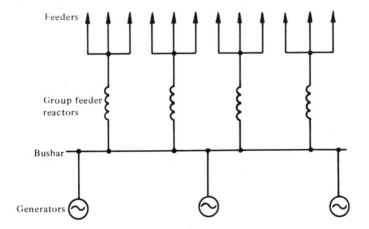

Fig. 14.3.4F   *Connection of group feeder reactors*

The disadvantages are that a continuous power loss and adverse effect on voltage regulation must be accepted, and the reactor affords little relief against busbar faults. If the total generating capacity of the station is increased it may be necessary to increase the size of the feeder reactors to limit the higher short circuit current, but this inherent reactance will of course have a similar effect on system regulation as the deliberate introduction of a reactor unit.

Group feeder reactors: An alternative to the arrangement with a reactor connected in each feeder is shown in Fig. 14.3.4F. Such units are called group feeder reactors since several feeders are grouped on to a single reactor. Economy in the number, and therefore the cost of reactors is the only merit of this method of connection, and it has the disadvantage that the disconnection of the reactor for either fault investigation or maintenance purposes deprives the system of not one feeder but three. It is used occasionally at voltages up to and including 33 kV.

14.3.5   Reactor protection

General: Although a reactor is often similar in appearance to a transformer and similar winding methods are employed, they differ in several other respects. Chief among these is the single winding of the reactor and the absence of magnetising inrush current when the unit is switched in. It is thus unnecessary, except for the iron-cored reactor, to go to the expense and complication of biased systems with the result that reactor protection is usually simpler than transformer protection.

In some cases the reactor may be included in the protected zone of another system element, such as a feeder, and little, if any, additional protection would be necessary. Examples of this are a reactor connected in a busbar run and embraced by the busbar protection, or a reactor connected in series with a feeder and embraced by the feeder protection. The additional protection for any important oil-immersed reactor would include a Buchholz gas- and oil-actuated relay and a winding temperature indicator, both of which are described later in this Section.

The types of fault which may occur include flashover of external bushings, earth faults on the windings or connections (phase faults if the three phases are mounted in one tank), core faults, interturn faults and overheating of the winding resulting from excessive loading or failure of the cooler equipment. It is usually considered unnecessary to protect against interturn faults since experience has shown that such faults very quickly spread to earth and are then detected by the earth-fault protection.

Series-connected reactors: overall differential protection: In deciding upon the protection required for a given reactor, the size and importance of the unit must be taken into account and, as will be seen later, the arrangement and number of terminals brought out from the winding has a bearing on the type of protection which can be applied.

For the larger three-phase series reactors with all six ends of the windings brought out to terminals, an overall system of protection is justified, and, as already mentioned, no biasing is required for this application. The emphasis on the number of ends brought out stems from the need for an overall system to be driven from two sets of current transformers, one set on each side of the reactor. The current transformers are connected by pilot wires and the relay connected differentially, as shown in Fig. 14.3.5A, giving protection against phase and earth faults. The six current transformers have identical ratios and may be housed in the reactor bushings, in the case of high-voltage reactors, or alternatively, in the associated switchgear. In reactors for lower voltages, bushings may not be fitted and the ends of the windings are brought out to a terminal chamber on each side large enough to accommodate the current transformers.

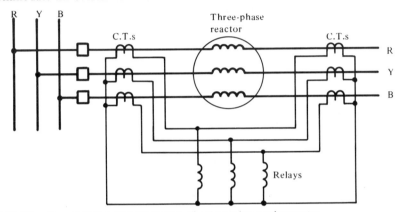

Fig. 14.3.5A   *Overall differential protection of a three-phase series reactor*

The modern relay used for the differential protection is a three-pole relay (or three single-pole relays) of the instantaneous, high impedance, attracted armature type. A tapped plug-bridge enables the setting to be varied, and in view of its high impedance it is necessary to connect a non-linear resistor in parallel with the relay and its associated components to limit the pilot voltage to a safe value during internal faults.

The operation of this balanced system of protection is based upon the well tried and reliable Merz-Price principle of circulating current protection. It compares the currents flowing in on one side of the protected equipment with those flowing out on the other. In such a system a fault occurring within the protected zone will cause primary fault current to flow through both sets of c.t.s in the directions shown by the heavy arrows in Fig. 14.3.5B, the resulting secondary currents circulating as indicated by the light arrows, the summated currents flowing through the differentially connected relay to cause operation. When a fault occurs outside the protected zone, primary fault current flows in the same direction through both sets of c.t.s as shown in Fig. 14.3.5C, and the secondary currents circulate in directions such that there is negligible current through the relay and no relay operation. Negligible current and not zero current, since in a balanced system of protection there is inevitably a little 'spill' current resulting from slight inequalities

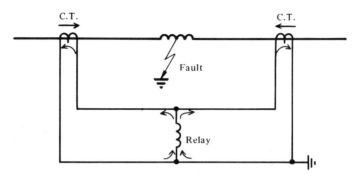

Fig. 14.3.5B   *Overall differential protection: operation on internal fault*

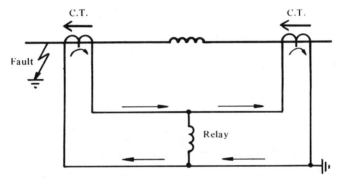

Fig. 14.3.5C   *Overall differential protection: non-operation on external fault*

in the c.t.s. at the two ends and, despite the use of pilot compensating resistors, some mismatch of the pilot burdens between the point at which the relay is connected and the c.t.s. at either side. Tests must be done during commissioning to check that the spill current is indeed negligible, since its presence in any significant quantity is tending towards instability of the protection under normal running or external fault conditions.

Overcurrent and earth-fault protection: The system of overall-differential circulating-current protection just described provides protection of the reactor against both phase-to-phase and phase-to-earth faults, but failure to operate would probably have serious consequences and it is prudent to add a back-up feature to guard against such an eventuality. This usually takes the form of a conventional inverse definite minimum time (i.d.m.t.) overcurrent relay driven from separate c.t.s. and connected as shown in Fig. 14.3.5D. Such relays have already been described in detail in Chapter 6.

A variation of this form of back-up protection to include an earth-fault feature is illustrated in Fig. 14.3.5E, and consists of residually connecting the centre element and applying a somewhat lower earth-fault setting to it. This element is virtually identical with the overcurrent element but would have plug bridge settings variable in seven steps between 10 and 40% compared with 50 and 200%.

On small reactors, where an overall differential system is not justified, the reactor may be protected by separate overcurrent and earth-fault systems, and this is dealt with more fully in the following section on shunt reactor protection.

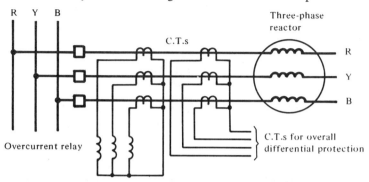

Fig. 14.3.5D   *Overcurrent protection as back-up to overall differential protection of three-phase series reactor*

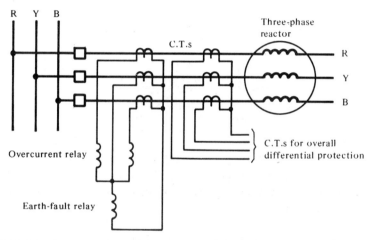

Fig. 14.3.5E   *Overcurrent and earth-fault protection as back-up to overall differential protection of three-phase series reactor*

The Buchholz relay: An oil-immersed reactor is not completely protected unless it is fitted with a gas and oil operated relay. This is because a very slowly developing core fault or incipient fault within the reactor tank will not be detected by the other forms of protection. It is well known that an internal reactor fault is accompanied by gases which the heat liberates from the oil. This phenomenon is utilised in the Buchholz relay which is fitted in the run of the pipework from the tank to the oil conservator. Fig. 14.3.5F shows a typical relay.

With an incipient fault producing gas the upper float, or in the illustration the upper bucket, operates when a specified volume of gas has been collected and causes an alarm to operate. With a heavier fault requiring immediate disconnection of the reactor, a surge of oil from the tank to the conservator operates the lower or

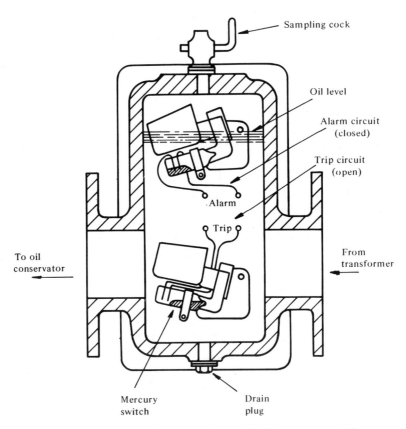

Sampling cock

Oil level

Alarm circuit
(closed)

Trip circuit
(open)

Alarm

Trip

To oil
conservator

From
transformer

Mercury
switch

Drain
plug

Fig. 14.3.5F   *Double float gas- and oil-actuated relay (GEC Measurements Ltd)*

surge float to complete the tripping circuit. Falling oil level also is detected by this relay giving first an alarm and, if the loss continues, initiating the disconnection before damage can occur.

One modern relay consists of a cast housing containing two pivoted buckets each counterbalanced by a weight. Each assembly incorporates a mercury switch which, owing to the weight distribution of bucket and counterweight, is normally in the open position. When an incipient fault occurs small bubbles of gas will be generated and these, in attempting to pass to the conservator, will be trapped in the relay housing. As the gas accumulates the oil level in the relay will fall and eventually the top bucket will be left full of oil. The bucket will not then be fully immersed and the weight of the oil left behind will cause the whole assembly to tilt, closing its mercury switch and completing the alarm circuit.

With a heavier fault the gas is generated much more rapidly and the displaced oil surges through the relay causing the lower bucket assembly to tilt closing its mercury switch and completing the tripping circuits to the h.v. and l.v. circuit-breakers.

Loss of oil from the tank is also detected by the Buchholz relay since the buckets will be left full of oil. This will cause first the alarm element and then the surge element to operate, completing the alarm and tripping circuits.

The relay is mounted in a straight run of pipework sloping up at about 10° from tank to conservator, as shown in Fig. 14.3.5G. The arrow on the relay must point in the same direction as the oil flow to the conservator or the relay will not function properly. It must be appreciated that the Buchholz relay is not a high speed relay compared with, say, a modern attracted-armature relay. The surge float may take as long as 0·5 s to operate if the magnitude of the fault current is limited, and on all but the smallest units it fulfils a role supplementary to the other protection arrangements already described.

It should be noted that although the relay described is of the double element pattern a single-element pattern is available, and in this the contacts would be connected to give a gas alarm only.

Winding temperature protection: A reactor winding, like that of a transformer, can withstand short periods of overloading without damage but overheating caused by prolonged overloading or failure of cooler equipment will, if allowed to persist, result in premature deterioration of the insulation and so shorten the useful life of the reactor. To obtain a warning of overheating of the winding, a hot-spot temperature indicator is fitted in the manner shown in Fig. 14.3.5H. This device indicates the temperature of the top oil and takes into account also the temperature of the reactor winding. The first is obtained by the thermometer immersed in the top of the tank, and the second by feeding a heater in the same pocket from a current transformer located in the reactor winding. To obtain maximum advantage from the reactor's ability to tolerate reasonable overloading for short periods, the thermal time-constant of the thermometer is made to match as closely as possible the thermal time-constant of the reactor winding.

In addition to serving as a winding hot-spot indicator the instrument incorporaates mercury switches: one to initiate an alarm if the temperature should reach a predetermined figure, 100°C is typical, and the other to complete the reactor trip circuit if the temperature should increase by a further fixed amount, say 20°C.

Shunt-connected reactors: overall differential protection. If all six ends of the shunt reactor winding are brought out an overall differential system of protection can be applied using an unbiased circulating-current system as for the series-connected unit.

Restricted earth-fault protection: In a shunt reactor it is not strictly necessary to bring out all six ends, and, for reasons of economy, the star connection is sometimes made internally and only four connections brought out. It is not then possible to apply an overall differential system of the type referred to above and recourse is made to a system requiring only four c.t.s. This is known as a restricted earth-fault system and, as the name implies, protects the equipment against earth faults only. Since approximately 75% of all faults are earth faults or at least begin

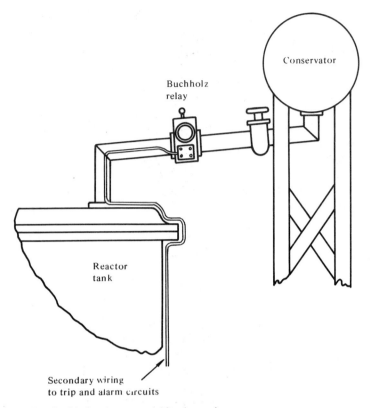

Fig. 14.3.5G *Buchholz relay mounted in pipework*

as such, this is not such a serious drawback as it may seem at first, and phase faults can be catered for with a separate relay.

The application of restricted earth-fault protection is illustrated in Fig. 14.3.5I and employs a single pole, high speed, attracted armature relay of the type described in Chapter 6. It is a balanced current system restricted to operation for faults within the zone spanned by the c.t.s. and therefore unresponsive to external faults. The setting applied should be the lowest possible compatible with stability and should have regard to the need to protect as much of the winding as possible.

Overcurrent protection: Phase faults on reactor installations are a considerably lower risk than earth faults and can be protected against by using a three-pole i.d.m.t. overcurrent relay of the type described in Chapter 6, and connected as shown in Fig. 14.3.5I. This relay is by its nature relatively slow in operation and it must be set to discriminate with other protective equipments.

Buchholz and over-temperature protection: A shunt-connected oil-immersed reactor would qualify for the fitting of a Buchholz relay and a winding temperature indicator, just as in the case of a series-connected unit.

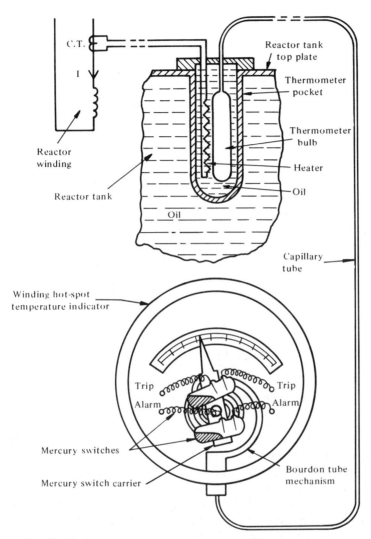

Fig. 14.3.5H *Winding hot-spot temperature indicator for oil-immersed reactor*

Intertripping: As the name implies, intertripping is a means of effecting the tripping of a circuit breaker at a point remote from that at which a fault has occurred. To do this it is necessary to transmit intelligence from the point at which the fault has been detected to the other end or ends of the circuit and to arrange for its reception to initiate the tripping of the appropriate circuit breaker or breakers without reference to any other conditions prevailing at the time. Intertripping finds its main application as part of the protection scheme of a transformer connected directly to the end of a feeder, that is without an h.v. circuit breaker local to the transformer, and as part of the protection of a reactor similarly lacking in circuit breakers which could be opened to isolate a reactor internal fault. It

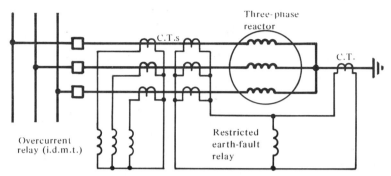

Fig. 14.3.5I   *Restricted earth-fault and back-up overcurrent protection of a three-phase shunt reactor*

consists of sending a signal, initiated by the reactor protection, over a rented Post Office pilot channel, or privately owned pilot channel if available. A carrier signal transmitted over the power system conductors may be used in certain circumstances. Fig. 14.3.5J illustrates a typical application.

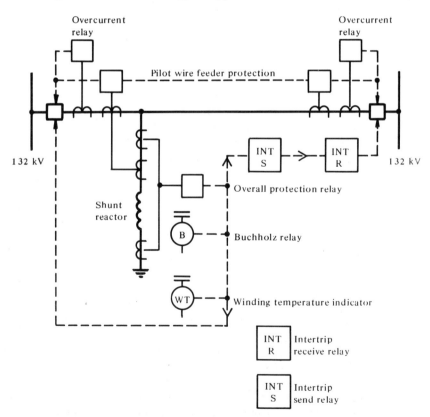

Fig. 14.3.5J   *Diagram of protection and intertripping for a 132 kV feeder and oil-immersed shunt reactor*

For further consideration of intertripping and protection signalling facilities and their application reference should be made to Chapter 7.

To obtain a figure for the total time required to isolate a fault from such a circuit it is of course necessary to add the intertripping time to the protection and circuit breaker operating times. Thus the absence of a circuit breaker has the effect of appreciably increasing the length of time a fault remains on the system with consequent increase of damage at the point of fault and a greater tendency towards system instability.

An alternative to conventional intertripping techniques for transformer or reactor faults uses a single-pole fault-throwing switch. Operation of the overall differential protection or the Buchholz protection trips the local circuit breaker and initiates the closing of the fault-throwing switch to apply a deliberate system fault between one phase and earth. The substantial fault current flowing under this condition is detected by the protection at the remote end and tripping takes place. It is simple and robust and functions independently of signalling channels and equipment but has disadvantages in that its operation will subject the power system to another, possibly more severe, fault condition than the one it is about to clear. Designs have been developed suitable for application on systems having a three-phase fault level of up to 2500 MVA at 132 kV.

14.4   Boosters

I4.4.1   The place of boosters in a power system

It is the responsibility of the Supply Industry to maintain within declared limits, the voltage at every consumer's premises. This is no small task, but, as will be seen later, it is one which is tackled in various ways depending upon the requirements of the system concerned. The practice has been to concentrate an increasing proportion of generating stations, with the exception of nuclear stations, in a few coal producing areas, resulting in long transmission lines and the inevitable voltage drops between the generation areas and the load centres. Voltage adjustments are usually made at transforming stations, but in a scattered distribution area supplied from one supply point adjustments may be made at the remote ends of the distribution lines.

In this chapter, the term 'booster' is not restricted to the booster transformer but embraces other forms of voltage regulating equipment. These include transformer tap-changing, the moving coil regulator and the induction regulator, and together with the booster transformer these are discussed in more detail in the following Sections. It should be noted also that although the term booster is most commonly used, these equipments provide facilities for reducing or 'bucking' as well as for boosting the voltage.

A transformer with tap-changing gear performs a double function; voltage transformation and voltage boosting or bucking by varying the setting of the tap-changing gear. The booster provides only the regulating facilities, but has advantages in size and cost and can be installed at any point in the system where voltage regulation is required. On the other hand, the lossses in the booster make the combined transformer and booster arrangement less efficient than the transformer with integral tap-changing. Features of the moving coil regulator and the induction regulator are the continuous regulation obtainable and the absence of switches and moving contacts, thus reducing the amount of maintenance required.

14.4.2   Transformer tap-changing

In this, the most obvious method, the transformer secondary voltage is varied by changing taps, that is by varying the number of effective turns in one of the windings, thereby changing by a small amount, and without phase-shift, the transformation ratio.

This is done by means of selector switches, and it is essential that there is no break in the winding circuit while the selector is passing from one tapping to the next. Since this means that there will be a short period when the selector is connected to two adjacent tappings, it is necessary to introduce resistors, or sometimes reactors, to limit the flow of short circuit current during the changeover period. One phase of the winding and tap-changing arrangements of a typical 275/132 kV autotransformer is shown diagrammatically in Fig. 14.4.2A.

Transformer tap-changing gear does not form part of this chapter and is mentioned here only for the sake of completeness. The tap-changing equipment is included in the zone embraced by the transformer protection and no separate protection is required, although the presence of the tap-changer does influence the design of the protection applied to the transformer unit as a whole.

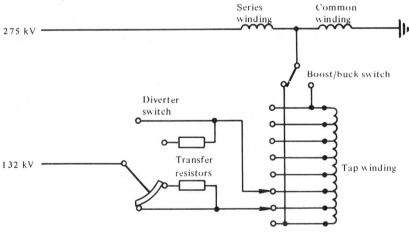

Fig. 14.4.2A   *Winding arrangement of one phase of 275/132 kV three-phase autotransformer*

14.4.3   Booster transformers

The booster is regarded as an adjunct to the main transformer, and consists essentially of an auxiliary transformer with its secondary winding connected in series with the main transformer, so that the output is the resultant of the secondary voltages of the two transformers. The secondary winding of the auxiliary transformer is provided with a number of tappings to give a variable voltage over a limited range. Thus the boosting voltage is governed by the number of secondary turns actually in circuit, and the regulation is adjustable in steps, rather than continuously as with the moving coil regulator and the induction regulator. The kVA rating of a booster may be defined as the product of the maximum change in voltage it can produce and the load current it can carry.

A simple form of booster for single-phase circuits consists of an autotransformer with tappings, the tap position being selected by a switch of the face-plate type. At voltages above, say, 3·3 kV and for high outputs on-load tap-changing gear is incorporated.

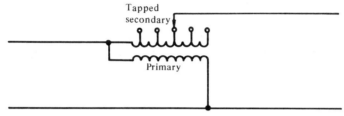

Fig. 14.4.3A *Diagrammatic arrangement of simple voltage booster*

If the equipment were connected as shown in Fig. 14.4.3A the tap-change gear would have to carry the full line current. Apart from other considerations this would make the cost prohibitive, and the usual method is to employ an untapped boosting winding with its secondary connected in the line and its primary energised from a tapped regulating or 'teaser' winding, as shown in Fig. 14.4.3B and more fully in Fig. 14.4.3C. It will be seen from these diagrams that the on-load tap-changing is performed in a circuit remote from the line whose voltage is being controlled. Bucking facilities also are available with this equipment, and are obtained simply by reversing the connections to the primaries of the regulating transformer, using the switch provided (not shown in diagram). The boosting and regulating transformers usually form a combined unit mounted in a common tank.

For lines having high power factor loads, for example distribution circuits to domestic consumers, a simpler and cheaper arrangement can be applied. It consists

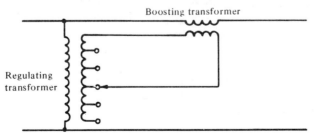

Fig. 14.4.3B *Connections of single-phase booster with regulating winding*

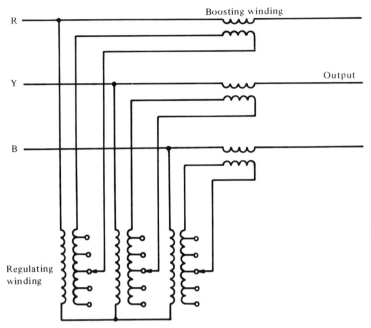

Fig. 14.4.3C *Connections of three-phase booster with regulating winding*

of an autotransformer with one tapping only and a reactor connected in series with the incoming line, as shown in the single-phase diagram Fig. 14.4.3D. Reference to Fig. 14.4.3E will show that under no-load conditions the no-load current I_0, that is the exciting current of the autotransformer, lags nearly 90° behind the incoming

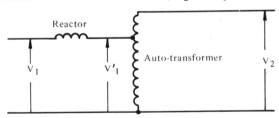

Fig. 14.4.3D *Single-phase booster (fixed boost)*

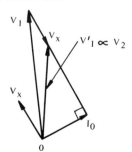

Fig. 14.4.3E *Phasor diagram of single-phase booster on no-load*

voltage V_1. The small reactor voltage drop V_x is in quadrature with I_0, and the resultant primary voltage V_1' is directly proportional to V_2.

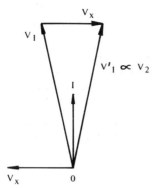

Fig. 14.4.3F *Phasor diagram of single-phase booster on high power-factor load*

Fig. 14.4.3F illustrates the conditions with load power factor approaching unity. The primary current I is now almost in phase with the incoming voltage V_1 and the voltage drop V_x across the reactor will be increased. With the increase in power factor this drop will be almost in quadrature with V_1; the resultant primary voltage V_1' being considerably higher than before but again proportional to V_2. Thus by judiciously choosing the turns ratio and reactor impedance the increase in the voltage V_2 can be made equal to any required value. This method provides up to about 6% boost and finds application in distribution systems supplying high power factor domestic loads.

In-phase boosting: The boosters so far described inject a voltage in phase with, or in phase opposition to, the line-to-earth voltage, that is they add or subtract a voltage in phase with the line voltage. This can be illustrated by considering two points A and B in an interconnected network, the voltages at these two points being V_A and V_B. If, as shown in Fig. 14.4.3G(*a*), the voltages are equal and in phase, the feeder between A and B will carry no current, but if an in phase voltage booster is

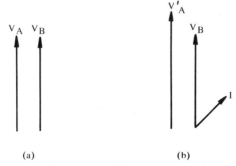

(a)   (b)

Fig. 14.4.3G *Voltage phasors (a) unboosted (b) boosted interconnected system*

connected at A, increasing the voltage there to V'_A, a current I will flow in the feeder. Fig. 14.4.3G(b) shows this current lagging behind the increase in voltage $V'_A - V_B$ by an angle determined from the expression $\tan^{-1} X/R$ where X and R are the feeder reactance and resistance values, respectively. The value of X is usually large compared with R so that, for most practical purposes, the current will lag by an angle approaching $90°$. Thus the effect of the in-phase booster is to introduce a lagging current, and so control the flow of reactive kVA (kVAr) in the system. The power component of current is thus not significantly affected by in-phase boosting.

Quadrature boosting: It is sometimes desirable to modify the phase of the line voltage without substantially affecting its magnitude, and this is achieved by combining with the line voltage V_1 another voltage V_2 lagging or leading it by about $90°$. The resultant voltage has undergone a phase change compared with the original line voltage, the direction of the phase-shift depending upon whether the injected voltage is lagging or leading. Little change in the magnitude of the voltage will occur for small angles of phase-shift. This is known as quadrature boosting and the resultant change in the current will be nearly in phase with the line voltage, so producing a change in the transmitted power. Thus the effect of the quadrature booster is to provide control of the power flowing in the system.

Considering Fig. 14.4.3H, the diagram for one phase, it will be seen that the

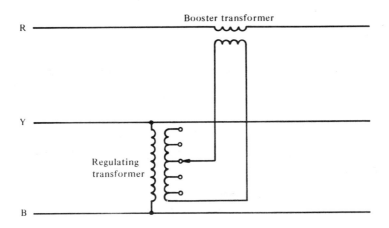

Fig. 14.4.3H *Connections of quadrature booster (only one phase shown)*

primary winding of the red phase boosting transformer is energised from the tapped secondary winding of the regulating transformer connected between the other two phases. As the voltage between these two phases is $90°$ out of phase with the red 'phase-to-neutral' voltage, the effect of the boosting voltage is to change the phase of this 'phase-to-neutral' voltage. For a complete three-phase quadrature boosting equipment, similar connections for two additional sets of transformers would be required, as indicated in Fig. 14.4.3I.

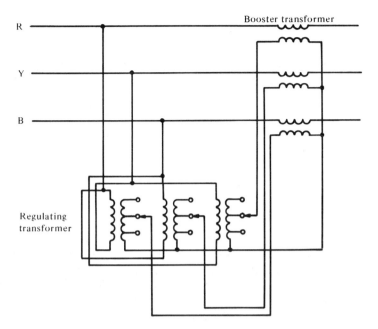

Fig. 14.4.3I   *Connections of three-phase quadrature booster*

14.4.4   The moving-coil regulator

Introduced many years ago by Ferranti Ltd., the moving-coil regulator has its windings wound on a two-limbed core much as in standard transformer practice. The laminated iron core carries the fixed coils a and b, one at either end of one limb of the core, and a short-circuited moving coil s which is free to move up or down the limb, over the fixed coils, as shown in Fig. 14.4.4A. The moving coil is isolated electrically, that is short-circuited on itself, and so does not require connections or slip rings.

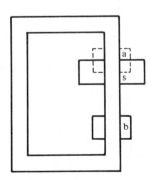

Fig. 14.4.4A   *Ferranti moving-coil regulator*

The effective impedance of coils a and b is governed by the position of coil s. As coil s is moved closer to coil a the lower the effective impedance of coil a will become until coil s is in the position shown in Fig. 14.4.4B, when the effective impedance of coil a will be a minimum and that of coil b a maximum.

If a voltage is applied across coils a and b in series, the greater part of this voltage will appear across coil b, as shown in Fig. 14.4.4B. Conversely, with coil s in the position shown in Fig. 14.4.4C, the impedance of coil a will be a maximum and coil b a minimum, and the greater voltage will appear across coil a.

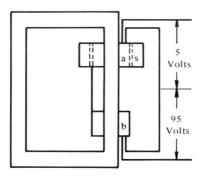

Fig. 14.4.4B   *Moving coil in upper position*

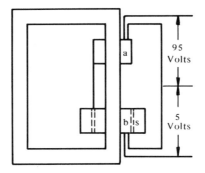

Fig. 14.4.4C   *Moving coil in lower position*

Since the core iron is run at a very low flux density the iron loss is small, and in order to reduce the current in the moving coil, coils a and b are connected in opposition, so that the currents they induce in the moving coil are to a large extent neutralised. The resultant force on the moving coil is therefore very small and at no-load is zero for any position of the regulator. The current in this coil when the regulator is on-load is proportional to the load and remains independent of the regulator position. Thus the power required to operate the regulator in very small and even large regulators can be operated by hand.

The voltage values quoted in the figures are for illustration purposes, and for use in a practical system a voltage variation of 25% would be adequate in most cases. Variations of this order can be obtained by using the regulator with an appropriately tapped transformer, as in Fig. 14.4.4D, or by adding windings on the regulator, as in Fig. 14.4.4E and Fig. 14.4.4F.

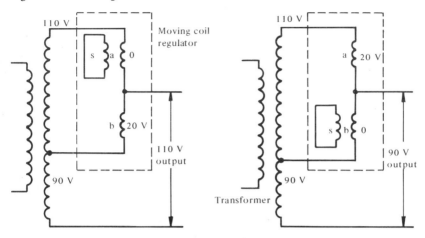

Fig.. 14.4.4D *Moving-coil regulator connections when used with fixed-tap transformer*

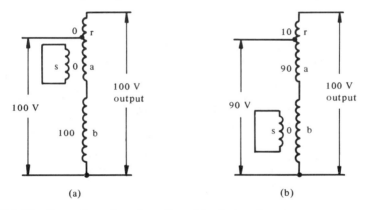

Fig. 14.4.4E *Connections of moving-coil regulator for boosting*

In the first case the regulator is connected across part of the transformer winding, and by a careful choice of tapping the required voltage variation can be obtained. The range shown gives a variation from 90 V to 110 V for one tapping position: anther tapping would give a different range.

The additional transformer is undesirable and the more usual method is to fit additional coils on the regulator. In Figs. 14.4.4E (*a*) and (*b*), coil r has been added at the top of the limb over coil a, and we will assume that coil a has nine times as many turns as coil r. It will be seen that the output voltage is maintained at a constant value of 100 V when the input voltage varies between 90 V applied in the maximum boost position and 100 V applied in the other extreme position. Reversing coil r would have the effect of subtracting its secondary voltage from the input voltage instead of adding to it.

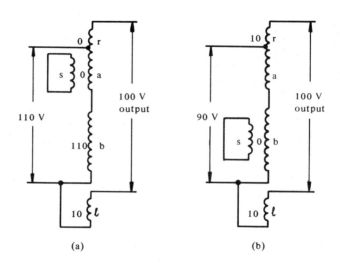

(a)   (b)

Fig. 14.4.4F   *Connections of moving-coil regulator for (a) bucking and (b) boosting*

To provide both buck and boost, another coil *l* is mounted at the bottom of the limb beneath coil b, as shown in Figs. 14.4.4F(*a*) and (*b*). Assuming that coil b is wound with eleven times as many turns as coil *l*, then, with 110 V input and the moving coil in the minimum boost (maximum buck) position, the output voltage will be 110 – 10 = 100 V (Fig. 14.4.4F(*a*)). If the moving coil is moved to the maximum boost position, the input of 90 V will be boosted to give an output of 100 V (Fig. 14.4.4F(*b*)). Thus with the turns ratio quoted for coils r and *l*, the output voltage can remain constant at 100 V over input voltage variations of ±10%.

One significant advantage of the moving coil regulator over the induction regulator is that by choosing appropriate turns ratios for coils r and *l* any value of buck or boost, including all boost and no buck, can be obtained. The induction regulator provides facilities for equal values of buck and boost.

One application of the moving coil regulator is as an alternative to on-load tap-changing gear on a distribution transformer, partly because it is economic and partly because it is more effective to apply the regulation at some point along the distributor. When used for this purpose it is usually automatic in operation. A voltage operated relay or contact-making voltmeter is used to initiate operation of the regulator in the correct direction when the voltage varies by, say, ±1% from the required value.

A relatively recent development of the moving coil regulator for control of processing work incorporates the means of releasing the moving coil instantly, so reducing the voltage to zero in under a second. Thus loads can be switched on or off without recourse to switches or contactors.

Figs. 14.4.4G, 14.4.4H and 14.4.4I show views of typical single-phase and three-phase regulators.

Fig. 14.4.4G   *Core and coil assembly of 100kVA, single-phase, 415-373/415V automatic moving-coil voltage regulator (Ferranti Ltd.)*

Fig. 14.4.4H   *Core and coil assembly of 10 000kVA, three-phase, 11000/10345 - 11 605V automatic moving-coil voltage regulator (Ferranti Ltd.)*

Fig. 14.4.4I *Core and coil assembly of part of 14 000kVA, 13 000V moving-coil reactor bank for h.v. cable testing equipment (Ferranti Ltd.)*

14.4.5   The induction regulator

An induction regulator is designed in much the same way as a three-phase, wound-rotor induction motor, with the exception that the rotor is locked to prevent it turning under the electromagnetic forces acting on it. The angular position of the rotor with respect to the stator can be varied by hand. Fig. l4.4.5A shows the method of connection, from which it will be seen that the stator or primary winding is connected across the supply and the rotor or secondary winding is in series with the line whose voltage is being controlled.

When the stator is connected to the supply a rotating magnetic field is set up which induces an e.m.f. in each phase of the rotor. This induced e.m.f. is of constant magnitude and, since it depends only on the strength and speed of the rotating field, it is independent of the rotor position. Although the position of the rotor does not

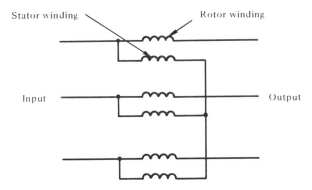

Fig. 14.4.5A   *Connections of three-phase induction regulator*

Fig. 14.4.5B   *Phasor diagram of one phase of three-phase induction regulator*

affect the strength or speed of the rotating field it does affect the phase angle between the rotor induced e.m.f. and the stator voltage.

The connection of the secondary windings in series with the line results in a total line voltage equal to the vector sum of the incoming voltage and the voltage induced in the secondary. This is illustrated in Fig. 14.4.5B, in which V_1 represents the supply voltage, V_2 the boosting voltage, and V the resultant voltage. Altering the position of the rotor has the effect of rotating the phasor V_2, which remains of constant magnitude whatever the position of the rotor. A phase-shift is introduced between the supply voltage V_1 and the resultant voltage V for all positions except when the boosting voltage V_2 is exactly in phase with V, the maximum amount of phase-shift depending upon the maximum boost of the regulator concerned. From Fig. 14.4.5B it will be seen that, when the rotor position is such that the secondary voltage is in phase with and in the same direction as the supply voltage, the resultant voltage is equal to the sum of the voltage V_1 and V_2. With the rotor moved to the opposite position, so that the secondary voltage is in antiphase with the supply voltage, the resultant is equal to the difference of the voltages V_1 and V_2. Intermediate positions of the rotor will, of course, give intermediate resultant voltages, so providing continuous unstepped adjustment of the resultant voltage.

The phase-shift of the line voltage is not of great practical importance when the induction regulator is associated with a line feeding an isolated section of the system, but is an embarrassment if the line forms part of a network interconnected with another source of supply. This is because the phase-shift gives rise to an exchange of current between the sources and to differences in the magnitude of the resultant voltages. Thus the two sources of supply which normally have equal operating voltages will not exchange current as long as these voltages remain in phase, but will do so if a phase-shift is introduced, for example, by the installation of an induction regulator. In such cases a double regulator with two rotors is used, each unit contributing one half of the total voltage added to each phase. Of these equal boosting voltages one is arranged to lead and one to lag so that the combined phase-shift is zero and the resultant voltage is always in phase with the supply voltage. Fig. 14.4.5C shows the main connections for this equipment and Fig. 14.4.5D the operating principle in phasor form. V_1 is again the supply voltage and V_2 and V_3 are the individual boosting voltages. Mechanical coupling of the two rotors ensures that V_2 and V_3 are inclined at the same angle to V_1 and the boosted voltage V is always in phase with V_1.

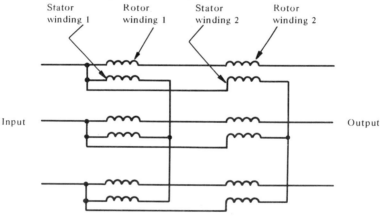

Fig. 14.4.5C *Connections of double three-phase induction regulator*

Fig. 14.4.5D *Phasor diagram of one phase of double three-phase induction regulator*

14.4.6   Protection of boosters

It was mentioned in Section 14.4.1 that the term 'booster' is not limited to the booster transformer but includes also transformer tap-changing, the moving-coil regulator and the induction regulator. Of these the tap-changing equipment is invariably included in the zone covered by the transformer overall differential protection, and for this reference should be made to Chapter 12. The protection requirements of the remaining types of booster can best be described by considering a typical scheme of protection for a booster transformer.

Let us consider a booster installed at one end of a 132 kV overhead line for the purpose of modifying the phase-angle of the line and improving the load sharing between this and other parallel-connected feeders. If the line is assumed to have a phase-angle of 70° lagging, the booster will have been designed to have a phase-angle of 70° leading, so enabling the overhead line to carry its full wattful load. A typical rating of such a booster would be 90 MVA at 132 kV, and the primary connections would be as shown in Fig. 14.4.6A. In Fig. 14.4.6B the location of the necessary current transformers is shown in, or adjacent to, the local 132 kV circuit breaker, on the line side of the booster and in the booster earth connection. Additional current transformers are shown for feeder distance protection (Z) and the back-up overcurrent protection.

The protection of the booster may consist of restricted earth-fault protection driven from current transformers in the circuit breaker, in the line and in the earth connection. The restricted earth-fault relay would be of the high speed, attracted armature type described in Chapter 6. With such protection, sensitive to earth faults only, it is necessary to add protection against phase faults. This can best be

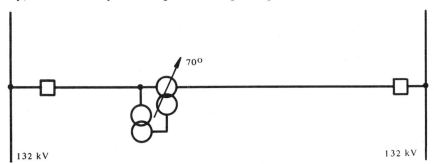

Fig. 14.4.6A   *Connection of a booster transformer*

provided as shown, by utilising the overcurrent relay which would be required, in any case, for feeder back-up protection. This relay will therefore provide back-up to the high-speed distance feeder protection and will afford protection against phase-faults on the booster or on the connections between the circuit-breaker and the booster.

When a booster is earthed via a neutral earthing resistor it is necessary to protect the resistor against the effects of uncleared earth faults elsewhere on the system.

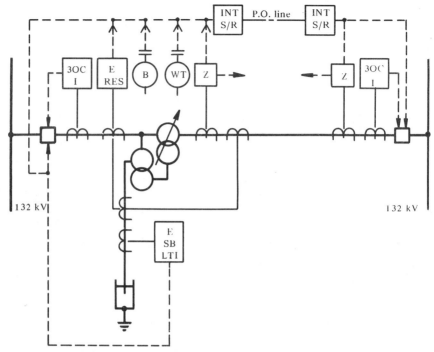

Fig. 14.4.6B *Diagram of protection and intertripping for a 132 kV feeder and oil-immersed booster transformer*

This is conveniently and adequately achieved by a standby earth-fault relay driven from a current transformer located in the resistor earthing connection, as shown in Fig. 14.4.6B.

As in the case of the oil-filled reactor and, of course, the conventional transformer, the booster requires protection capable of detecting faults within the tank, preferably before they develop to the stage in which severe damage will be caused. The only relay capable of detecting incipient booster internal faults of this type is the Buchholz relay of which one type is described in Section 14.3.5 of this chapter and another type in Chapter 12.

Again, as with reactors and transformers, a winding hot-spot indicator would be fitted to provide a warning of any overheating of the booster windings. The two mercury switches incorporated are arranged to provide first, an alarm to indicate that the winding temperature has risen to a certain value, and second, a signal to initiate tripping of the circuit-breakers if the temperature rises by a further fixed amount. The instrument is described in Section 14.3.5 and shown in Fig. 14.3.5H of this chapter.

Intertripping: Since the booster is connected solidly to the feeder, faults within the booster can only be cleared by opening the local circuit breaker and the circuit breaker at the remote end. The local end can obviously be tripped direct from the booster protection but intelligence has to be sent from the booster protection to 'instruct' the remote end to trip. As explained in Section 14.3.5, this is known as 'intertripping' and is usually effected by signalling over a Post Office line rented for the purpose. The application of intertripping is shown in Fig. 14.4.6B, the restricted earth fault, Buchholz and distance protection all being connected to initiate the sending of an intertrip signal in the event of the operation of any one of them.

14.5   Capacitors

14.5.1   Capacitors in an interconnected power system

The transmission system in England and Wales is a closely interconnected one providing facilities for the bulk transfer of power from centres of generation in the coal producing areas to other large load centres, for interconnection between centres with both generation and load, and for the supply of power in bulk to the Area Boards for distribution to their consumers. Although an unloaded transmission or distribution line is capacitive in character a fully loaded line has inherent inductive and resistive characteristics. On main transmission lines operating at near unity power factor, the power which can be transmitted is determined largely by the system stability limit (the system will remain stable provided the phase angle between the voltages at the sending and receiving ends does not exceed a certain critical value). On distribution networks, especially those operating at low power factors, the inductive reactance makes a major contribution to the voltage drop, and it is voltage drop considerations which frequently dictate the amount of power which can be distributed.

The effect of series inductance in a power network is to cause

(*a*)   a phase shift between the different parts of the network tending towards instability at an undesirably low power level,

(*b*)   excessive voltage drops between the ends of feeders, and

(*c*)   unequal sharing of the load between parallel feeders, thus limiting the total power which can be transmitted.

Of these the stability problem affects primarily the transmission system, and the regulation problem the distribution system. Inequalities in load sharing of parallel feeders pose problems for both systems. When such problems arise it is sometimes possible to postpone costly system reinforcement by installing reactive power compensation equipment, although it is necessary to study each case on its merits.

Overall improvements in operating conditions will be brought about if means are introduced of reducing the system reactance or of reducing the phase angle between the system current and voltage. This can be done by installing static plant, namely series or shunt connected capacitors, shunt connected reactors or rotating plant in the form of large synchronous machines capable of being over-excited to generate reactive power or under-excited to absorb reactive power, that is operating as shunt capacitors or shunt reactors respectively, depending upon the system requirements at the time. These machines are operated by the CEGB as capacitors (overexcited) during periods of heavy active load transfer, and as reactors (underexcited) during periods of light load transfer.

With a static capacitor or reactor bank the reactive power can be varied only by switching sections of the installation in or out as required, thus altering the capacitance in steps. With a synchronous machine immediate variation is obtained by automatic variation of the excitation, but disadvantages are complexity and cost, the latter being approximately three times that of static plant of equivalent rating. The remainder of this Section is devoted to consideration of the application of static series and shunt capacitors and synchronous shunt compensators together with measures necessary to protect them.

14.5.2   Series-connected capacitors

The simplified equivalent circuit of a transmission line with series connected capacitor is shown in Fig. 14.5.2A and the associated phasor diagram in Fig. 14.5.2B. Fig. 14.5.2C shows how the voltage drop increases with the distance from the sending end and how the voltage rise is concentrated at the capacitor.

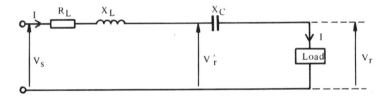

Fig. 14.5.2A   *Simplified equivalent circuit of transmission line with series capacitor connected at receiving end*

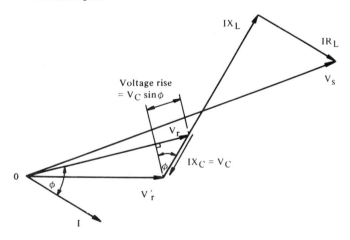

Fig. 14.5.2B   *Phasor diagram of equivalent circuit*

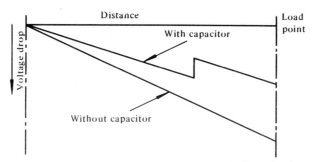

Fig. 14.5.2C *Diagram showing voltage drop with distance and effect of series capacitor*

In the Figures, R_L and X_L are the total series resistance and inductive reactance in ohms, X_C is the ohmic reactance of a series capacitor, V_s and V_r' are the sending and receiving end line voltages, V_r is the voltage on the load side of the capacitor, and I is the load current.

Neglecting the effects of line charging current, or shunt capacitance, and considering lumped values for the line constants, as shown in Fig. 14.5.2A, the phase-to-neutral voltage drop between V_s and V_r can be expressed as

$$\text{voltage drop} = I\left[R_L \cos \phi + (X_L - X_C)\sin \phi\right]$$

The conditions $X_L < X_C$, $X_L = X_C$ and $X_L > X_C$ are referred to as overcompensation, full compensation and undercompensation, respectively.

Overcompensation is not used in transmission systems, but applications of this type are sometimes found in distribution systems. Examination of the regulation formula above shows that by varying the quantity X_C the regulation can be increased or decreased at will, provided that $\sin \phi \neq 0$. As ϕ is the phase angle, the condition $\sin \phi = 0$ represents unity load power factor.

The compensation of the line reactance obtained when a series capacitor is applied has the effect of

(*a*)   increasing the line carrying capacity,

(*b*)   improving the load sharing of two or more parallel connected feeders, and

(*c*)   improving voltage regulation chiefly at the point of installation.

The voltage change obtained takes the form of a sudden rise at the capacitor terminals so that its beneficial effects are felt on the load side of the capacitor. Thus the load voltage V_r will be larger than the received voltage V_r'. Since the voltage rise is dependent on the load current and power factor (that is voltage rise $V_C \sin \phi = IX_C \sin \phi$) a change in I produces a change in V_C and the capacitor acts automatically as a voltage regulator.

14.5.3   Shunt-connected capacitors

The simplified equivalent circuit of a transmission line with shunt connected capacitor is shown in Fig. 14.5.3A and the associated phasor diagram in Fig.

14.5.3B. Fig. 14.5.3C shows that, unlike the effect with a series capacitor, the voltage rise is distributed uniformly along the length of the line.

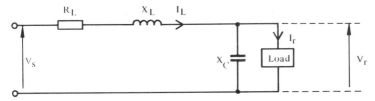

Fig. 14.5.3A   *Simplified equivalent circuit of transmission line with shunt capacitor at receiving end*

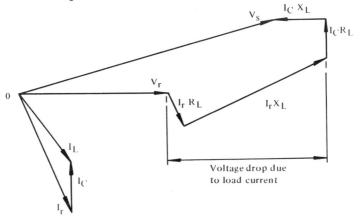

Fig. 14.5.3B   *Phasor diagram of equivalent circuit*

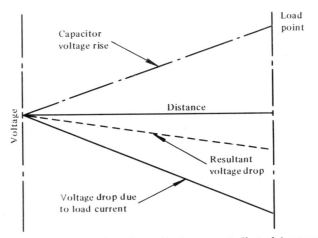

Fig. 14.5.3C   *Diagram showing voltage drop with distance and effect of shunt capacitor*

The reduction of the phase angle between the voltage and the current, which is obtained when a shunt capacitor is applied, has the effect of

(*a*) reducing line current losses owing to the generation of reactive power,
(*b*) reducing the transmission line current to a value less than the current in the load (Fig. 14.5.3B),
(*c*) improving the power factor of the transmitted power, and
(*d*) reducing the voltage drop uniformly along the length of the line (Fig. 14.5.3C). This should be compared with the step-function voltage rise across the terminals of the series capacitor.

The response to voltage dips is not as rapid as with series capacitors since the switching of sections of the bank is initiated by the change in voltage, and at best, the regulation is in steps.

14.5.4 Series or shunt connection

From what has already been said, it will be appreciated that series and shunt capacitors serve a broadly similar purpose in improving operating conditions, the series connection by compensating for line reactance, that is reducing it, and the shunt connection by compensating the phase angle, that is reducing the phase diplacement between system current and voltage. Clearly, there are several factors governing the choice of connection and these may be summarised as follows.

With a series capacitor the regulation, or reduction in voltage drop, achieved depends mainly on the reactive power of the load, and it follows that this type of capacitor is of little use unless the conditions are such that reactive power is consumed by the load. With a shunt capacitor the regulation achieved depends mainly on the reactance of the system, and a useful increase in voltage will be obtained only if the reactance is substantial.

If continuous and automatic voltage regulation is the main objective, a series capacitor installation is most likely to satisfy the need. On the other hand a shunt capacitor bank with means of automatically increasing or decreasing the number of sections of the bank in service will provide a measure of regulation, albeit in steps and with some delay.

A capacitor connected in series with a line must have a current rating equivalent to that of the line, the output of reactance power from the capacitor being dependent upon the line current

$$\left(\text{output} = \frac{I^2 X_C}{10^3} \text{ kVAr per phase}\right).$$

With a shunt connected capacitor the output of the bank is independent of the current, compensation being determined by the applied voltage.

On transmission circuits there are technical advantages in siting a series capacitor at some point in the line route, but this introduces the need to acquire a suitable site and problems of maintenance. A shunt capacitor, however, can conveniently be connected to the low voltage side of a grid transformer situated at a substation and need be insulated only for the lower voltage level. The cost per kVAr installed of either series or shunt capacitors varies little over a wide range of capacity, and recent figures for losses indicate the negligibly low level of 3 W per kVAr.

In the mid 1960s, the CEGB embarked on a programme of providing reactive compensation at appropriate points throughout the transmission system and in the short term this took the form of hydrogen-cooled synchronous machines of up to 60 MVAr rated output at 13 kV, operating as referred to in Section 14.5.1 of this chapter. As an immediate measure, a few such machines rated at 40 MVAr were commissioned at 275 kV substations to be followed soon after by shunt-connected static capacitors at other 275 kV sites (see Fig. 14.5.4A for a typical example of the static shunt capacitor arrangement). An important feature of these equipments, whether rotating or static, was their transportability and the value of this facility was demonstrated when it subsequently became necessary to deploy them at other sites as dictated by the operating requirements of the system. Since that time all new autotransformers have been supplied with 13 kV tertiary windings suitably rated for the possible connection of compensation equipment of up to 60 MVAr.

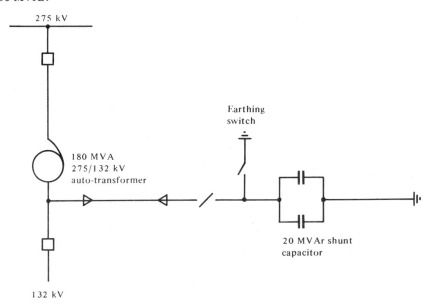

Fig. 14.5.4A   *Primary arrangement of typical shunt capacitor*

Several series connected capacitors have been installed in Area Board 11 kV circuits for the purpose of reducing 'flicker', particularly in the vicinity of steelworks and arc furnaces. The duty cycle during the melt at an arc furnace is particularly onerous, and it is in such areas that applications for small series capacitors are most likely to be found in this country.

Abroad, notably in Sweden and the USA, it is the practice to install large banks of series capacitors in the very long, high voltage transmission lines common in those countries.

14.5.5 The capacitor unit

A capacitor unit (See Fig. 14.5.5A for illustration of typical unit) consists of a number of small capacitor elements in a single case suitable for assembling with other similar units to form a capacitor bank, or tank-type capacitor complete with terminal bushings and protection.

Initially it was the practice in Great Britain to make capacitors of the tank type, and examples of these are to be found at Kenfig (950 kVAr, 33 kV, installed in 1942) and Llanelly (7500 kVAr, 33 kV, installed in 1951). Following the establishment of a need for large high-voltage capacitors on the transmission system, the unit type built up to form a capacitor bank has found favour and such installations are in service at Fleet, West Weybridge and Elstree. These are all shunt connected in the 132kV side of 275/132kV autotransformers and are of 40, 20 and 20 MVAr, respectively.

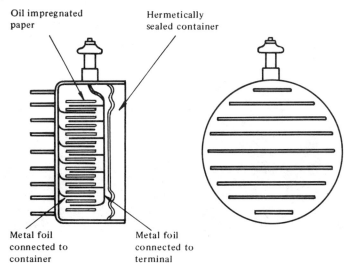

Oil impregnated paper

Hermetically sealed container

Metal foil connected to container

Metal foil connected to terminal

Fig. 14.5.5A *Arrangement of typical ASEA foil cooled capacitor unit*

Each element consists of the capacitor plates or foils with interleaving tissues of special paper, the whole wound up to form a cylindrical roll. In a tank-type capacitor a number of such elements are mounted on wooden supports and connected in series-parallel to give the required kVAr output. The tank is then filled with an impregnating fluid to ensure that all the interstices of the paper tissues are filled and moisture excluded. Unit type capacitors are usually of rectangular metal-box construction and employ similar elements in flat form, a relatively small number being housed in each unit.

One interesting design of the unit type is made by the ASEA Company of Sweden. The container is circular about 1 ft in diameter and 6 inches deep, excluding cooling fins, and contains seven rolled elements mounted in star form,

Fig. 14.5.5B   *General view of 20 MVAr,132kV capacity bank (British Insulated Callenders Cables Ltd.)*

that is, six arranged around one centre element. The impregnant used is a mineral oil, under a low pressure, to improve the dielectric strength of the impregnated paper.

The unit construction has the advantage of greater flexibility, in that units can be assembled on open-type outdoor construction as in Fig. 14.5.5B, and to any size required.

14.5.6   Protection of capacitors

The need for adequate protection against damage is evident when consideration is given to the vulnerability of such equipments to system faults, for example lightning flashovers, and the loss of compensation which would follow the removal of a damaged capacitor from service. The loss of a capacitor would, of course, result in a return to the very conditions it was intended to prevent.

The protection may be looked upon as comprising two parts: protection of the individual capacitor elements within a unit or tank ('internal' protection) and protection to prevent excessive stressing of the dielectric by system disturbances ('external' protection).

Internal protection consists of detecting any abnormal unbalance of the nominally balanced impedances of the sections of each phase bank. It will be appreciated that because of manufacturing tolerances in the capacitor elements a small standing ubalance is inevitable, but this is kept to an absolute minimum by careful selection and matching of elements and, where relays are used, is allowed for in setting the relay. Requirements of the protection are:

(*a*) disconnection of a faulty element before damage or case rupture occurs, and with a minimum loss of kVAr,

(*b*) indication of the location of a faulty element, and

(*c*) non-operation when the capacitor is subjected to non-injurious system disturbances.

External protection is necessary to protect against the heavy currents which will flow when a short circuit occurs on the capacitor itself, or its connections, or on that part of the system to which it is connected. The effect of such currents is to produce correspondingly high voltages across the capacitor which, if allowed to persist, will overstress the dielectric. External protection may be provided in several differing forms depending upon the size and connection of the capacitor.

For small series capacitors in distribution networks, spark gaps in one form or another are generally used and are described in more detail later in this Section. It might be supposed that a non-linear resistor would find an application as a simple protector for a series capacitor, but the thermal characteristics of the resistance material used in its manufacture are such that the resistor would have to be very large, and therefore costly, to be able to carry the fault current for times of the order of seconds.

14.5.6.1 Series capacitor internal protection: The choice rests between the use of an individual fuse for each element within the unit or tank, or sometimes one fuse for a group of elements, and the use of current or voltage transformer driven relays connected to detect any significant out of balance between the two associated sections. Sometimes a combination of fuses and instrument transformer driven relays is considered desirable.

The practice of using fuses for element protection was adopted many years ago in shunt connected capacitors and is now used extensively in series capacitors also. The fuses are of the high breaking-capacity type incorporating a pin which projects when the fuse has blown, or the expulsion type, from which a tail hangs down to indicate a blown fuse; in either case the element is disconnected permanently. The disconnection of an element in one section results in a small change in the capacitance of the bank and therefore a small out of balance, of the order of 1%, between that section and the other sections. This in itself is relatively insignificant, but assumes importance if it is followed by the failure of further fuses, thus increasing the stress of the remaining elements. A capacitor is designed so that the failure of, say, one element will not result in the rest of the elements being overstressed, that is the voltage across the remainder will be within the continuous rating of the elements. Care must, of course, be taken to ensure that the fuses remain intact when the external protection operates.

The introduction of current or voltage transformers brings with it the need to divide each phase bank into two equal parallel halves, so that the detection equipment can be connected across the midpoints. Under normal conditions no current flows in the relay (other than the very small amount due to the minor difference in individual elements), but the failure of, say, two elements would be arranged to give an alarm and the failure of any further elements to trip the capacitor from the system.

The cost of providing current or voltage transformers, and the space required to accommodate them, renders this method of protection most suitable with large installations where a case can be made out for providing a capacitor short-circuiting switch.

14.5.6.2 Series capacitor external protection: As already mentioned, small series capacitors such as are used in distribution circuits for voltage regulation purposes are usually provided with spark-gap protectors to prevent damage to the capacitors on the occurrence of faults on the capacitor or the network to which it is connected. There is a wide variety of gaps available embracing the extinguishable and nonextinguishable, the triggered and the nontriggered and those employing electronic techniques. Detailed consideration will now be given to a selection of these gaps:

(*a*)   *Nonextinguishing, nontriggered gaps:* The electrodes of these gaps are of copper or stainless steel and their useful life can be extended by adding a switch to automatically short circuit them immediately after operation. One example of such a gap is the English Electric Type HH device which consists of a spark gap connected in parallel with a normally open spring-operated isolating switch (Fig. 14.5.6.2A). The current transformer operated inverse-time relay determines the time for which the gap is permitted to arc, and if this is exceeded the isolating switch is closed to short circuit the gap and the capacitor. They will remain short-circuited until the isolating switches on all three phases are re-set by means of an insulated pole.

Since these simple gaps do nothing to assist in extinguishing the arc they are unlikely to survive more than one or two operations, and so their use is limited to small series capacitors in places where the through-fault incidence is low. They are sometimes applied to such capacitors in low-voltage cable networks.

(*b*)   *Extinguishing, nontriggered gaps:* There are at least two devices in this general

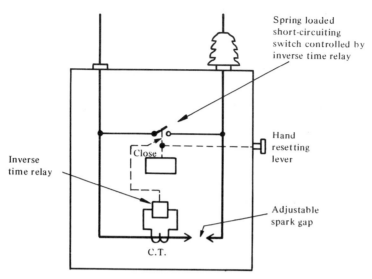

Fig. 14.5.6.2A *Type HH series capacitor protector*

classification and these may be considered as the open type and the sealed type. A desirable feature of any self-restoring gap is that the voltage at which it will flash over after resetting shall be sensibly the same as the original setting, and it is claimed that both the gaps described approach this requirement.

(i) *Open type:* Designed and first applied by Electricité de France on the Ayergues Valley 10 kV network, this type of gap consists of two concentric copper electrodes, the inner one carried at the top of a vertical copper spindle (Fig. 14.5.6.2B). The electrodes are so shaped that the space between them is in the form of an annular gap slightly larger at the top than at the base. The size of this gap determines the setting and is adjusted by raising or lowering the spindle. A coil wound round the outer electrode carries the short-circuit current. When subjected to a through-fault, the electrodes flashover at the base, the magnetic effect of the coil causing the arc to rotate. As it does so it climbs in a spiral to the top of the electrodes and continues to burn until it extinguishes itself when the fault is cleared. The advantage of rotating the arc and moving it away from the point at which flashover occurs lies in reducing the amount of burning at that point and helping to maintain the setting. In service these gaps have withstood up to 50 operations without requiring polishing or re-setting.

(ii) *Sealed type:* An example of the sealed type of self-restoring gap is one designed by BICC Ltd. and developed by the then AEI Ltd (Fig. 14.5.6.2C). Essentially it consists of a BICC gap sealed in a glass envelope filled with hydrogen at low pressure. Adjustment of the gap is obtained by varying either the spacing of the electrodes or the gas pressure. A coil is wound round the glass envelope and under fault conditions carries the short-circuit current. Its purpose is to protect the

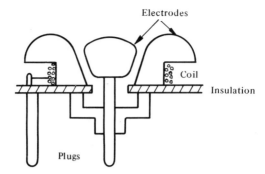

Fig. 14.5.6.2B   *Open type, self-extinguishing spark gap for series capacitor protection*

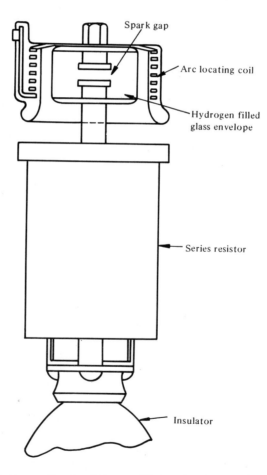

Fig. 14.5.6.2C   *Sealed type, self-extinguishing, gas-filled spark gap*

glass envelope by restricting the arc to the centre of the device during flashover conditions, thus permitting the gap to be used at higher levels of fault current. Approximately four times the fault current rating is obtained with the arc control coil compared with the rating without the coil. Typical values are 250 A for 1 s or 500 A for 0·25 s without the coil, and from 250 A for 2 s to 2000 A for 0·2 s with the coil. It is considered that further development up to 3000A fault current rating is possible.

(*c*) *Nonextinguishing triggered gaps:* By 'triggered' is meant the method by which the arc is struck on a calibrated, or trigger, gap and very quickly transferred to more substantial electrodes where it continues to burn until the fault is cleared. An example of this type was made by A. Reyrolle & Co. Ltd. and known as the Spinner Gap (Fig. 14.5.6.2D). Multiple intermediate gaps in series are connected

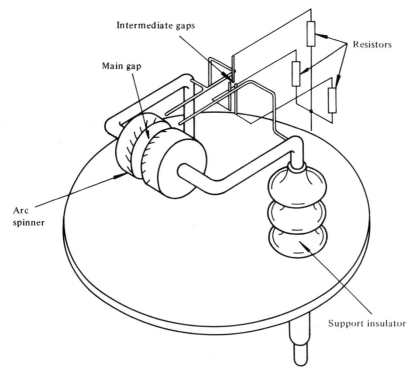

Fig. 14.5.6.2D   *Diagrammatic arrangement of 'spinner' gap*

together at one end through resistors to form the trigger element. The arc is struck initially at the calibrated gap, the current being limited by the resistors. It spreads to other electrodes of the intermediate gaps and then to the main electrodes when the current ceases to be limited by the resistors. From the main electrodes it is transferred by magnetic effects to the 'spinners' which cause the arc to rotate until the fault is cleared by the feeder protection. The setting at which the gap flashes over can be varied within the range 3 kV to 6 kV and the current rating at approximately 6000 A for 0·25 s is higher than with the other gaps described.

Another example of the triggered gap is that produced by the ASEA Company and used in their large, high voltage series capacitor installations, for example at Alfta and Djurmo in Sweden. Flashover takes place across the gap between the spherical surfaces of metal electrodes (Fig. 14.5.6.2E) and is forced up rapidly to the graphite electrodes by the action of electromagnetic forces and the upward flow of air due to the heat generated. It is claimed that this design ensures rapid and reliable ignition and that the flashover voltage remains unchanged after a number of operations of the device.

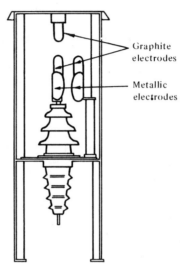

Graphite electrodes

Metallic electrodes

Fig. 14.5.6.2E *ASEA triggered spark gap*

In these large Swedish installations this spark-gap forms but part of the equipment provided to protect the capacitor. The arrangement for one phase is shown diagrammatically in Fig. 14.5.6.2F, and in addition to the spark-gap comprises a bypass circuit breaker, isolating switches, damping resistors, discharge reactors, current transformers and a protective capacitor.

The protective capacitor is connected in parallel with the spark-gap to eliminate any risk of flashover by steep-fronted overvoltage waves. This amounts to an added safeguard since the main capacitor provides some protection against such flashover. The damping elements reduce the stresses in the gap and the bypass breaker and also serve to moderate the stresses in the capacitor when the gap flashes over. The damping provided reduces the first current amplitude to about 70% of the undamped oscillation and the second to about 40% of the first.

The discharge reactor is fitted to discharge any remanent energy in the capacitor on the disconnection of the compensated line, thus reducing the risk of gap flashover when the line is reconnected. The discharge is accomplished in approximately

0·3 s to permit the use of high speed autoreclosing facilities. The purpose of the bypass circuit breaker is to short circuit the series capacitor and spark-gap in the event of a fault in the bank or an inadvertent flashover of the gap.

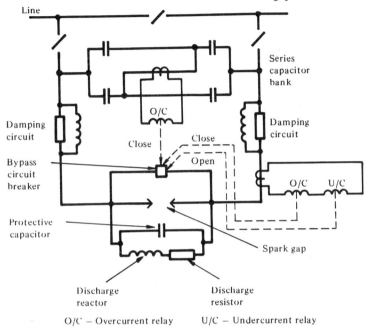

Fig. 14.5.6.2F *Protection of large series capacitor for Swedish State Power Board (only one phase shown)*

Faults in the capacitor installation causing unbalance are detected by a relay in each phase driven from a current transformer connected across equipotential points. Operation of the relay initiates, via a timing relay, the closing of the bypass circuit breaker, the timing relay having a setting of 1 sec. This delay is necessary to ensure that operation of the relay does not cause closing of the bypass breaker on the occurrence of faults in the compensated line, or by discharge current on bypassing the capacitor.

The three-phase current transformers drive time-lagged current relays which initiate closing of the bypass breaker only if the spark-gap re-ignites after the tripping, and automatic reclosing, of the circuit breakers at the ends of the compensated line. Timing relay settings and the waiting period or 'dead time' before the line breakers reclose are carefully chosen to prevent the bypass breaker being closed when the line fault occurs and the spark-gap flashes over the first time. A continuation of the automatic sequence reopens the bypass breaker after several seconds and if the spark-gap re-ignites again the breaker recloses and remains closed.

(*d*)   *Electronic devices:* A development by BICC Ltd. consists essentially of a gas-filled spark-gap and two ignitrons, and is shown in Fig. 14.5.6.2G. The ignitrons are connected in opposition across the capacitor terminals and are triggered by the common spark-gap. If a fault on the load side of the capacitor is severe enough to

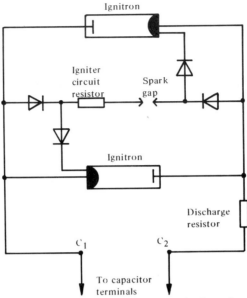

Fig. 14.5.6.2G *Diagrammatic arrangement of electronic device for series capacitor protection*

cause the spark-gap to flash over, a pulse of current flows through the igniting circuit of one ignitron or the other, depending upon polarity. The ignitron operates and carries fault current in addition to a capacitor discharge current during one half-cycle of the fundamental power frequency. The sequence is repeated with the other ignitron during the next half-cycle, the capacitor being temporarily returned to service at each fault-current zero and permanently returned to service at the first current-zero after clearance of the fault. The discharge resistor is provided to limit the value of the capacitor discharge current carried by the ignitrons, and the igniting circuit resistor to limit the ignitron igniting current.

A device of this type has been laboratory tested up to 1000 A for 1 s and is in service at the Alston 11 kV series-capacitor installation of the North Western Electricity Board.

14.5.6.3 Shunt capacitor internal protection: As with series-connected capacitors, the choice rests between the use of fuses, current transformer or voltage transformer driven relays, or both, for the detection of unbalance between the nominally equal capacitances of two sections of the bank. In the case of large shunt capacitors with which this section is chiefly concerned, it is usual to fit fuses and relays to provide complete protection against the consequences of element failure.

The fuse will, of course, merely disconnect the faulty element or group of elements and provide an indication that it has operated. The relay operated by an instrument transformer in the midpoint connection between two sections will usually be a 'two-stage' device, the first stage giving an alarm for the loss of one or two elements, that is the blowing of one or two fuses, and the second stage disconnecting the capacitor bank from the system in the event of further failures.

Relay protection: The use of relays for the detection of capacitor unbalance brings with it the need to provide current or voltage transformers with consequent increase in overall cost, particularly if voltage transformers are used. For this reason the arrangements described below are usually applied only to the larger capacitor banks.

(*a*) *Star-connected bank:* (Fig. 14.5.6.3A). A voltage transformer is connected across part of the series capacitance of each phase of the bank with its secondary windings connected in broken delta to a sensitive relay. Any redistribution of voltage caused by the failure of capacitor elements will be detected, but this method, applied to a bank with earthed neutral, is liable to be affected by system disturbances and by third harmonics.

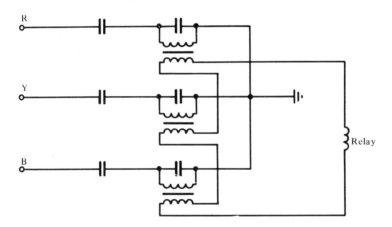

Fig. 14.5.6.3A   *Protection of star-connected shunt capacitor bank with earthed star point*

(*b*) *Delta-connected bank:* (Fig. 14.5.6.3B). An arrangement of overvoltage protection similar to (*a*) may be applied to the unearthed delta-connected bank shown in Fig. 14.5.6.3B. Again the single relay will detect any abnormal unbalance between sections, but will be unaffected by harmonics.

(*c*) *Split star-connected bank:* (Fig. 14.5.6.3C). When an unearthed star-connected bank is large enough to be split into two sections it is convenient to protect it against capacitance unbalance by connecting a voltage or current transformer between the neutral points of the sections. The two sections must be designed to have identical capacitances or unacceptably high out-of-balance currents will flow in the neutral. It has the advantage of low cost and is unaffected by harmonics.

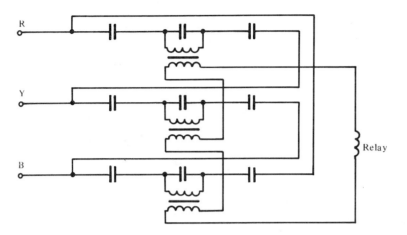

Fig. 14.5.6.3B *Protection of delta-connected shunt capacitor bank*

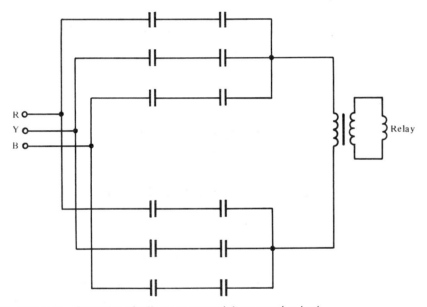

Fig. 14.5.6.3C *Protection of split star-connected shunt capacitor bank*

(*d*)   *Star-connected bank (two limbs per phase):* (Fig. 14.5.6.3D). When each phase is split into two equal sections the current transformers may be mounted at either end of the phase connections, but since much less insulation is required at the neutral end, there is a clear economic advantage in mounting them there.

This basic method was employed at the CEGB's 132 kV shunt capacitor installations at West Weybridge and Elstree, the current transformers being mounted at the neutral end. It is very sensitive and can be applied to delta or star connected, earthed or unearthed banks. The currents in each phase are individually compared rendering the protection inherently stable under unbalanced system conditions and, assuming equal values of third harmonic in each section, unlikely to be affected by such currents.

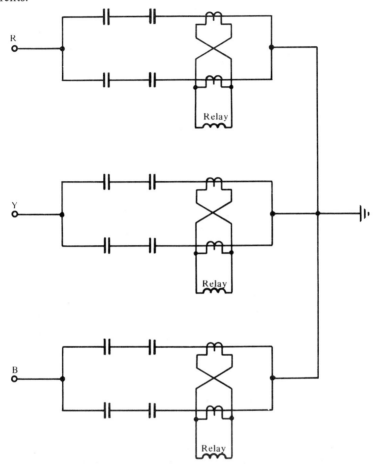

Fig. 14.5.6.3D   *Protection of star connected shunt capacitor bank*

(*e*)   *Star-connected bank (two limbs per phase):* (Fig. 14.5.6.3E). An alternative to (*d*) is shown in Fig. 14.5.6.3E. This method of detecting unbalance may be used when each phase is split into two equal parallel limbs, each limb consisting of a number of units in series. The current transformer driving the relay is then connected across equipotential points of the two limbs. It has the advantage over (*d*) in requiring only one current transformer per phase.

It will be apparent that all the methods described above suffer from the disadvantage that they rely on the comparison of the capacitance of one section of the bank with that of another. Thus, if elements fail simultaneously in the sections being compared, symmetry of capacitance will be maintained and the protection will be unable to detect the failures.

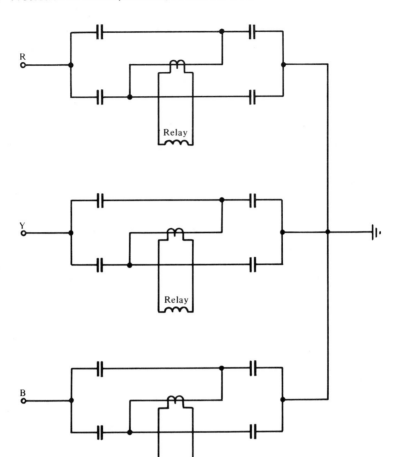

Fig. 14.5.6.3E *Protection of star-connected shunt capacitor bank*

Thermal overload protection: A two-stage feature per phase is used to achieve protection against overloads in excess of the level allowed in BS 1650:1955. These overloads may arise from system conditions producing:

(i)   increased voltage (kVAr loading is proportional to voltage squared).
(ii) increased frequency (kVAr loading is proportional to frequency), and
(iii) harmonics, that is frequencies other than the power frequency.

The first stage consists of a thermal element having a minimum setting of 130% nominal bank current and an inverse time characteristic matching that of the capacitor up to 300%, and is arranged to sound an alarm. The second stage uses an instantaneous overcurrent element which will initiate tripping if the overload exceeds 300%. The two-element relay is operated from a current transformer located in the 13 kV capacitor circuit breaker.

14.5.6.4 Shunt capacitor external protection: The early shunt capacitors in the British transmission system were directly connected to the 132 kV side of the 275/132 kV autotransformers but it is now usual practice to connect them, via their own circuit breakers, to the 13 kV tertiary windings of the autotransformers. Thus in the early installations the capacitors were controlled by the autotransformer h.v. and l.v. circuit breakers so that a capacitor fault resulted in the temporary disconnection of its associated transformer. However, there is clearly some merit in providing protection which enables operational staff to determine, from relay operations and indications, whether the fault is on the capacitor, the transformer or the connections between them. To this end subsequent installations have been provided with discrete protection systems covering each of these main elements so that if it is established that the capacitor alone is faulty, it can be isolated and the transformer returned to service.

The remainder of this Section is devoted to a description of the protection arrangements usually applied to star connected static capacitor installations supplied from the autotransformer 13 kV tertiary windings. A diagram showing all these arrangements is given in Fig. 14.5.6.4A, and Fig. 14.5.6.4B shows the d.c. circuitry associated with them.

13 kV connection protection

The connections between the transformer tertiary winding bushings and the 13 kV capacitor circuit breakers are protected by a differential circulating current system. This takes the form of instantaneous high-impedance relays in the differential circuit formed by balancing, phase by phase, a set of three current transformers in the transformer bushings against similar sets of c.t.s of identical turns ratio in each capacitor circuit breaker or its associated c.t. housing. The setting of the protection should be capable of adjustment in excess of the full load current of the circuit.

Capacitor circulating current protection

The individual capacitor banks are each protected by a separate differential system. This consists of two sets of three current transformers one set located in the capacitor bank circuit breaker or its associated c.t. housing and the other set in the capacitor neutral end connections, all the c.t. turns ratios being the same. The setting of the high impedance circulating current relays is of the order of 20% of capacitor bank full-load current. Operation of this capacitor differential protection would trip only the 13 kV capacitor circuit breaker associated with the faulty bank, leaving the transformer and the remainder of the capacitor bank in service.

Restricted earth-fault protection

With unearthed capacitor banks an earthing transformer and resistor are required to tie the 13 kV equipment down to earth and this is teed to the 13 kV connections between the tertiary winding and capacitor circuit breaker. A differential system of restricted earth fault protection consisting of a single pole high impedance relay driven from c.t.s located in the bushings or associated c.t. housing of each 13 kV capacitor circuit breaker, and in the earthing transformer neutral connection, is applied to cater for faults producing very low values of earth-fault current in the earthing transformer or autotransformer tertiary winding. The relay is connected to trip the autotransformer h.v. and l.v. circuit breakers.

13 kV standby earth-fault protection

The neutral earthing resistor is designed to limit the earth fault current to 300 A and it is important to ensure that it is not loaded beyond its rating. A single stage of standby earth-fault protection is therefore provided and this also affords earth-fault protection to the capacitor banks and back-up protection for 13 kV earth faults. A relay with an i.d.m.t. characteristic is used and is supplied from a c.t. located in the connection between the earthing transformer and the earthing resistor. It is set to operate at 15% of the rated earthing resistor current with an operating time of 2 s at this setting. The trip circuit is designed to open the autotransformer h.v. and l.v. circuit breakers.

Overcurrent protection

To cater for the possible failure of the main differential protection an i.d.m.t. back-up overcurrent relay is provided driven from c.t.s in the transformer tertiary winding bushings. The relay is connected to trip all circuit breakers capable of providing fault current infeeds.

Overvoltage protection

Under light system loading conditions the capacitor banks may be subjected to symmetrical three-phase overvoltages. The value of the maximum permissible overvoltage and its allowable duration will depend upon the overvoltage character-istic of the capacitors and upon the system operating requirements.

Overvoltage protection is provided by two overvoltage relays with i.d.m.t. characteristics one connected for alarm and the other for trip and both supplied from the same single-phase 13 kV voltage transformer. The trip contacts are arranged to trip sequentially the capacitor 13 kV circuit breakers at intervals of 30 s. Subject to system operating requirements and to the characteristics of the capacitor banks, the overvoltage alarm relay is set to operate at 130% and the overvoltage trip relay to operate at 140% of capacitor rated voltage. Both relays would have an operating time of about 30 s at their respective settings.

Other protection

Overloading of the capacitors may result from increases in system voltage or system frequency, or from the effects of harmonic currents. Two-stage thermal overload protection for each capacitor bank is provided by a two-element relay supplied from c.t.s located in the 13 kV capacitor bank circuit breaker, with settings as described in Section 14.5.6.3. The first i.d.m.t. stage is set to alarm only and the second, instantaneous element is connected to trip its associated 13 kV circuit breaker.

Protection to detect capacitor out-of-balance resulting from the failure of individual capacitor elements or the blowing of their fuses, takes the form of a c.t. and relay scheme, the choice depending upon the size and configuration of the capacitor bank. A number of typical arrangements are described and illustrated in Section 14.5.6.3.

The earthing transformer is provided with a double float gas and oil operated Buchholz relay generally of the type described and illustrated in Section 14.3.5. The relay has alarm and trip functions, the trip contact being connected to trip all circuit breakers capable of supplying fault current infeeds.

The tertiary winding of the autotransformer can withstand short periods of overloading but prolonged overheating will hasten insulation deterioration and eventually shorten the life of the transformer. To prevent this happening a winding temperature indicator (w.t.i.), previously described in Section 14.3.5., is fitted. Appropriate alarm and trip settings are applied and the trip contact is connected to trip the 13 kV main oil circuit breaker.

14.5.6.5 Protection of synchronous shunt compensators: Synchronous compensators like the modern versions of their static capacitor counterparts are connected to the 13 kV tertiary windings of the autotransformers. In addition to a main 13 kV circuit-breaker two similar circuit breakers, 'start' and 'run' are required in the synchronous compensator starting and control circuits. Again discrete protection systems are provided for the machine, the 13 kV connections between it and the autotransformer, and for the transformer itself. Each of these systems is described below together with the appropriate back-up protection features and these composite arrangements are shown diagrammatically in Fig. 14.5.6.5A. The d.c. circuitry associated with them is shown in Fig. 14.5.6.5B.

13 kV connection protection

The connections between the transformer tertiary winding bushings and the 13 kV main oil circuit breaker are protected by a differential circulating current system. This takes the form of a set of current transformers in the transformer bushings balanced phase by phase against another set in the main oil circuit breaker or its associated c.t. housing. High-impedance relays are used and the setting of the protection should be capable of adjustment to above the full load current of the circuit. The c.t. turns ratio must be the same for each location.

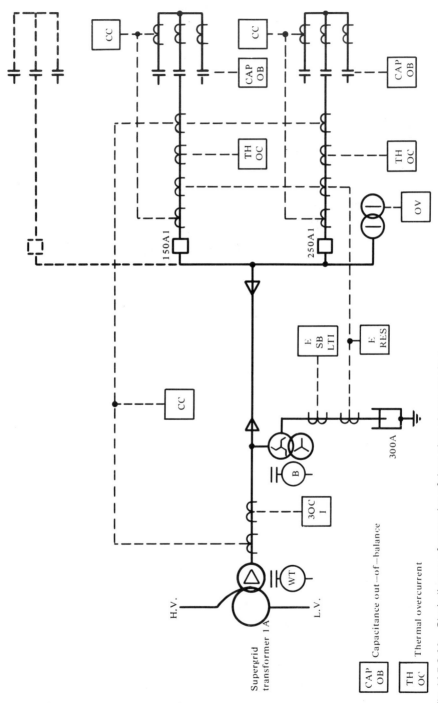

Fig. 14.5.6.4A   *Block diagram of protection of three-phase shunt capacitor*

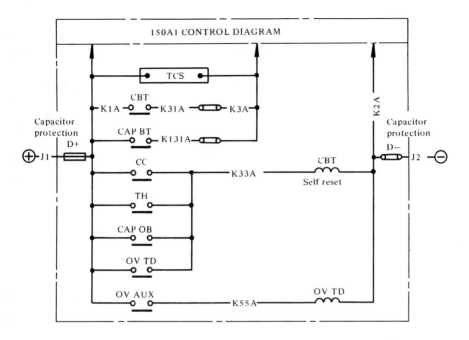

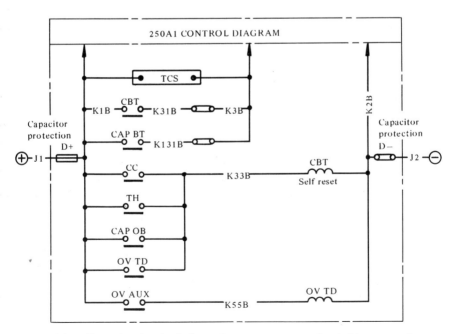

Fig. 14.5.6.4B *Protection d.c. circuits for static compensators associated with autotransformers*

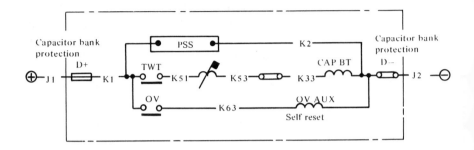

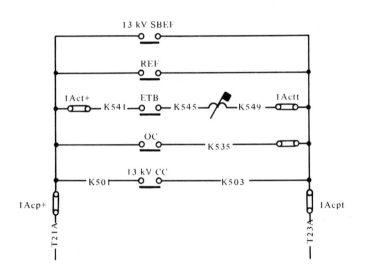

CAP BT	— Capacitor bank trip relay
CAP OB	— Capacitance out-of-balance
CBT	— Circuit-breaker trip relay
CC	— Circulating current
13 kV CC	— 13 kV circulating current
ETB	— Earthing transformer buchholz
OC	— Overcurrent
OV	— Over voltage
OV AUX	— Over voltage auxiliary relay
OV TD	— Over voltage time delay relay
PSS	— Protection supply supervision
REF	— Restricted earth-fault
13 kV SBEF	— 13 kV standby earth-fault relay (IDMT - 2 sec.)
TCS	— Trip circuit supervision
TH	— Thermal
TWT	— Tertiary winding temperature

Machine circulating current protection

The connections between the machine neutral, the starting transformer neutral and the 13 kV main oil circuit breaker are protected by their own differential circulating current system. This consists of a set of c.t.s in the 13 kV main oil circuit breaker, or its associated c.t. housing, balanced phase by phase against two further sets of c.t.s located one each in the netural connections of the machine and the starting transformer, respectively. High-impedance relays are used here also and the differential protection setting should be approximately 20% of full load current. Again, all the c.t. turns ratio must be the same.

Restricted earth-fault protection

As the machine is unearthed, an earthing transformer and resistor are required to tie the 13 kV equipment to earth and, as shown in Fig. 14.5.6.5A, this is teed to the connections between the tertiary winding and the machine main oil circuit breaker. A differential system of restricted earth-fault protection is applied consisting of a set of c.t.s in the machine main circuit breaker, or associated c.t. housing, and one c.t. in the earthing transformer neutral connection. It is designed to detect low level earth-fault currents in the earthing transformer or autotransformer tertiary winding. The d.c. circuit of the high-impedance relay used is connected to trip the autotransformer h.v. and l.v. circuit breakers.

13 kV standby earth-fault protection

Two-stage standby earth-fault protection is provided. Stage 1 affords earth-fault protection for the machine and stage 2 provides back-up protection for uncleared 13 kV earth faults and ensures that the neutral earthing resistor is not loaded beyond its rating. Both relays are supplied from the same c.t. located in the connection between the earthing transformer and the earthing resistor. The stage 1 relay is instantaneous in operation, usually has a setting of 10% and is connected to trip the 13 kV main oil circuit breaker only. The stage 2 relay which trips all the h.v. and l.v. circuit breakers associated with the autotransformer as well as the 13 kV machine main oil circuit-breaker is of the induction type with an i.d.m.t. characteristic. This relay should have a setting of 5% and an operating time of about 2 s at twice the setting.

Overcurrent protection

To guard against the possible failure of the 13 kV connection protection an i.d.m.t. back-up overcurrent relay is provided supplied from c.t.s located in the bushings of the 13 kV main oil circuit breaker or its associated c.t. housing. The relay is connected to trip the 13 kV main oil circuit breaker only.

Reverse power protection

If the supply to a synchronous compensator were to be lost while its associated

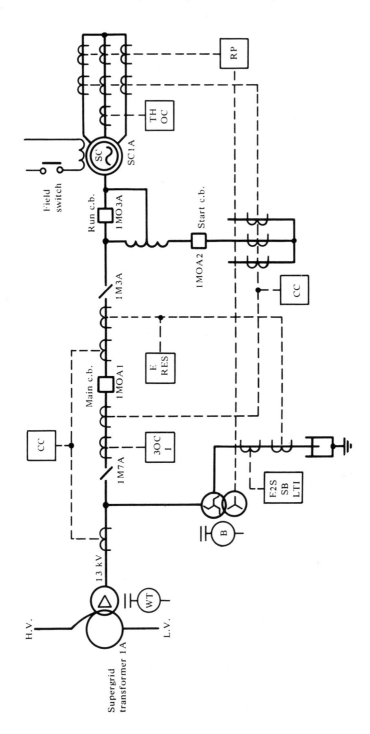

Fig. 14.5.6.5A *Block diagram of protection of synchronous shunt compensator*

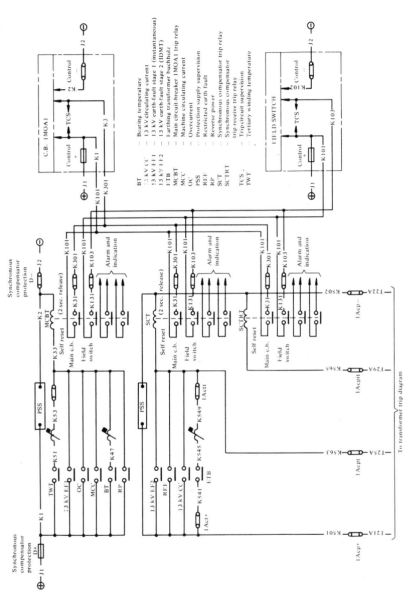

Fig. 14.5.6.5B *Protection d.c. circuits for synchronous compensators associated with auto-transformers*

circuit breakers remained closed, subsequent restoration of supply could result in the machine being re-energised out of synchronism. Although this situation is unlikely to occur at busbar type stations it is a possibility at stations with a limited number of infeeds.

To cater for this eventuality, which could result in serious damage to the machine, reverse power protection is usually considered necessary at stations other than those of the busbar type. The trip circuit is arranged to trip the 13 kV main oil circuit breaker only.

The low internal losses of the synchronous machines necessitate the use of a highly sensitive relay for the detection of loss of power following an interruption of supply. The voltage supply to these relays must therefore be of high accuracy if malfunctioning is to be avoided. The phase angle errors resulting from the internal regulation of the earthing transformer preclude its use for this purpose if there is any likelihood of its being used to supply varying loads, such as motor starting loads. In such cases a separate voltage transformer of high accuracy should be used.

The relay is, of course, designed to measure power and thus requires a current as well as the voltage supply just described. This current source is provided by a set of c.t.s located in the neutral end connections of the machine.

Other protection

To prevent the machine suffering damage from excessive thermal effects it is usual practice to provide a thermal overload relay supplied from a c.t. in one phase of the machine neutral end connections. Ideally, the characteristic curve of the relay should match the thermal characteristic of the machine over its whole range: in practice this may not be possible but it is essential that it does so over the working part of it. The relay setting adopted will thus be based on the thermal characteristics of the machine and the relay contacts are connected in the machine control circuit so that following relay operation the machine excitation is reduced.

Temperature indicators with facilities for providing alarm and tripping functions are provided on the machine bearings. The trip contact is connected to trip the 13 kV main oil circuit breaker.

The earthing transformer is provided with a double float gas-and oil-operated Buchholz relay generally of the type described and illustrated in Section 14.3.5. The relay has alarm and trip functions, the trip contact being connected to trip all circuit breakers capable of supplying fault current infeeds.

The tertiary winding of the autotransformer can withstand short periods of overloading but prolonged overheating will hasten insulation deterioration and eventually shorten the life of the transformer. To prevent this happening a winding temperature indicator (w.t.i.), previously described in Section 14.3.5., is fitted. Appropriate alarm and trip settings are applied and the trip contact is connected to trip the 13 kV main oil circuit breaker.

14.6   Bibliography

British Standards

BS.587:1957, 'Motor starters and controllers'
BS.4941:1973, 'Motor starters for voltages up to and including 1000 V a.c. and 1200 V d.c.'
BS.4999:Part 72 (1972) 'Thermal protection for electric motors rated at 660V a.c. and below
BS.5000:1973, 'Rotating electrical machines of particular types for particular applications'
BS.171:1970, 'Power transformers'
BS.1650:1971, 'Capacitors for connection to power frequency systems'

Books

Motor selection and application by C Libby Charles (McGraw-Hill)
The protective gear handbook by F E Wellman (Pitman)
Automatic protection of a.c. circuits by G W Stubbings (Chapman & Hall)
Protective relays: their theory and practice by A R Van C Warrington (Chapman & Hall)
Application of power capacitors (BICC Ltd. Publ.)

Papers and articles

'Short circuit rating and testing of reactors' by J G Wellings and R V Wheeler (*J.IEE*, 1942, Pt. 2, p. 473)
'Technical and economic aspects of the supply of reactive power in England and Wales' by W Casson and H J Sheppard (*Proc.IEE*, 1961, **108**, Part A)
Report on the use of series capacitors in power systems (ACE Report No. 3, 1956)
'The protection of shunt capacitor banks: a critical review of published information' by J A Nicholson (ERA Report No. Q/T136, 1953)
'Protection of series capacitors against external disturbances and internal faults' by R Pellissier (BE Translation No. 391)
'380 kV series capacitors in Sweden' by G Jancke, K S Smedsfelt and P Hjertberg (CIGRE Paper 322, 1954)
'Self-extinguishing gaps in large series capacitor stations' by L Ahlgren and B Grundmark (CIGRE Paper 317, 1956)
'The use of series capacitors on high voltage transmission systems' by S Lalander and L Norlin (CIGRE Paper 330, 1958)
'Series capacitors for distribution networks' by K S Smedsfelt and P Hjertberg (ASEA Paper 7407E)

'Series capacitors for high power transmission' by I Herlitz (ASEA Paper 7251E)
Report on the protection of series capacitors (up to 33 kV) (Protection Sub-
Committee M2, ad hoc Panel on Capacitor Protection, 1961)

Chapter 15

The application of protection to rural distribution systems

by J.Harris

15.1 Introduction

The growth in demand for electricity supplies in rural areas has led to rapid increases in the extent of rural high voltage networks, and consumers in these areas have come to demand supplies comparable in reliability to those provided in urban districts. In view of the type of construction employed for rural electrification, this demand has called for considerable skill and ingenuity on the part of electricity supply engineers.

Because of the savings achieved thereby, rural feeders are almost entirely of overhead construction, backbone lines radiating from step down transformer substations fed from the primary system and from these tappings are made to afford supplies to small groups of consumers. A typical system is illustrated in Fig. 15.1A. In order to take advantage of the impulse strength of the wood poles, these overhead lines are generally of 'unearthed construction', that is the pole top steelwork is earthed only at transformer and section switch positions and where pole type cable boxes are installed at junctions between lines and cables. The performance of lines with this type of construction is improved under certain conditions of fault liability compared with the older type with all steelwork earthed, but overhead lines generally are susceptible to faults due to lightning and other climatic conditions, birds, cattle and a variety of additional causes. A large proportion of these faults, amounting to approximately 80% are, however, of a transient nature and bring about the operation of the protective device without causing permanent damage to the system. As will be seen later, this fact enables automatic restoration of supplies to be employed with consequent improvement in the continuity of supplies to consumers fed from such lines.

Manual restoration of supplies in rural areas after interruption is often rendered difficult by inclement weather and rough terrain and frequently involves journeys of considerable length.

The fault power level on a rural network may be as high as 250 MVA at the source substation. Such a condition may cause burning through of small section line conductors if clashing occurs during gales or storms and it may be necessary

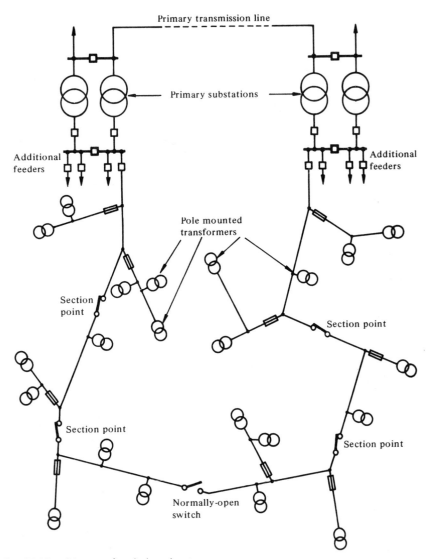

Fig. 15.1A   *Diagram of typical rural system*

to restrict the fault level by the isolation of infeeding transformers to discrete sections of switchgear. In such cases automatic sequence closing of busbar section circuit breakers may be employed to restore supplies in the event of a transformer failure.

Due to the comparatively high reactance of overhead lines, the attenuation of fault power along the line is high and the current values resulting from faults at points remote from the substation are considerably reduced as will be seen from Fig. 15.1B.

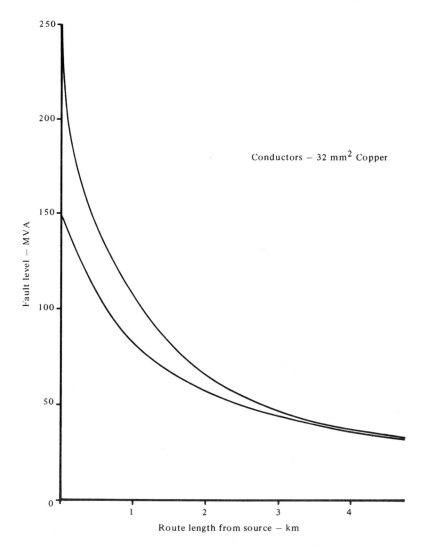

Fig. 15.1B

In the case of earth faults, a further reduction may occur due to high resistances caused by difficult earthing conditions. Protective devices for rural lines must therefore be capable of withstanding the thermal effects of heavy current whilst being sufficiently sensitive to operate on restricted currents. Furthermore, protective equipment, such as fuses or circuit breakers, which is installed on line supports must perform reliably after prolonged exposure to varying climatic conditions. It is the provision of devices meeting these requirements, at a cost in accord with the overall economics of rural electrification, that poses the problems of rural system protection.

15.2   Fuses

15.2.1   Types employed

One of the oldest and simplest methods of protecting rural systems is the use of fuses. Early designs consisted of little more than an enclosed wire and their performance was somewhat erratic. A large amount of research and development has, however, been carried out and the modern fuse is a much more reliable device.

Two types of high-voltage fuse are now generally available for the protection of rural systems, namely

(i)   Expulsion type
(ii)   Powder filled (high breaking capacity) type.

The construction and characteristics of these fuses have already been discussed in Chapter 5.

The liquid filled fuse was once widely used but troubles were experienced due to breakage of the glass and leakage of liquid. Furthermore, its application was somewhat restricted by its limited breaking capacity as system fault levels increased. The expulsion type is cheaper in capital cost and fuselink replacement and with available ratings being suitable for the fault power levels normally encountered in rural networks, its use has now superseded that of the liquid filled fuse.

For fault levels in excess of 150 MVA at 11 kV, an adaptation of the expulsion fuse carrier to incorporate a cartridge type powder-filled fuse link may be employed.

The construction of the expulsion type fuse readily permits the removal of the fuse link to be used as a means of isolating the protected equipment.

15.2.2   Application

Early applications tended to fuse each spur line and individual transformer separately, as in Fig. 15.2.2A(a), the fuse rating being related to the full load current rating of the plant protected. Whilst fuse blowing due to transformer failure was infrequent, surges during lightning storms often resulted in widespread fuse operation without permanent damage to apparatus. This led to the concept of 'group fusing', that is the protection of a number of transformers on a spur line by a single set of fuses at the spur tapping point, as shown in Fig. 15.2.2A(b). This safeguards the main line from disturbances on the spur and is the principle generally employed today. It is usually accepted that h.v. fuses be employed for short circuit rather than overload protection, and it is usual, therefore, to install 'group fuses' of comparatively high rating to prevent unwanted operation due to switching surges and l.v. faults. This, however, has the disadvantage that low current faults, such as transformer interturn failures and certain broken conductor faults, may not cause the fuse to operate. The number of such incidents is, however, negligible in comparison with those caused by lightning and, with the high reliability of modern distribution transformers and present day overhead line design, the principle of h.v. group fusing is undoubtedly justified. Overload protection of individual transformers is provided by l.v. fuses.

Current flowing to a fault on the l.v. side of a transformer is supplied via the h.v. group fuse and, under these conditions, the l.v. fuse protecting the faulty circuit should operate first in order that the h.v. supply to healthy transformers is not

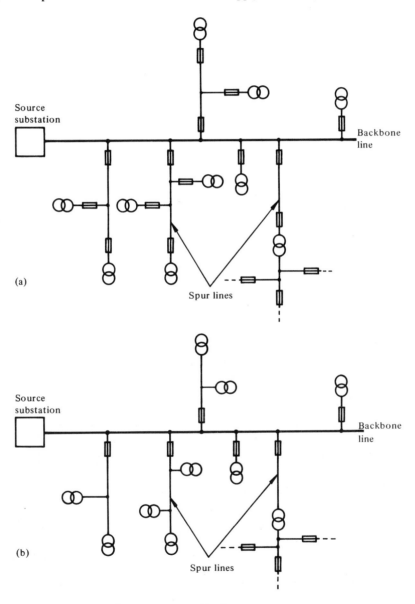

Fig. 15.2.2A   *Diagrams of systems protected by fuses*

affected. The use of high breaking capacity powder filled fuses, with their inherent high speed of operation, on the l.v. side, combined with the comparatively high current rating of the h.v. group fuse, materially assists in obtaining this discrimination.

This is shown in Fig. 15.2.2B where the h.v. and l.v. fuse protection of three-phase 11 000/440 V transformers is illustrated. A 100 kVA transformer having an impedance of 4·75 per cent and connected to an h.v. system having a fault

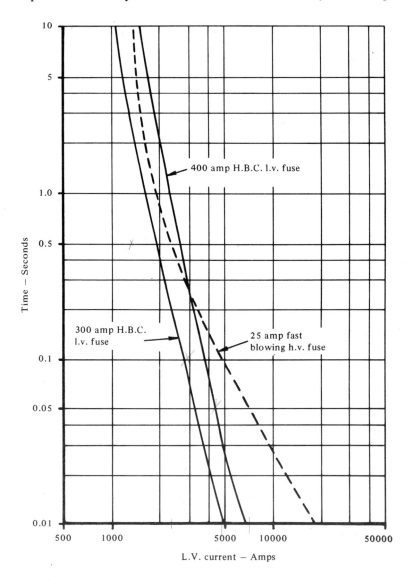

Fig. 15.2.2B   *Discrimination between h.v. and l.v. fuses protecting a 11 000/440V transformer*

level of 150 MVA will pass a maximum l.v. fault current of 2760 A. For all values
of fault current up to this figure discrimination will be obtained between the h.v.
expulsion type fuse of 25 A rating and the high breaking capacity l.v. fuse of 300 A
rating, tolerances on fuse characteristics being neglected. The ratio between l.v. and
h.v. fuse ratings is 12:1, although the transformation ratio is approximately 25:1,
discrimination with fuse ratings of this ratio being made possible by the high speed
of the filled type of fuse relative to that of the expulsion type.

An l.v. fuse of 400 A rating will not discriminate with the 25 A h.v. fuse at fault
currents below the maximum that can occur on the l.v. side of the 100 kVA trans-

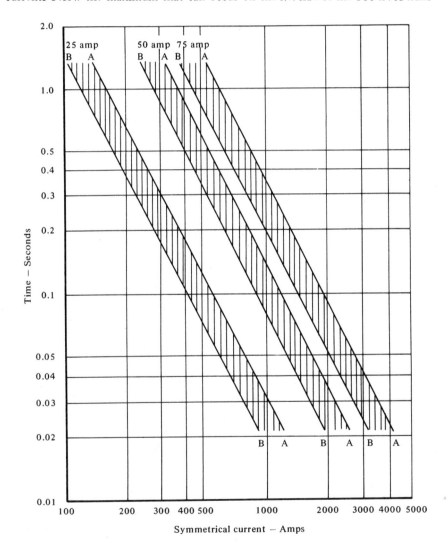

Fig. 15.2.2C   *Discrimination between h.v. fuses in series*

former but will do so at higher values of fault current which may be experienced on the l.v. side of larger transformers.

In order to check the discrimination between fuses in series, it is necessary to plot the total clearing-time characteristic of the fuse remote from the source and the prearcing-time characteristic of the fuse nearer the source to a common current base. In the case of transformer h.v. and l.v. fuses, the current values must be converted to a common voltage base. Discrimination will result if the characteristics are separated by an interval of at least the sum of the permitted characteristic tolerances for the fuses in question. Prior to the advent of BS 2692, tolerances on

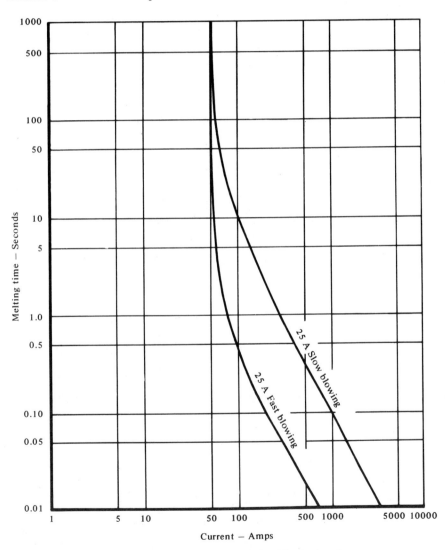

Fig. 15.2.2D   *Time/current characteristics of fast and slow blowing h.v. fuses*

the time/current characteristics of high-voltage fuses were noι specified and a simple rule-of-thumb method of ensuring discrimination between h.v. fuses was to employ a major fuse having a current rating twice that of the minor fuse. The tolerance on the characteristics of fuses to BS 2692 is ± 20% and in the absence of more specific information from the fuse manufacturer, this tolerance must be allowed when comparing fuse characteristics. With certain designs of expulsion fuse, however, greater accuracy is possible and a discrimination factor, that is minor fuse rating/major fuse rating, of 0·75 is obtainable. Fig. 15.2.2C shows the discrimination limits for three commonly used sizes of expulsion fuse. The lines AA represent for each rating the published characteristic whilst the lines BB have been plotted with the current ordinates reduced to 0·75 of the values represented by AA. These fuses will discriminate since the shaded area between the lines for any rating does not overlap that of the other ratings. Fuses of intermediate rating will not discriminate if overlapping of their characteristics, plotted as above, occurs.

In some instances, the use of fuse links with a slower operating characteristic at the higher currents may be required to obtain adequate discrimination. Fuse links with such characteristics are available in the liquid filled and expulsion types but are not available with the powder-filled h.b.c. type which is inherently fast in operation. A comparison of the relative prearcing times of fast and slow blowing h.v. fuse links is illustrated in Fig. 15.2.2D.

Some types of fault on the low-voltage side of transformers employing certain winding connections will give rise to unbalanced currents on the high voltage side and currents in excess of those carried by a balanced three-phase fault may occur. It is essential therefore to ensure that adequate discrimination can be obtained with these particular fault conditions.

Experience has indicated that the time/current characteristics of overhead line h.v. fuses change after a length of time in service and maldiscrimination may occur between fuses in series, even though correct discrimination is indicated by a comparison of their published characteristics.

For this reason and because of the wide tolerances on the characteristics sometimes encountered, the use of such fuses in series is not recommended.

15.3 Automatic circuit reclosing

15.3.1 Principle

As mentioned in the Introduction, approximately 80% of the faults occurring on rural systems are of a transient nature and cause no permanent damage to lines or plant. Such faults, however, require the operation of a protective device, for example a fuse or circuit breaker, for clearance, and an interruption of supply results until the fuse has been replaced or the circuit breaker reclosed. In rural areas a long journey may be involved often at an inconvenient time and in inclement weather, and in consequence the supply may be interrupted for a very long time. It will be apparent therefore that an improvement in the continuity of supply to consumers and a reduction in operating costs will result if the supply can be restored automatically. Automatic circuit reclosing is now extensively applied to rural networks and has resulted in a high standard of security of supplies to rural consumers.

Of the factors bearing on successful automatic reclosing, the most significant is the speed of operation of the circuit breaking device. If the opening of the circuit is delayed more than a few cycles, the thermal and other effects of the fault current may cause permanent damage at the fault position thus creating a persistent fault, preventing immediate supply restoration. High speed fault clearance, however, will, in most cases, prevent such damage and permit successful restoration of supplies.

The time interval between tripping and subsequent reclosure is usually referred to as the 'dead time' and may vary over a wide range. It is influenced by the characteristics of the circuit-breaking device, the nature of the faults likely to be encountered and the type of load supplied. In this latter connection, differing types of motors have conflicting requirements, synchronous machines requiring a dead time sufficiently long to ensure operation of their undervoltage protection whilst for induction motors the period needs to be short to enable them to coast through the open-circuit period. The dead time must in all cases however, be of sufficient duration to ensure deionisation of the fault path and stabilisation of the breaker mechanism. In practice times ranging from 0·4-120s are employed but evidence from field trials suggests that a time of 10-15s affords the best performance under typical system conditions.

An important characteristic of reclosing schemes is that known as reclaim or resetting time, i.e. the time following a successful reclosing operation after which the scheme will provide a full operating sequence in the event of subsequent faults. It is of particular significance under repetitive fault conditions, e.g. lightning storms or conductor clashing in high winds, when reclaim times in excess of the interval between the incidence of successive faults may cause unnecessary lockout and interruption of supply. Service experience indicates that good results are obtained by the use of reclaim times of the order of 5s, although in the case of spring actuated mechanisms it may be governed and extended by the spring winding requirement.

The use of single phase interruption and reclosing produces a tendency for the voltage on the faulty phase to be maintained by the sound phases via the magnetic circuits of three phase transformers connected to the system. Whilst this may assist induction motors to continue to run, it may delay the disconnection of synchronous machines. Since induction motors are the more commonly used in rural areas, however, the scheme has been used with considerable success.

In a large proportion of non-persistent faults, estimated to be some 80% of the total, the circuit may be successfully re-energised at the first attempt, but with the remainder a second or third reclosure may be necessary. Considerable improvement in the continuity of supply can therefore be obtained by the use of 'single shot' reclosing, and any further improvement which may be achieved by multishot reclosing must be judged against the cost of the additional equipment required to provide this feature.

15.3.2 Repeater fuses

Where protection of the h.v. system is by fuses, automatic restoration of supplies may be achieved by the use of repeater fuses. These are of the drop out expulsion type and one, two or three restorations may be obtained by the installation of the appropriate number of fuses per phase. Only one of these is normally in circuit, and following its operation on fault the energy of the falling carrier in isolating the spent fuse is utilised to actuate a spring loaded changeover contact to bring the next fuse into circuit. By the incorporation of a time lag device this action may be delayed to ensure that any fault arc path has become sufficiently deionised to permit the circuit to be successfully re-energised.

The disadvantages of the use of repeater fuses are the amount of equipment which it is required to accommodate on an overhead line support and the number of replacement elements required after clearing a persistent fault.

15.3.3 Pole-mounted automatic circuit reclosers

(*a*) *Construction:* The repeater fuse permits only a limited number of operations before resetting becomes necessary and periodical inspections are therefore required to ensure full availability.

A form of reclosing circuit breaker which overcame the disadvantage of this limitation, by virtue of an operating mechanism which is self resetting if the fault is removed before the completion of its operating sequence, was developed in America about the mid 1940s. This type of equipment offered other advantages for the protection of rural overhead lines, and designs are now available in this country.

Units of this type have been commonly termed 'high speed reclosers' but this term is something of a misnomer since, although the open circuit interval is reduced to approximately one second, their main attribute is a very high tripping speed which minimises fault damage to apparatus and prevents unnecessary operation of

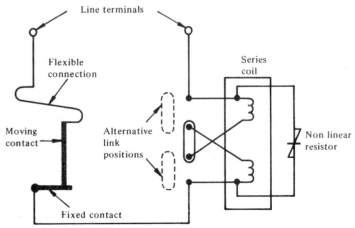

Fig. 15.3.3A   *Internal connections of recloser (AEI Ltd.)*

associated fuses. For certain applications, however, some delayed tripping operations may be required and units with variable tripping characteristics have therefore been produced.

The first recloser of this type produced by a British switchgear manufacturer was a single phase per tank design which utilised the energy of the fault current to open the circuit-breaking contacts, and, at the same time, to charge springs which subsequently reclosed the contacts. It was essentially a series solenoid device, the eletrical arrangement being as shown in Fig. 15.3.3A. The thermal characteristics

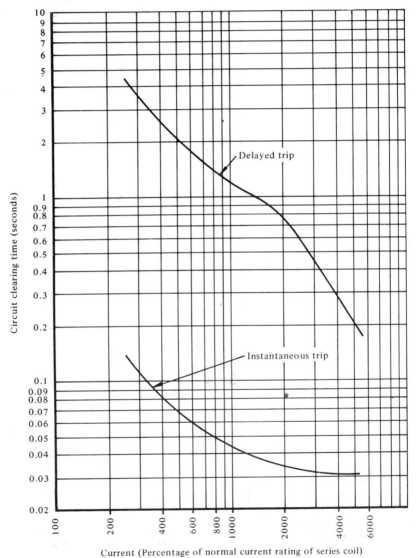

Current (Percentage of normal current rating of series coil)

Fig. 15.3.3B   *Recloser time/current tripping characteristics (AEI Ltd.)*

of the solenoid imposed some limitation on the maximum breaking capacity, particularly on units for the lower normal current ratings.

The timing mechanism incorporated an oil dashpot which provided a full operating sequence of two high speed and two delayed trips, or alternatively up to four high speed tripping operations. On the delayed trips it imparted an inverse time characteristic modified to improve discrimination with time fuses fitted to the source circuit breaker. This characteristic is indicated in Fig. 15.3.3B.

If a fault was cleared before completion of the full operating sequence, the recloser remained closed and the mechanism reset. When, however, the fault persisted for the duration of the full sequence, the recloser locked in the open position after the final trip and then had to be reclosed manually after the fault had been removed.

Following a manual reclosure, the recloser had only one delayed trip to lock out in order to prevent tripping due to inrush currents and to prevent unnecessary reclosing, if a fault still existed on the line. If no such tripping occurred however, the mechanism reset within a short time to provide a full operating sequence.

This type of recloser was manufactured with ratings up to 200 A in single phase units with mechanical interphase coupling. It was arranged to provide tripping and reclosing on the faulted phase or phases only, but for locking open or manual operation all three phases were actuated simultaneously.

The minimum operating current was approximately twice the normal current rating and thus tripping on low values of fault current, such as may obtain on some types of earth fault, was not possible. This type of recloser is therefore no longer in production having been superseded by the current design which affords this latter feature.

The design now available encloses three phase units in one tank and is arranged for three-phase tripping and reclosure. The energy for charging the reclosing spring is derived from a multistroke electromagnet, the coil of which is connected across two of the incoming terminals through auxiliary switches coupled to the main contacts which ensure that the coil is in circuit only for the time necessary to charge the spring. The electrical arrangement is as shown in Fig. 15.3.3C. It should be noted that the act of manual closing merely closes the coil auxiliary switches, and closing of the main contacts is by the action of the electromagnet and closing springs.

Under certain circumstances, such as when maintenance or repair work is being carried out, it may be necessary for the current flow through a recloser to be in a direction reverse to that normally employed. When operating under this condition, a recloser with the closing arrangement described above will trip once to clear a fault occurring on the side remote from the new source of supply, but cannot be reclosed, either automatically or manually, since the reclosing coil is then isolated from the supply by the main contacts. To avoid unnecessary interruptions due to this cause, a 'lock-closed' feature has been introduced which is brought into action by the operation of an external handle and which prevents the recloser from tripping. Protection against faults on the recloser protected section is then provided by another recloser or a circuit breaker nearer the source.

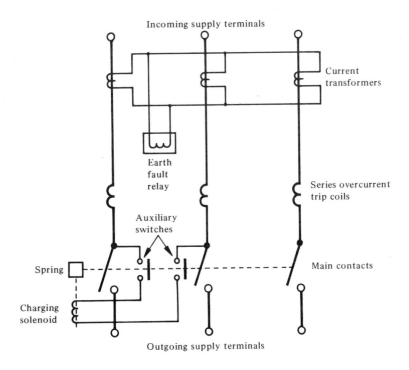

Fig. 15.3.3C   *Internal connection diagram of recloser with earth fault feature
(A Reyrolle & Co. Ltd.)*

Overcurrent protection is provided by conventional series trip-coils with a dashpot type mechanism to give an inverse time characteristic shown in Fig. 15.3.3F. For instantaneous tripping, the dashpot action is bypassed by the opening of a valve in a cylinder, the control of this valve being by means of a cam which thus provides a ready means of sequence control.

As a consequence of the fine mechanical clearances employed in the construction of the dashpot, some increase in operating and resetting times occurred in cold weather due to the increased viscosity of the oil. Under repetitive fault conditions, e.g. conductor clashing during winter storms, this had the effect of cumulative progression to the lockout position due to incomplete resetting between consecutive operations. One method of alleviating this situation was to use a special low viscosity insulating oil which produced operating characteristics at 0°C approximating to those at 20°C with normal oil to BS 148.

This cold weather problem is now overcome by the incorporation in the design of a modified timing and sequencing mechanism. In the modified tripping dashpot, the clearances are controlled by a bimetallic strip and thus afford delayed overcurrent tripping times which are comparatively independent of temperature. The resetting mechanism is now noncumulative and resets to provide a full sequence of operations in a constant time irrespective of the number of trip operations which have occurred. The standard reset time is 90s, but this time can be reduced to some 5-10s by drilling a small hole in the controlling dashpot.

Provision is made for an instantaneous earth-fault trip coil operated from current transformers in turrets at the base of the terminal bushings. This feature is operative on earth fault currents down to 20 amps.

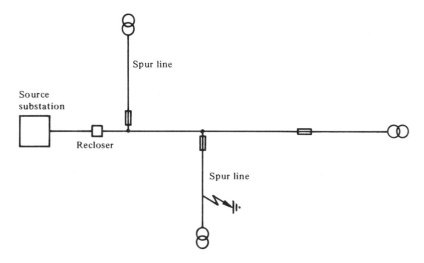

Fig. 15.3.3D   *Recloser and fuse protected line*

A range of trip coil ratings up to 200 A is available with this design and the full breaking capacity of the unit is maintained with all ratings throughout the range. Owing to the single tank construction, the unit may be mounted on a single line pole.

Both types of recloser described above have nominal dead times of one second.

(*b*)   *Application:* In order to protect as large a section of network as possible, a recloser should be installed as near to the source of supply as limitations of normal current and breaking capacity will permit, the actual location being determined largely by these factors. Reclosers in series may be justified on extensive or important networks and in some cases individual spurs may be protected by a recloser.

The method of application of reclosers based on their use in conjunction with h.v. fuses is indicated on Fig. 15.3.3D. The recloser and fuses are so co-ordinated that transient faults are cleared by the high speed initial tripping of the recloser. The fuse, or fuses, operate during the delayed tripping period to isolate persistent faults and minimise the section of network without supplies. This requires a recloser with an operating sequence of instantaneous followed by delayed tripping operations, as shown in Fig. 15.3.3E. The fuse should remain intact during the instantaneous trips and suffer no deterioration due to partial melting so that its performance on subsequent faults may be in accordance with its published characteristic. On the delayed tripping operations, however, the fuse should melt and isolate the faulty section before lockout of the recloser occurs.

In order to determine the current range over which these requirements may be achieved it is necessary to compare the total heat input to the fuse during the relevant portion of the recloser operating sequence with the time/current characteristic of the fuse. Over the portion of the sequence during which the fuse should remain intact, however, some modification of the published fuse curves is required, in order to take into account the effect of preloading and progressive deterioration of the fuse element with consequent loss of characteristic after carrying repeated transient fault currents. This is done by derating the melting time curve of the fuse by the application of a factor of 0·75, a figure which may be used in the absence of specific information on this point relating to the particular fuse employed. On the other hand, some degree of cooling of the element takes place during the open circuit interval of the recloser, and the correction time to be added for this effect is given by the formula

$$t = \frac{I_m^2}{I_f^2} T$$

where t is the correction time to be added to the fuse melting time characteristic, I_m is the minimum melting current of fuse, T is the total open-circuit time for the portion of reclosure sequence considered, and I_f is the circuit fault current.

In practice the error introduced by neglecting the cooling effect is so small as to be of little consequence.

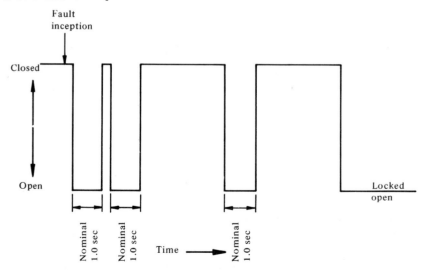

Fig. 15.3.3E   *Travel/time diagram for instantaneous and delayed tripping recloser*

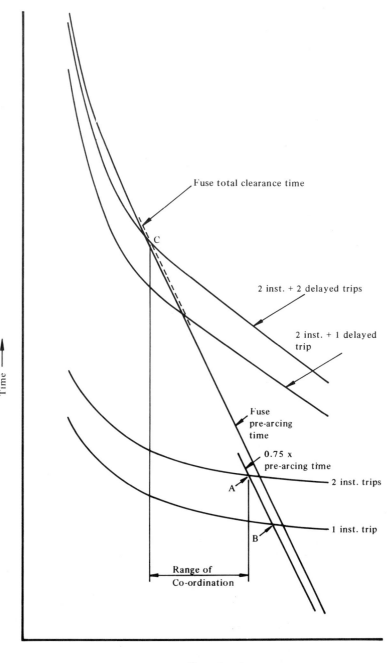

Fig. 15.3.3F

The modified fuse characteristics are then superimposed upon the cumulative time/current curves of the recloser, as shown on Fig 15.3.3F. The upper limit for correct co-ordination is given by the intersection of the derated fuse melting curve and the last instantaneous tripping curve of the recloser (shown as A), whilst the lower limit is obtained from the intersection of the fuse total clearing time curve with the recloser final delayed tripping curve (shown as C).

With fault currents between A and B, co-ordination will be obtained only if the fault is removed before the second instananeous trip, and currents in excess of B will cause the fuse to blow before any operation of the recloser. Point A is there-fore regarded as the upper limit since above this value the full advantage of a second instantaneous trip is not obtained. At currents below the lower limit, locking open of the recloser will occur before the clearing of the fuse, provided that the current is in excess of the minimum value required to trip the recloser, normally twice its rated current.

The range of co-ordination is obviously influenced by the slope of the fuse characteristic curve, the steep slope of the fast blowing fuse restricting the range in comparison with that of the slow blowing type. The latter type are therefore employed with reclosers, and it has been found that the size of fuse is dictated by co-ordination requirements rather than load currents, and fuse ratings somewhat higher than those in use on systems without reclosers are generally employed.

The dual mode fuse referred to in Chapter 5 is designed to afford improved co-ordination with reclosers by having fast blowing characteristics at low currents and slow blowing characteristics at high currents.

(c) *Development of alternative operation cycles:* Operational experience of reclosers and fuses in combination initially indicated that the number of supply interruptions on the protected line were reduced by some 90% of their original number, and that the operation of a fuse was a definite indication of a persistent fault. After two or three years, however, a sharp increase in the number of fuse operations on transient faults occurred inferring that fuse deterioration in service had, in fact, taken place.

The effect of this deterioration can be offset, and the initial performance of a recloser/fuse combination maintained, by the replacement of all fuse elements at intervals of approximately two years. Alternatively, the fuse deterioration factor of 0·75 may be reduced, but this is attended by a reduction in the range of co-ordina-tion and may not, in any case, be the complete solution. In view of the small number of persistent faults occurring on recloser protected systems, however, consideration was given to the elimination of fuses entirely. In addition to reducing installation and operating costs and avoiding unnecessary interruptions due to transient faults, this course permitted an improvement in the overall system per-formance since delayed recloser tripping operations could be eliminated and dis-crimination with back-up relays thereby facilitated. It was appreciated that all persistent faults would result in the locking open of the recloser causing a greater number of consumers to be affected by interruption of supply, but it was felt that against the reduction in interruptions on transient faults this could be tolerated.

Reclosers having all instantaneous tripping operations, as indicated in Fig. 13.3.4J were therefore introduced.

Reclosers with delayed trips have been used without associated fuses, but they impose unnecessary strain on the system due to the long clearance times for persistent faults. In addition, the problem of discrimination with back-up relay protection still remains.

Operating experience of reclosers on systems from which fuses have been eliminated indicates that the incidence of supply interruptions is reduced to a consistently low level. The main criterion to be employed when comparing this method of application with that employing fuses, however, is that of the product of the number of consumers and time for which supplies are interrupted, taken over a period of time rather than for an isolated incident.

(*d*) *Fault indicators:* On systems protected by reclosers with the all instantaneous tripping sequence, damage due to persistent faults is greatly restricted due to the very short duration for which the fault current is allowed to persist. At times this renders fault location difficult, and adequate line sectionalising facilities are necessary to assist the location of faults. Where fuse mounts already exist, these may be converted to sectionalising points by the fitting of solid links in place of the fuses.

The installation of fault indicators at strategic positions on an overhead-line circuit aids the location of faults by indicating the passage of fault current. One such device provides a fixed phase fault setting of 100, 200 or 400 A and a minimum earth fault setting of 5% of the phase fault setting. Indication is displayed whilst the setting current is exceeded or the line is dead after fault clearance, resetting taking place automatically on restoration of supply.

The device is activated by three detector coils located inside special insulators mounted on the line crossarm. The magnetic flux surrounding each line conductor supported by the insulators induces a voltage proportional to the line current in the associated coil and these voltages are applied via flexible leads to solid-state phase and earth-fault measuring circuits contained in a weatherproof housing mounted on the pole below the crossarm.

At the set current value, a signal is applied to a trigger circuit which discharges a capacitor into the indicator operating coil. Whilst the line is energised the device receives a pulse every few seconds from a second capacitor to retain it in the reset state but the operating circuit is arranged to override the resetting circuit.

The device derives the energy necessary for operation of the measuring and indicating functions from the line itself by means of capacitors formed by conducting glazes on the upper shed and internal coil housing of the insulator. Since there is no stored energy available prior to energising the line, the device takes approximately two seconds to operate when closing a line on to a fault and this time may be increased if the source impedance is high and the voltage reduced. If the line protection clears the fault within that time, no indication is made.

For close-up faults when the line voltage may fall to zero, sufficient energy is stored to allow normal operation for up to 4 s after the loss of voltage.

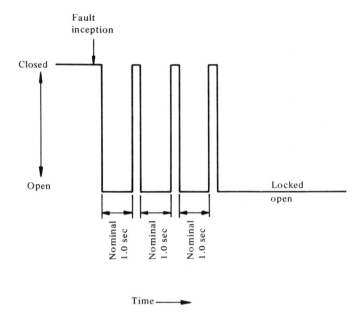

Fig. 15.3.3G   *Travel/time diagram for all-instantaneous recloser*

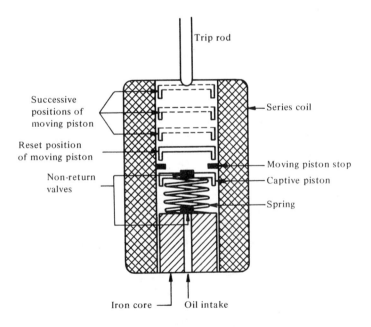

Fig. 15.3.3H   *Line sectionaliser timing device*

The indicator housing and the detector coils may be installed or removed by the use of live line techniques.

Another type of line fault indicator may be used as a portable device for attachment to poles at strategic points on a line during fault finding operations and subsequent removal for use on later faults on other circuits. Alternatively, a version suitable for permanent installation is available.

The device is fixed to the pole near to the base and is responsive to changes in the magnetic field produced at this level by currents flowing in the line conductors, this field being zero under normal balanced load conditions since the vector sum of the phase currents is zero. Under the unbalanced conditions obtained during faults however, a resultant field is produced and an earth fault current of 20 A is sufficient to cause operation of the indicator. The phase to phase fault current required to operate the device is dependent on the conductor configuration, the minimum value for lines of horizontal construction to BS 1320 being 900 A and somewhat less for lines of triangular formation, although operation may not occur in the case of faults which cause currents to flow in the outer conductors only.

The operating sequence of the instrument is initiated when a system disturbance causes the rate of change of the magnetic field to be sufficient to induce a voltage of the set value in the detector coil. Irrespective of its state, the device immediately resets to the start of its sequence and for 50 ms operation is inhibited. This delay is introduced to avoid unwanted operation on magnetising inrush transients but if at the end of this period the field is still adequate to produce the required voltage in the detector coil, the device will indicate after a further 20 ms. Following this, further operation, i.e. resetting, is prevented for one second so that the device is unaffected by the change in field caused by the clearance of the fault by a circuit breaker. The detector circuit is then reinstated and any further system disturbance will reset the device and restart the operating sequence. If, however, no such signal is received, the device resets automatically after 8 h. The times quoted above are preset during manufacture but may be varied to suit particular requirements.

Operating power is derived from internal batteries, a ten year life being claimed for those used in the permanently installed version.

(*e*) *Sectionalisers:* A method of isolating faulty sections of a recloser protected network without employing fuses is the use of automatic line sectionalisers. These devices are pole mounted oil disconnectors which are arranged to open automatically during a predetermined 'dead time' of the associated recloser, thus isolating the fault before lockout of the recloser occurs. This characteristic ensures co-ordination with the recloser at all values of fault current up to the full rating of the device.

The sectionaliser functions by counting the passage of pulses of fault current let through by the recloser, these pulses flowing through the operating solenoid causing a captive piston in an oil filled cylinder to be pulled down against a spring. A non-return valve in the crown of the captive piston allows oil from the underside to pass through to, and be trapped in, the space above the piston, forming an oil column which is forced upward by the spring when the recloser operates to cut off the fault current in the solenoid. The oil column in turn lifts a moving piston. After a preset number of pulses, the oil column formed is sufficient to lift the moving piston against the trip bar of the sectionaliser, the contacts then being opened by the action of a spring which has been charged during manual closing of the device. The basic arrangement of the sectionaliser is shown in Fig. 15.3.3H.

(*f*)   *Grading of reclosers with other forms of protection:* In a typical recloser protected system, as depicted in Fig. 15.3.3D, the operating characteristic of the recloser must be between those of the fuse and the protective relay on the source substation circuit breaker. Any maldiscrimination, in addition to causing unnecessary loss of supplies, may also delay the restoration of these supplies by presenting a false indication of the location of a fault to the operating staff.

A method for determining the co-ordination between recloser and fuse has been set out in Section 15.3.3(b), and it is essential to ensure that the size of fuse installed permits a range of co-ordination adequate to cover fault currents likely to be encountered on the protected spur.

The protective relay associated with the substation circuit breaker will usually be of inverse definite minimum time type, and when a persistent fault occurs beyond the recloser this relay may be energised for two very brief periods followed by two somewhat longer time intervals.

Since little resetting of the relay disc can take place during the very brief dead times, cumulative forward movement of the relay will occur. In order that discrimination between the circuit breaker and the recloser is obtained, it is therefore necessary to take this into account when choosing the time setting of the relay. An operating time of approximately twice that of the time delay tripping characteristic of the recloser, as in Fig. 15.3.4L, is usually satisfactory.

Compliance with this requirement may at times be difficult against the background of the overall scheme of protection further back towards the source of

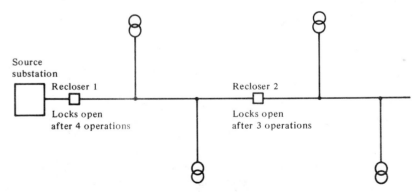

N.B. If only one recloser is fitted with an earth fault relay this should be employed as recloser No. 2.

Fig. 15.3.3J   *Grading of all-instantaneous tripping reclosers*

supply. Where, however, full discrimination cannot be obtained, the installation of reclosers will still show a considerable improvement in the quality of supply since some 90% of the faults occurring will be cleared in the nonpersistent stage by the instantaneous trips of the recloser which permit discrimination. The disadvantage of this arrangement lies in the fact that when maldiscrimination occurs, the operating staff may be presented with a misleading indication of the location of the fault and valuable time lost in restoring supplies.

With all-instantaneous tripping reclosers the difficulty of obtaining discrimination between the recloser and circuit breaker is greatly reduced. When reclosers of this type are operated in series, however, the differences in the operating times of units of various ratings are so small as to render time grading unreliable. Recourse must therefore be made to grading by the number of operations to lockout, as in Fig. 15.3.3J. The recloser most remote from the supply source is set to lock open after two or three unsuccessful reclose operations, whilst the one nearer the source is arranged to complete a full sequence of four trips before locking open. Thus, if the current to a fault beyond the more remote recloser is of such value as to cause simultaneous operation of both reclosers, the more remote recloser will lock open to isolate the fault whilst supply to the healthy section is maintained through the recloser nearer the source.

When a recloser with an earth-fault tripping feature is employed in series with a recloser not so fitted, as may occur due to piecemeal growth of a network, it must be borne in mind that all earth-fault tripping operations are instantaneous. The recloser with the earth-fault feature must therefore be employed as the more remote unit of the pair; otherwise false indication of fault position may be given, since the magnitude of the fault current may be high enough to operate the earth-fault feature but insufficient to cause overcurrent tripping of the recloser not so fitted.

15.3.4   Substation circuit breakers

The location on a rural system of the pole-mounted reclosing devices previously mentioned may be governed by considerations of normal current rating and breaking capacity, and these may demand that the recloser be installed some distance from the primary substation. In such cases, the section of line between the substation and the device is without the benefit of high speed automatic reclosing and faults on that section, whether persistent or nonpersistent, will affect the continuity of supply to the remainder of the line. The advantage of providing automatic reclosing of the substation circuit breaker to minimise interruptions of supply on this section will therefore be apparent.

Control relays for circuit breaker reclosing schemes have been available for a number of years. The simplest of these provides a single closing impulse after a predetermined time delay, whilst another form permits a preselected number of reclosures with selected time intervals between them. This latter relay, known as a periodic reclosing relay, consists of a motor driven disc around the periphery of which are spaced a number of tapped holes. Into selected holes are screwed pins which project through the disc, and as this is rotated the projections in turn actuate a contact to energise the closing circuit, the time between reclosures (the dead time) being determined by the spacing of the pins. If the circuit breaker remains closed after a reclosure, the relay is reset by the energising of the motor reverse field through an auxiliary switch on the circuit breaker. The final pin has a somewhat longer projection than the others and if the reclosure initiated by it is unsuccessful, continued rotation of the disc causes it to operate a lockout contact which disconnects the supply to the foward field of the driving motor, preventing further reclosure. The electrical circuits of this type of relay are indicated in Fig. 15.3.4A.

The time interval between tripping and reclosure generally employed with the above relays is comparatively long and may vary from 10 to 120 s. The number of reclosures permitted is dependent on the nature of the system protected and may be two or three where it consists almost entirely of overhead lines, and somewhat less where the proportion of underground cable is appreciable. Operating experience indicates that with the use of these relays, in conjunction with inverse time protection, successful reclosure occurs in approximately three out of four faults, the number depending on the speed of operation of the protection.

The improved quality of rural supplies obtained by the use of the pole-mounted automatic circuit recloser indicated the advantages of high speed fault clearance and the desirability of providing a similar operating sequence on substation circuit breakers. This course removes the normal current and breaking capacity limitations of the recloser and extends the reclosing facilities to the whole of the protected line.

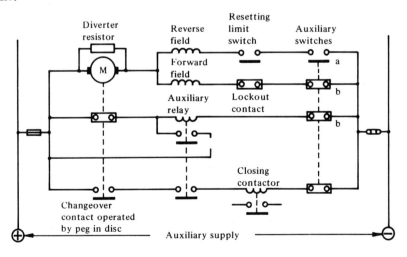

a — made when o.c.b. closed

b — made when o.c.b. open

Fig. 15.3.4A   *Connections for periodic reclosing relay*

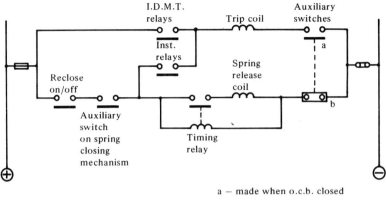

a — made when o.c.b. closed

b — made when o.c.b. open

Fig. 15.3.4B *Basic reclosing scheme for substation circuit breaker*

To provide this feature, the circuit breaker is fitted with a combination of high speed and inverse-time protection, each having approximately the same range of settings. On the occurrence of a fault, the high speed protection operates to trip the circuit breaker, which is reclosed by an auxilliary timing relay after a brief time interval. The tripping circuits of the high speed relays are then held open, either by an auxiliary switch on the discharged spring closing mechanism or by an auxiliary relay, so that if the fault persists after reclosure, further tripping of the circuit breaker is accomplished by i.d.m.t. relays. The control scheme is arranged to lock open the breaker on the operation of the inverse time relays, but if the reclosure is successful, the relays reset to provide a full operating cycle on subsequent faults. The basic circuit arrangement of a simple spring closing scheme is shown in Fig. 15.3.4B and the operating sequence diagram in Fig. 15.3.4C.

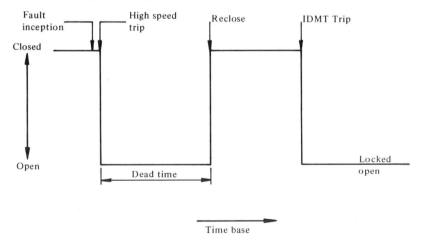

Fig. 15.3.4C *Travel/time diagram for reclosing circuit breaker with high speed and i.d.m.t. protection*

This sequence is known as repetitive single-shot reclosing and was adopted to limit the number of breaking operations at the higher source substation fault levels to a figure within the capability of standard circuit breakers. Subsequent investigations and service experience have shown that breakers currently available in this country are capable of carrying out many more breaking operations before maintenance becomes necessary than those required by certification tests, particularly at the lower duties.

In the early 1960s, a number of Area Boards introduced individual auto reclosing schemes for use with ground mounted circuit breakers but in 1966 a report recommending standard reclosing schemes was issued by the Electricity Council. The schemes, all incorporating the single shot sequence with optional short or long dead times were for:

(i)   Single-shot reclosing for circuit breakers having hand charged spring mechanisms.

(ii)   Repetitive single shot reclosing for breakers with motor wound spring closing mechanisms. This scheme utilises an auxiliary switch on the spring charging mechanism to use the rewinding time as the reclaim time of the sequence.

(iii) Repetitive single-shot reclosing for circuit breakers with solenoid closing mechanisms. In this case the dead and reclaim times are determined by a timing relay.

(iv)   Repetitive single shot reclosing for breakers with solenoid or motor wound spring mechanisms and incorporating precumulative lockout and cumulative lockout alarm features.

In all these schemes reclosing is initiated only by the operation of the high speed protection thus ensuring that it takes place only after a fault and not following manual tripping of the breaker. The repetitive schemes incorporate cumulative operation counting relays which limit the number of tripping operations on faults to an extent determined by the maintenance requirements of the breaker. When the preset number of operations has been achieved, the inverse time protection only is effective and further reclosing is inhibited.

The schematic diagram for scheme (iv) is shown in Fig. 15.3.4D.

A subsequent report concerning protection against lightning discussed the use of automatic circuit reclosing in this context and recommended the adoption of long dead times and short reclaim times, the figures quoted being 10-15s and 5s, respectively. These times enable the system to recover fully from a fault and minimise the possibility of unnecessary lockouts on repetitive faults. This report also suggested that, with improved knowledge of circuit breaker capabilities, multi-shot reclosing schemes might be employed with advantage. Modifications of the original standard schemes have therefore been made to permit the optional use of an additional counting relay to extend the operating sequence up to a maximum of three reclosures, (i.e. four tripping operations) on any one fault.

Comprehensive relay equipment providing both protection and reclosing

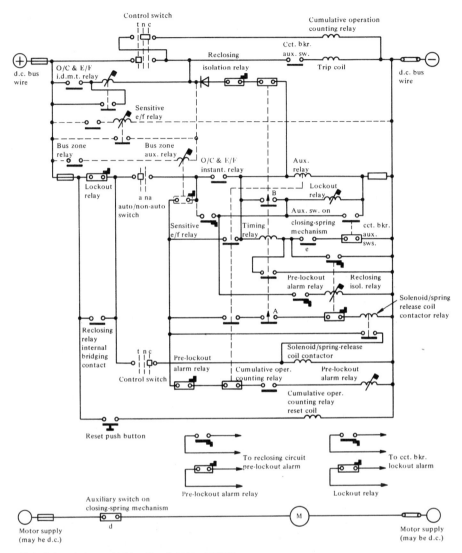

Mechanical counter to record total number of opening operations.

Auxiliary switch d on closing spring mechanism is open when spring is charged. Auxiliary switch e on closing spring mechanism is closed when spring is charged.

Timing relay to have a normally open time delay contact A closing after a preset time delay of 0.5−1.0s or 5−20s for a period of not less than 0.6s and not greater than 2s and a normally open time delay contact B closing after a preset time delay of 30−35s or 35−60s. The remaining contacts operate instantaneously.

Auxiliary relay must operate in not more than 8ms. The normally open contacts must have a 100ms delay on drop off when the relay is shorted.

Normally open contact on the cumulative operation-counting relay must not close in less than 15ms.

Reclosing relay internal-bridging contact is closed when the relay assembly is withdrawn from the case.

Fig. 15.3.4D *Circuit diagram of repetitive single-shot reclosing scheme for circuit breaker with motor-wound spring or solenoid-closing mechanism and having prelockout and lockout alarm facilities*

facilities is now available in solid-state form. These relays afford high speed protection with characteristics shaped to prevent operation by transformer magnetising inrush currents together with a choice of various inverse time overcurrent and earth fault characteristics by means of interchangeable plug-in modules. Sensitive earth fault options are also available.

Flexible control of the auto reclosing sequence and protection operation selection is provided by changeover links mounted on the face of the relay. Up to 3 or 4 reclosures per fault incident may be obtained and the instantaneous protection can be inhibited for any trip operation of a multiple-reclose sequence. Both dead and reclaim times are adjustable but whilst the former may differ for each reclosure, the preset reclaim time is applicable following all reclosures. An operations counter and circuit breaker inspection and lockout alarms are provided.

In addition to greater flexibility in application, the solid-state protection and reclosing control relays have the merit of occupying little control panel space compared to their electromagnetic counterparts.

The suitability of a circuit breaker for autoreclosing duties depends upon its total break time, the mechanical stability of its operating mechanism and, in the case of oil circuit breakers, the effect of any residual gas pressure in the tank when successive breaking operations occur within a very short time. In addition, taking an

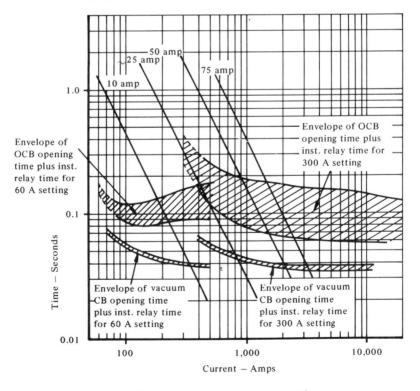

Fig. 15.3.4E   *Limits of co-ordination between circuit breakers and fuses*

overall view, the breaker's ability to perform a number of operations before requiring maintenance must be taken into account.

The vacuum interrupter is ideally suited to this duty. This device possesses high speed of fault clearance, the current being interrupted at the first current zero after trip initiation unless opening of the contacts takes place within 3 ms of that point when clearance is effected at the next zero point. Such a characteristic permits a high degree of co-ordination between the vacuum breaker and any associated fuses. This is illustrated in Fig. 15.3.4E which shows the co-ordination between both oil and vacuum circuit breakers and fuses. The fuse characteristics have been plotted at 75% of the published data to allow for deterioration of the fuse link and the intersection of the fuse and circuit breaker characteristics determines the limiting current beyond which co-ordination will not be obtained.

It is not possible to employ sectionalisers in series with substation circuit breakers having repetitive single shot reclosing facilities. Since the sectionaliser has no breaking capacity and must open during a dead time interval in the operating sequence, it would isolate the line section before the single reclosure irrespective of whether the fault was of a transient or permanent nature. Reclosers having all high-speed tripping sequences may be used in the role of sectionalisers in conjunction with substation breakers, however. Whilst the first trip of both breaker and recloser may occur simultaneously, the subsequent high-speed trips of the recloser will ensure discrimination with the inverse time protection of the circuit breaker and final clearance by the recloser.

The application of multishot reclosing schemes to substation circuit breakers permits the use of associated sectionalisers at a lower cost than that of reclosers.

Interruptions of supply on lines protected by this form of reclosing are reduced to a level similar to that obtained by the use of pole-mounted reclosers and circuit breaker maintenance requirements have been found to be light.

The provision of any form of automatic reclosing on a circuit breaker requires some form of power closing mechanism. If full advantage is to be derived from this feature, this mechanism must be of the solenoid, motor wound spring or other self-charging type.

15.4   Sensitive earth-fault protection

It has been mentioned earlier that earth-fault currents on rural networks may be of very low magnitude owing to long line lengths, the use of neutral earthing resistors, and difficult earthing conditions. Such circumstances arise when an overhead conductor breaks and falls on ground of high resistivity or across a hedge or haystack.

The 1947 edition of the Overhead Line Regulations required that such a conductor should be rendered dead but compliance with this requirement was in some cases not possible since the fault current under such a condition might be less than the minimum setting of the earth fault relays then available. This particular requirement is not included in the current (1970) edition of the Regulations but in view of the implications of a broken conductor remaining alive, some means of automatic disconnection is clearly desirable.

To avoid a dangerous condition arising on broken conductor faults, a sensitive form of earth-fault protection, responsive to primary earth-fault currents of the order of 5-10 A, is required. Such values represent the minimum setting which can be satisfactorily employed, since normal system unbalance currents, for example due to the unequal line to earth capacitance currents of varying lengths of single phase spur lines, may approach the lower value. Even so this sensitivity may be insufficient to detect broken conductor faults in which the conductor on the side of the break remote from the source falls to the ground. The conductor in this instance remains energised via the high-voltage windings of any transformers connected to the line beyond the point of fault and the fault current may be limited to a very low value by the impedance of these windings. Its magnitude will be determined by the number of transformers connected and the load connected to them, but in the extreme case of transformers on open circuit will consist of the magnitising currents only.

Whilst possessing a low fault setting, the components must be sufficiently robust to withstand the effects of much heavier fault currents which may occur from time to time.

With a relay which operates at such low primary currents, the effect of the magnetising current drawn by current transformers in idle shunt has an appreciable bearing on the value of primary current required to cause operation of the relay.

For this reason, therefore, early installations utilised a moving-coil relay element energised by a core balance current transformer mounted on the cable termination. The ratio of such a current transformer may be independent of the circuit rating and fault level and can be arranged to provide the optimum setting, generally of the order of 5 A.

When applying such a scheme to existing switchgear installations, however, considerable expense and inconvenience may be involved as it may be necessary to break down the cable end box in order to mount the core balance transformer and to fit the insulated glands essential for such a scheme, if the current transformer is mounted externally.

The development of relays having extremely low burdens, of the order of 0·01 VA or less, has enabled sensitive earth-fault protection to be provided by connection of the relay in the residual circuit of the current transformers employed for the conventional earth-fault protection. Such relays of the polarised element type enable settings as low as 2% or 3% of the primary current rating to be obtained whilst the corresponding static version provides a setting range of 1% to 16% of the rated current.

High-speed clearance of the low fault currents in question is unnecessary and indeed may be undesirable, since the high sensitivity of the protection might then give rise to operation on momentary system abnormalities. It is usual, therefore, to apply a time-lag to the tripping operation and values of approximately 10 seconds are in common use. A typical co-ordination of sensitive earth-fault protection and reclosers having delayed tripping and earth-fault features is shown in Fig. 15.4A.

The operation of sensitive earth-fault protection applied to an overhead line is frequently an indication of the existence of a dangerous condition on the circuit, e.g. a broken conductor lying on the ground. For this reason, some earlier auto-reclosing schemes are arranged to inhibit the reclosing feature after tripping initiated by sensitive earth-fault protection. Experience has shown however that the condition to which this form of protection is designed to respond arises frequently during normal operation of an overhead system and some undertakings now employ automatic reclosing in such circumstances. A reasonable degree of successful re-

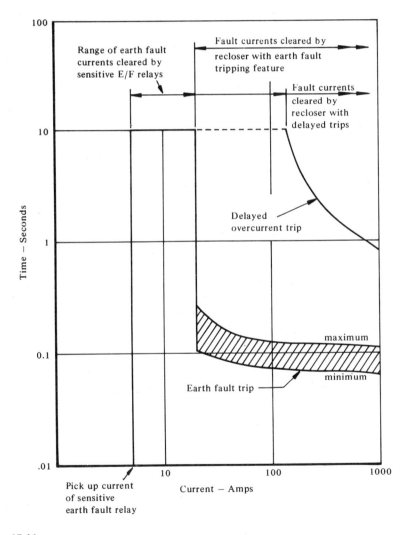

Fig. 15.4A

closing has been achieved and the more recent schemes include an option for selection of autoreclosing following the operation of sensitive earth-fault protection.

Sectionalising devices on overhead lines protected by sensitive earth-fault protection should be of the type which breaks all three phases simultaneously, otherwise the unbalance caused by the sequential opening of individual phases may exceed the set time delay and cause the relay to operate. In some cases, switches are provided in the tripping circuit to render the protection inoperative whilst carrying out switching operations.

15.5   Arc-suppression coils

Prior to the introduction of the unearthed crossarm form of overhead line construction, faults on rural systems were predominantly to earth. To minimise interruptions due to these earth faults some systems were designed to operate with the neutral point unearthed, but it was found that under fault conditions the capacitance currents between the healthy phases and earth were sufficient to permit arcing at the fault position. The capacitance currents were invariably of low magnitude and consequently were difficult to detect by the normal protection. Furthermore the arcing could be prolonged and dangerous overvoltages might occur. Such systems are not now permitted by statute.

To overcome this, the arc-suppression or Petersen coil was introduced. As described in Chapter 1, this takes the form of a reactor connected between the system neutral point and earth, the coil impedance being such that under earth fault conditions the capacitance current to earth of the sound phases is neutralised by the inductive current of the coil. The system line-to-earth capacitance will, of course, vary with the amount of line in service at any one time, and tappings must therefore be provided on the coil to cater for different operating conditions. With a limited number of tappings, however, it is virtually impossible to neutralise exactly the capacitance current for every system combination, and in practice the current at the fault is the difference between the system capacitance and coil currents.

The difference current is normally very small and can be tolerated by the system. If the coil is continuously rated, an earth fault may be allowed to persist for a period sufficient to enable switching operations to be carried out to isolate the faulty section with the minimum loss of supplies. This facility is invaluable where no standby supplies exist, but suffers from some disadvantages. Under earth-fault conditions the voltages to earth of the sound phases of the whole system are raised to the full line-to-line voltage and this increase may cause insulation breakdown on these phases at points on other lines of the system, as indicated in Fig. 15.5.A. The resultant condition is termed a 'cross-country' fault and constitutes a phase-to-phase fault against which the arc-suppression coil is ineffective. For this reason, the transfer of existing networks to arc-suppression coil working is generally done in small sections, as the number of breakdowns of

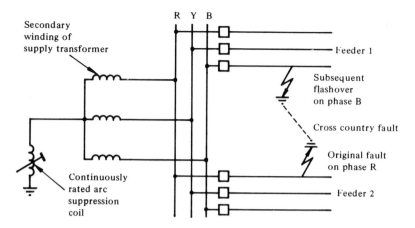

Fig. 15.5A   *Cross-country faults on system protected by an arc-suppression coil*

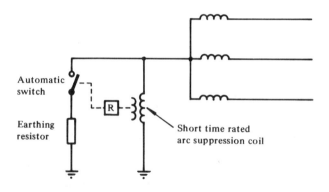

Fig. 15.5B   *Automatic short-circuiting scheme for short time rated arc-suppression coil*

insulation weak spots occurring during a fault is thereby reduced and their location facilitated.

Where alternative supplies are available or the persistence of the voltage increase cannot be tolerated, a short time rated coil fitted with automatic short-circuiting equipment, as in Fig. 15.5.B, may be employed. With this arrangement, if the fault condition persists for more than a few seconds, the system neutral point is automatically connected to earth, either direct or through a resistor in parallel with the coil, thus permitting the passage of sufficient earth-fault current to be detected and the line isolated by the normal feeder protection. In some installations, the short circuit applied to the coil is automatically removed after a time-lag sufficient to permit the isolation of the faulty line. This ensures that the system is without the benefit of the arc-suppression coil for the minimum of time but may lead to the system being overcompensated if the line to earth capacitance current of the isolated faulty feeder is large. To overcome this, coils with automatic tap changing may be employed, but this naturally adds to the cost of the coil.

As an arc-suppression coil is effective for a fault anywhere on the complete system, it is desirable to provide indication of the faulty feeder when the coil is brought into operation. With automatic short circuiting, the tripping of the feeder circuit breaker is a clear indication. Where a continuously rated coil is used, indication of a faulty feeder may be obtained by the use of a wattmetric type relay sufficiently sensitive to detect the small difference currents referred to earlier in this section. To energise such relays, however, it is necessary to provide a voltage transformer on each feeder circuit breaker and the arrangement is therefore costly.

The adjustment or tuning of a coil in relation to the protected system is carried out by applying an earth fault to the system and varying the coil tapping to give maximum voltage across the coil with the normal amount of system connected. The reactance is then reduced slightly to ensure that a reasonable balance will exist when a section of the network is removed for any reason. Some degree of mistuning is permissible without seriously affecting system operation, and for 11 kV systems this tolerance is sufficient to allow sections of networks to be transferred from other substations when necessary to maintain supplies. For systems where frequent variations in length of line connected occur, automatic on-load tuning equipment is available but is normally not considered economic.

When viewed in the light of the amount of line which it may protect, an arc-suppression coil is a comparatively cheap item of equipment. This advantage may be somewhat offset by the cost of strengthening insulation weak spots and the possible transfer of single phase spur lines or line transposition in order to achieve a phase balance of capacitance currents. Its operation is, however, independent of fault current levels and the co-ordination of existing protection is not affected by its use. Statistics indicate that a reduction of some 40% in the number of supply interruptions compared with fuse protected systems is achieved on systems protected by arc-suppression coils, although a greater reduction might be expected on older lines with a greater number of points having earthed metalwork.

15.6   Performance/cost comparison of protective equipment for rural systems

It will be appreciated from the preceding sections of the chapter that in the application of protection to rural systems, the primary function of the clearance of faults is allied to the rapid restoration of supplies. In comparing the performance of various forms of protection available, therefore, some cognizance must be taken of this factor. Unfortunately, in such an assessment, an infallible criterion is difficult to find and the influence of particular local conditions must be weighed.

The quality of rural supplies may be judged in terms of

(*a*)   Interruptions per 100 km of line per annum.

(*b*)   The product of the number of interruptions and the km of line affected per 100 km per annum.

(c)   Total consumer hours lost per annum.
(d)   Consumer hours lost per consumer per annum.

None of these takes into account all the factors which cause irritation or inconvenience to the consumer, such as time of day or a spate of interruptions of supply to a particular consumer, but that of interruption per 100 km per annum is usually most readily available and is therefore most commonly used.

The cost of each form of protection must enter into any comparison which is made between them, and since the amount of network protected by each form varies, the cost per kilometre of line protected may serve as a useful basis. This cost should take into account operating costs such as maintenance charges and cost of fuse replacement, in addition to capital cost, and may well be expressed in terms of total annual charges.

Operating experience with the types of protection covered by this Chapter indicate that the performance figures shown in Table 15.6A may be expected.

Table 15.6A   *Performance figures for various types of protection*

Type of protection		Interruptions per 100 km per annum
H.V. fuses		31
Arc-suppression coils		16
Pole-mounted recloser		2
Substation reclosing circuit breaker	Periodic reclosing	7
	Single-shot high-speed reclosing	3

The significance of these figures should be viewed in the light of the following observations.

(a)   *Fuses:* Individually these call for only a small capital outlay, but for adequate protection of a network a large number may be required. The incidence of a fault requires the replacement of the fuse element and this may involve high labour and transport costs. Deterioration which occurs in service may cause unnecessary supply failures.

(b)   *Arc-suppression coils:* A single coil will protect the whole of the system to which it is connected and it is therefore low in terms of capital cost per mile of line. In addition, very little maintenance is required. It is, however, effective only against single phase-to-earth faults, which amount to some 50% of the total number of faults on overhead lines of unearthed construction, and, in addition, requires that the line insulation be in sound condition in order to withstand transient overvoltages as well as the rise in line-to-earth voltage during fault operation. Some form of remote alarm system is desirable when the coil is installed at an unattended substation.

(c)   *Pole-mounted reclosers:* Each main line of the network requires a separate recloser for protection and, as the capital cost of each installation is some 40% of the cost of an arc-suppression coil, the total cost may be higher than that of a coil protection system. The high degree of protection is provided only on that portion of the line on the side of the recloser remote from the source of supply, and rated current and breaking capacity limitations may restrict the extent of this portion. Nationally, the average length of line protected per recloser installed is of the order of 12 kilometres. The cost of periodical maintenance must be taken into account but, due to the reduced number of supply interruptions with the use of reclosers, system operating costs are greatly reduced.

(d)   *Substation reclosing circuit breakers:* The cost of providing automatic reclosing features on substation circuit breakers is that of additional relay equipment only and is generally but a small percentage of the cost of the circuit breaker itself. There is merit, too, in the fact that such features may also be readily applied to existing switchgear. High-speed tripping may, with considerable advantage, also be provided at low cost.

The use of reclosing circuit breakers affords the benefits of automatic restoration to the whole of the associated feeder in contrast to restrictions imposed by the limited breaking capacity of the pole-mounted recloser. The average length of line protected by substation reclosing circuit breakers is nationally some 20 km per circuit breaker.

Rapid fault clearance combined with automatic reclosing provides the lowest incidence of supply interruptions and, because of its performance, low cost and other advantages, the provision of this feature on substation circuit breakers has considerable advantage.

Multiple reclosure sequences offer some improvement in system performance compared with single-shot schemes and also permit the use of sectionalisers to limit the extent of supplies interrupted. The cost of the sectionaliser at present available is however some two-thirds of that of a recloser and largely on this account they have not been widely used in this country.

Fault passage indicators, whilst greatly facilitating fault location, are generally too expensive to permit their permanent installation in the profusion required to derive their full benefit whilst the portable form involves delay and expense in setting out and collection for each fault location.

The elimination of h.v. fuses from networks utilising automatic reclosing offers economic and operational advantages.

15.7   Primary networks in rural areas

Economic considerations play a large part in the design of the 66 kV and 33 kV primary networks in rural areas. Ring main schemes are commonly employed to afford alternative supplies and use is also made of feeder transformers and teed feeders. Overhead lines are generally supported on wood poles and switchgear is kept to a minimum, single circuit breaker substations being common practice even though involving some loss of operational flexibility.

Pilot channels for protection are seldom available. Sometimes combined with an earthing conductor, they may be carried on the overhead line supports but such circuits are expensive and liable to faults caused by climatic conditions and other external influences. In addition, it is necessary to guard against the effects of induction from the primary conductors.

On some 33 kV systems, particularly those having a predominance of steel tower lines, arc-suppression coils are sometimes used for protection against earth faults. With the increasing use of wood pole unearthed type construction, however, their use is rarely extended to new systems.

On simple ring main systems, current and time graded directional overcurrent and earth-fault protection has been employed for many years. Such protection, however, has long operating times for some types of faults and is limited in application to ring mains having not more than five substations. These limitations together with a general lack of pilot channels for unit schemes, have provided the incentive for the development of the cheaper forms of distance protection incorporating switched measuring elements, as described in Chapter 9.

The protection of feeder transformers has been discussed in Chapter 12 but on rural systems overall schemes utilising pilots are rarely used for the reasons stated above. Instead simpler forms of protection are usually employed. One such scheme for a single circuit is shown in Fig. 15.7A. At the source end of the line the circuit breaker is equipped with instantaneous earth-fault and inverse definite minimum time overcurrent relays, the latter incorporating high-set instantaneous elements. The rapid clearance of line faults by the use of relays without time lags minimises damage at the fault point and consequently increases the possibility of successful reclosure of the circuit breaker.

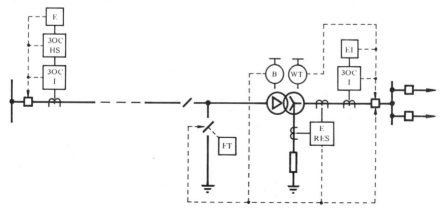

Fig. 15.7A   *Scheme of protection for single feeder transformer*

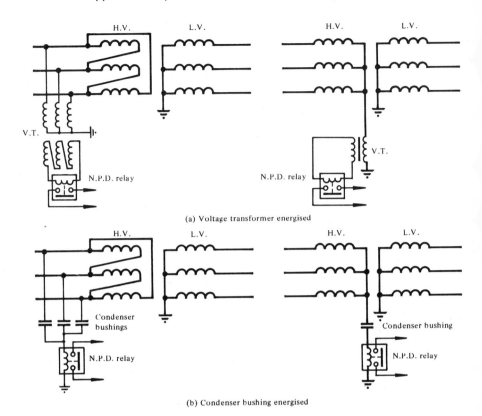

(a) Voltage transformer energised

(b) Condenser bushing energised

Fig. 15.7B   *Neutral point displacement protection*

Faults on the h.v. winding of the transformer are detected by the protection at the source end whilst restricted earth-fault protection is applied to the secondary winding. In addition, overcurrent and earth-fault protection is fitted on the secondary side to guard against busbar faults or the failure of circuit breakers to clear faults on the outgoing feeders. Protection against interturn and other internal faults which cause gas evolution is provided by a Buchholz gas and oil relay.

As an alternative the transformer may be protected by an overall scheme, but such an arrangement requires current transformers on the h.v. side, usually accommodated in the terminal bushing turrets.

Intertripping of the source circuit breaker is necessary on the occurrence of a transformer fault, and this is accomplished by a fault throwing switch connected between one phase and earth or, in the case of arc-suppression coil systems, between two phases. The fault throwing switch is closed on the operation of the transformer protection by an electrically released manually charged spring mechanism and will ensure the tripping of the remote h.v. circuit breaker.

Where duplicate feeder transformers afford supplies to a substation, similar schemes of protection to those used for single units may be applied. An earth fault on the line, however, will cause the appropriate circuit breaker at the source end to

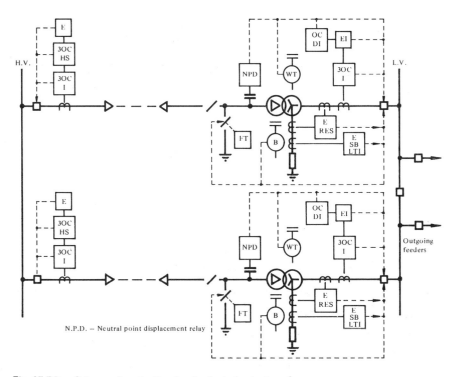

Fig. 15.7C   *Scheme of protection for duplicate feeder transformers*

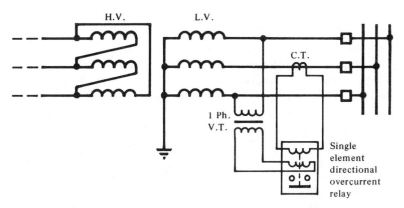

Fig. 15.7D   *Single element directional overcurrent relay for protection of duplicate feeder transformer*

trip but the fault will still be back-fed through the transformer. Since the neutral point of the transformer h.v. winding is not usually earthed, the voltage to earth of the two healthy lines will rise to the full line-to-line voltage. This condition may be detected, and the transformer l.v. circuit breaker tripped, by the use of neutral point displacement protection at the receiving end. This form

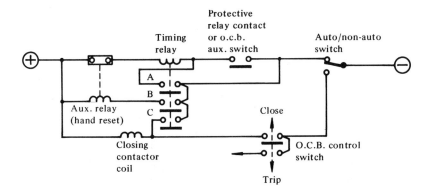

Fig. 15.7E   *Simple nonrepetitive single-shot reclosing scheme*

of protection uses a relay connected to respond to a residual voltage, the relay being energised by a voltage transformer or condenser bushings, the latter method being somewhat cheaper. The arrangements for differing transformer connections are shown in Fig. 15.7B. A time-lag relay having a setting of approximately 5s is normally employed in conjunction with the neutral displacement detecting relay to prevent operation when faults occur on other sections of the network. A typical scheme for the protection of duplicate feeder transformers is shown in Fig. 15.7C.

Another form of protection which has been successfully employed experimentally to bring about tripping under the condition described above uses a sensitive reverse power relay to detect the reverse magnetising current of the transformer. With modern transformers utilising cold rolled steel cores, however, the loss and magnetising currents are very small and special relays and current transformers may be necessary. Compensation for phase angle errors on the current transformers may be required and is provided as an integral part of the relay, this feature being cut-out during heavy through fault currents. The application of this scheme is generally limited to unteed parallel feeder transformers since tees introduce the possibility of incorrect operation.

Protection against the back-feeding of phase-to-phase faults occurring on the lines of duplicate feeder transformers may be afforded by directional overcurrent protection installed on the lower voltage side of the transformer. For this purpose the 30° relay connection is unsatisfactory and the 90° (or 90° minus 45°) connection should be used. Where the transformers are delta/star connected, a single-element relay, connected as shown in Fig. 15.7D, may be employed for this purpose since a phase/phase fault on the delta side will produce a 2:1:1 current distribution on the secondary side. (See Chapter 12).

The principles of automatic circuit reclosing discussed in Section 15.3.1 apply equally to rural 33 kV and 66 kV systems. Feeder circuit breakers on such systems are therefore generally fitted with reclosing facilities, usually of the nonrepetitive single shot type, that is the type in which only one reclosing operation is provided, lock out of the circuit breaker occurring on subsequent tripping. For this purpose

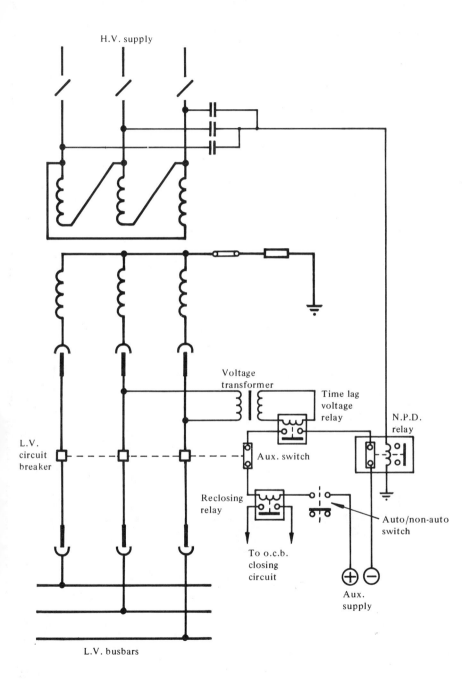

Fig. 15.7F   *Initiation of circuit breaker reclosing by voltage relay*

a simple reclosing scheme may be used, a typical example being shown in Fig. 15.7E.

The use of automatic reclosing features permits the use of instantaneous protection in addition to the more usual i.d.m.t. forms, as described in Section 15.3.4 and such schemes are being increasingly used on rural primary systems. As a result, fault damage is minimised and the number of prolonged interruptions of supply due to line faults is reduced.

With some control arrangements it is necessary to reclose automatically the circuit breakers on the lower voltage side of some system transformers. This should

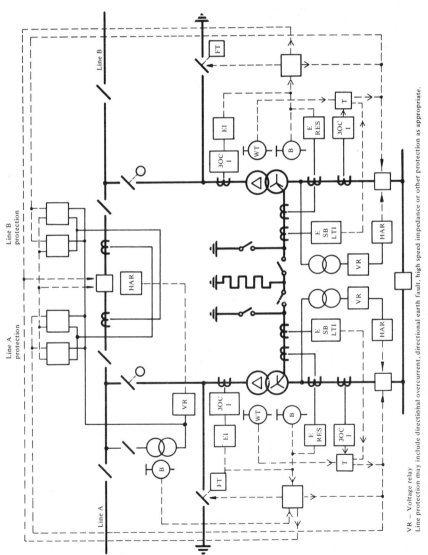

VR — Voltage relay
Line protection may include directional overcurrent, directional earth fault, high speed impedance or other protection as appropriate.

Fig. 15.7G   *Block diagram of single circuit breaker substation*

only be carried out if the primary circuit is healthy, consequently the reclosing feature is initiated by a voltage relay energised from a voltage transformer on the secondary side of the main transformer. A typical scheme is shown in Fig. 15.7F.

Extensive use is made of automatic reclosing in a single circuit breaker substation, the schematic diagram of which is shown in Fig. 15.7G. In considering the functioning of this scheme, let it be assumed that line A is normally the incoming supply, whilst line B is the outgoing supply to an adjacent substation. A fault on line A is cleared by the tripping of the local and remote h.v. circuit breakers together with the intertripping of transformer A lower voltage circuit breaker to prevent a back feed to the fault. The line is subsequently re-energised by the automatic reclosing of the remote breaker and this is then followed by the reclosing of the local h.v. circuit breaker if the voltage relay controlling the reclosing feature of this breaker remains energised for a period exceeding its time-lag setting. This time-lag is set to a value in excess of the operating time of the protection at the remote end of the line so that on persistent fault no reclosing of the local breaker occurs. The automatic reclosing of the transformer lower voltage circuit breaker is governed by restoration of supply to the transformer as mentioned in the previous paragraph.

Operation of the scheme in the event of a fault on line B is similar to that described above, except that the local h.v. circuit breaker recloses automatically after a predetermined time lag without voltage restoration control. It thus acts to clear persistent faults on the outgoing feeder in a manner similar to that in which the circuit breaker at the remote end of line A clears such faults on that line.

On transformer faults the transformer protection is arranged to trip the local h.v. and appropriate transformer l.v. circuit-breakers and to close the fault-throwing switch to ensure the tripping of the remote h.v. circuit breaker. After a time-lag sufficient to ensure operation of this latter circuit breaker, the faulty transformer is isolated by the opening of the power operated disconnector, following which the local and remote h.v. circuit breakers are reclosed automatically.

15.8 Bibliography

Regulations
Overhead line Regulations, HMSO

Articles
'Line protection by Petersen coils' by H Willott Taylor and P F Stritzl (*J.IEE* 82, page 387, April 1938)
'Automatic circuit reclosers' by Peirson, Pollard and Care (*J.IEE*, 102 Pt.A, (6), 1955)
'Auto-reclosing switchgear in distribution practice' by S H Money and J Harris (*Proc. IEE*, 115, (2), 1968)
'Discrimination with expulsion fuse switches' (*Elec. Times*, January 1962)

'High speed reclosing on 11 kV rural networks' by S H Money (*Elec. Times*, 18 June 1959)
'High speed tripping and reclosing on rural networks' by S H Money (*Elec. Times*, 15 & 22 June 1961)

Reports
'Arc suppression coils and auto-reclosing switchgear', The Electricity Council, (DRP Report No. 1, 1962)
'Report on standardisation of auto-reclosing facilities on 11 kV ground mounted metalclad distribution switchgear', The Electricity Council, (ACE Report No.11, 1966)
'Lightning protection of distribution networks', The Electricity Council, (Report Ref. ECR/R 566, 1972)
'Report on auto-reclosing schemes for 11 kV distribution networks The Electricity Council (ACE Report No. 54, 1977)

Chapter 16

The application of protection to urban and metropolitan systems

by K.A.J.Coates

16.1 Introduction

In the early days of electricity supply, many small generating stations supplied their own local areas and there was little interconnection. As the load grew, larger stations were built and transmission networks were superimposed which interconnected the larger stations and augmented supplies to areas where the local generation was inadequate. A complex system of generation, transmission and distribution evolved having a variety of different voltage levels for generation and transmission, although distribution was usually at 6·6 kV or 11 kV. Much of this still exists but with the siting of new stations away from large concentrations of population and the introduction of 275 kV and 400 kV transmission a new pattern is emerging. Typically, energy will be received at a 400 kV supergrid point where it will be transformed down and distributed by systems operating at 132 kV and 33 kV to primary substations which in turn will transform to 11 kV. At the higher load densities, for example, in city centres there are economic advantages in having only one system level between 400 kV and 11 kV and if the 33 kV level is dispensed with, as may be the case, the whole system needs only two stages of transformation namely 400/132 kV and 132/11 kV.

At the higher system levels, the units, e.g. transformers, busbars, cable circuits, are large and repair and replacement times are lengthy. Failures at this level tend to affect large numbers of consumers for long periods. To safeguard against such extensive outages, plant and circuits are duplicated and usually operate in parallel. Protection is required to identify correctly and initiate the disconnection of any faulty unit at the same time remaining stable against faults at lower system levels for which other protection exists. The provision of adequate, often complex, protection at high system levels is expensive but its cost is usually a small percentage of the capital value of the main plant.

At the lower system levels the units become progressively more numerous, duplication ceases, fewer consumers are supplied until finally only the consumers' service remains to be protected. To correspond with these conditions the protection becomes simpler and cheaper but must remain reliable so that the scale of servicing involved is contained within reasonable limits.

Economic considerations demand attention to the fault susceptibility of the various classes of equipment and if faults are rare then only minimal protection may be justified and some risks accepted. Protection at some other point is then relied upon to give disconnection.

Protection may be necessary to comply with an explicit or implied statutory requirement; the provision of protection on a consumer's service is a requirement under the Electricity Supply Regulations.

Although the primary function of protection is usually to minimise loss of supply due to faults it may also be valuable in reducing damage to capital plant by limiting fault current duration.

Thus the extent and type of protection afforded at any point may depend upon a number of factors. The availability of comprehensive fault statistics enables fault probabilities to be calculated which serve as a guide to the value of protection at a particular point on a system. Because protection affects the way in which a system operates under fault conditions it is rarely that protection arrangements can be assessed in isolation from broader system design considerations, however.

16.2   Characteristics of urban and metropolitan areas

Towns and cities usually have a concentration of commercial premises at the centre, surrounded by predominantly residential areas which in turn merge with surrounding semi-rural areas. Industrial premises may be present, scattered in small pockets or concentrated in a particular area.

Typically, the distribution system comprises a 415/240 V network supplied from 11kV/415/240V substations with a capacity ranging from 300 kVA to 1000 kVA. 11kV feeders each supplying perhaps a dozen such substations, emanate from primary substations which in turn may be supplied at 33 kV, 66 kV or 132 kV. In these primary substations there are usually two or more transformers ranging in capacity from 5 MVA to 60 MVA. This type of distribution system commonly supplies the whole range of load densities from, say, 100 MW/km^2 in the centre of the largest cities to the 5-12 MW/km^2 typical of residential areas down to the much lower densities of semirural areas. At the highest load densities substations may be only 30m apart compared with 200m apart in residential areas. In the latter areas voltage regulation in the 415/240 V network may affect the spacing of substations, a consideration which does not apply in the high density areas where spacing is determined entirely by the load and substation transformer capacity.

In the central areas substations are of necessity often situated in the premises of the larger consumers. As an alternative to 415/240V supply, some large consumers may be afforded supply at 11kV but this arrangement is more common where the load is industrial. The 415/240V and 11kV distribution is carried out almost invariably by underground cable.

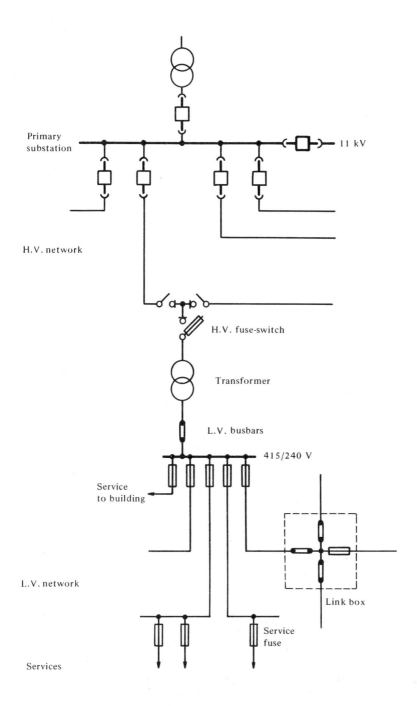

Fig. 16.3A *Elements of a distribution network*

16.3   Distribution system protection – radial l.v. systems

The elements of a distribution system are shown in Fig. 16.3A, and will be used to discuss the protection aspects.

16.3.1   Services

The first part of the distribution system to be protected is the service cable, and this is achieved by a service fuse at the termination of the Board's service cable on the consumer's property. For special reasons this may take the form of a circuit breaker, but in the majority of cases the best and cheapest protection is a high breaking capacity (h.b.c.) fuse. Usually, the size of the fuse should be related to the current-carrying capacity of the service cable and not to the load applied for or taken by the consumer.

16.3.2   L.V. cables

The cables which make up the l.v. distribution network require protection against faults and it is common practice to fit cartridge fuses in the phase conductors of each outgoing cable at the l.v. busbar in the substation. Fuses may also be inserted in the underground network at cable junctions where link boxes exist.

In choosing the size of fuse the following three points need to be taken into consideration, bearing in mind that they are not always compatible and a compromise is often necessary.

(*a*)   The fuse provides protection for overcurrent as a result of faults and not overload. Overloads can occur on distribution cables through increasing demands, but these are unlikely to be of such a magnitude that they cannot be carried safely for several hours without damaging the cable. Overloads can also occur through alteration due to load transfers, and in these cases the increase in load may be much greater. Nevertheless there is still an interval of time before the cable may be damaged. The size of fuse must be chosen so that it does not blow at times of peak load, but at the same time safeguards the cable against overcurrent due to breakdown of insulation. The size of fuse is therefore chosen more in relation to the short-term rating of the cable than the size of the load. Thus a cable considered appropriate for a 300A load could be fused with a 600A or 800A fuse. A further factor which needs to be considered is the degree of discrimination which should be obtained between the l.v. fuse on this cable and the protection on the transformer in the substation.

(*b*)   Faults on the consumer's premises which are not cleared by the consumer's own fuses or which occur between the Board's cutout (fuse) and the consumer's fuses, must be cleared by the Board's fuse, and therefore the fuse at the substation or in the network must be such as to discriminate with the largest fuse in the

Board's cutout.

It should be noted here that the remark made previously, that is that the size of fuse in the Board's cutout should be related to the current-carrying capacity of the service cable, requires no modification by the points made above. That is to say, where the distribution cable and service cable are of the same size, the fuse on the distribution cable should be the larger. This fact will help discrimination.

(c) The minimum fusing current of the fuse must be less than the minimum earth-fault current. This is often difficult to achieve when the density of the load is low, or in distribution systems where the size of distributor is chosen to suit the current at every point (that is a tree or tapered system), and therefore where the conductors become smaller and smaller as the distances from the source become longer.

In order to ensure that an earth fault at the end of a long length of small section cable is cleared, a fuse could be used in a link box where the cables are joined, the fuse rating being chosen to discriminate with a larger fuse further back in the network. Fuses can also be used in this way in an attempt to improve the continuity of supply by trying to limit the number of consumers which will be without supply in the event of a cable fault.

16.3.3 Substation transformers

Consider now the protection of the transformers in the substation. Due to their large number, the relative unimportance of each unit to the system as a whole, their good record of reliability, and the high percentage cost of giving complete protection, economics play a large part in determining the type of protection to be used.

In the simple case of a single transformer, plain h.v. fuse protection is the cheapest, but careful consideration must be given to the choice of fuses. In urban areas it is not unusual to give a supply to a single consumer in the order of 250 kVA at 415/240 V. While it might be felt desirable to supply such loads direct from separate substations, this is not always economical or practicable, and they will have to be supplied from the 415/240 V networks. For such a load, the service fuse should be rated at 400 A, which necessitates an 800 A fuse on the outgoing distributor at the substation in order to maintain a ratio of 2.

On an 11kV system, the ratio of transformation would be something under 25, and therefore to maintain a ratio of 2 with an l.v. fuse rating of 800 A, the h.v. fuse rating should not be less than 64 A. The discrimination which would be produced by such an arrangement is illustrated in Fig. 16.3.3A which shows typical curves for the fuses mentioned. The curves used, however, must be those for the actual fuses employed. It must be remembered that the reactance and size of the transformer sets an upper limit to the prospective l.v. fault current, and that any impedance in the fault itself will further reduce this current. There is no point in trying to achieve discrimination at currents greater than those likely to be found in practice.

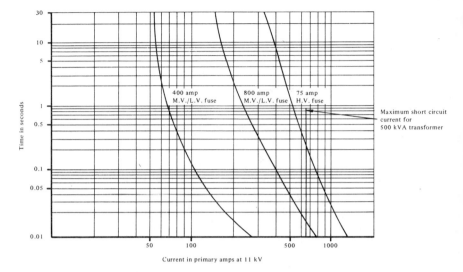

Fig. 16.3.3A   *Typical fuse characteristic for discrimination*

No mention has yet been made of relationship between the size of the h.v. fuse and the size of the transformer, but in considering this aspect it must be remembered that simple fuse protection may give little or no protection for earth faults at the middle of the h.v. winding and that, as the ratio of the size of fuse to full load current increases, less of the winding is covered for earth faults.

Furthermore, fuse protection is not intended to guard against overcurrents due to overloading of the transformer, but primarily against overcurrents due to faults. These facts, coupled with a limited choice of h.v. fuses, makes for a certain lack of relationship between the full load current of a transformer and the rating of the h.v. fuse.

In the UK, the ratings of h.v. and l.v. fuses appropriate to the various sizes of distribution transformers in use have been standardised and an Electricity Supply Industry Standard No. 12-8 deals comprehensively with this subject.

Where economic considerations justify a greater degree of protection, then the single transformer can be protected by a circuit breaker with overcurrent and earth-fault protection. If relays are used instead of direct-acting trip coils, then the protection can be set more accurately, but this introduces the problem of providing the necessary source of supply for tripping the circuit breaker. If only two-pole overcurrent relays are installed, the setting must be chosen to ensure that the relay will operate for a phase-to-phase fault on the secondary side of a delta star transformer which produces a 2:1:1 distribution of current in the primary circuit. Whatever the type of protection chosen for a substation transformer it is necessary to bear in mind that it is required to operate and clear the fault before operation of the protection on the outgoing feeder at the primary substation from which it is fed.

When two transformers feed a common busbar, steps may need to be taken to ensure discrimination when the healthy transformer feeds the faulty transformer through the l.v. side. In such a case neither fuses nor overcurrent and earth-fault relays will provide this discrimination and furthermore circuit breakers must be provided on both the h.v. and l.v. sides of the transformers. The protection of two such transformers could take five forms:

(a) Suitable unit protection, for example Merz-Price, which will provide discrimination for phase and earth faults on both sides of the transformers.

(b) Overcurrent and earth fault on the primary side, restricted earth fault on the secondary side, and intertripping, which will provide discrimination for earth faults on both sides of the transformer.

(c) H.V. and l.v. overcurrent and Buchholz, which will provide discrimination for faults inside the transformers.

(d) Overcurrent and earth fault on the primary side, directional protection on the secondary side, and intertripping, which will provide discrimination for phase and earth faults on both sides of the transformers.

(e) Frame leakage, Buchholz, h.v. overcurrent and intertripping which will provide discrimination for internal faults and earth faults on both sides of the transformers.

In practice, in radial l.v. systems, transformers are rarely operated in parallel on a common l.v. busbar because their failure rate is not high enough to justify the cost of the additional switchgear and protection equipment involved.

. The question of whether to apply unit busbar protection to either the l.v. or h.v. busbars cannot be seriously considered. The cost is out of all proportion to the risk of failures and the small advantage to be gained by installing it.

16.3.4   H.V. cables

For the protection of the h.v. cable feeding the substations, the same considerations apply as in the case of the protection of the substation transformer. If there is only one h.v. cable and the possibility of back-feed need not be considered, then plain overcurrent and earth-fault protection at the main substation is sufficient. If the h.v. cable is run either directly or indirectly in parallel with other h.v. cables, some form of unit or directional protection is necessary.

Again, the relatively heavy cost of providing protection in such circumstances has to be considered, and therefore a layout is often chosen which avoids h.v. cables running in parallel, yet gives facilities for alternative means of supply. Such a layout uses ring mains, as illustrated in Fig. 16.3.4A and the ring is normally open at a convenient point. Under such circumstances the protection at the main substation would again be overcurrent and earth fault. The setting of the earth fault relay should be as low as possible consistent with sufficient discrimination against the earth-fault relays or fuses for the transformers in the substations. The overcurrent setting should be as high as possible consistent with the size of cable and its short-term rating, as already described in connection with fuses for l.v. cables, and provide discrimination with relays closer to the source of supply.

If grading with overcurrent and earth-fault protection at the primary substation is possible, there is advantage in installing similar protection at a point on the ring midway between the primary substation and the normally open point. For those consumers nearer the primary substation this gives a probability of a 50% reduction

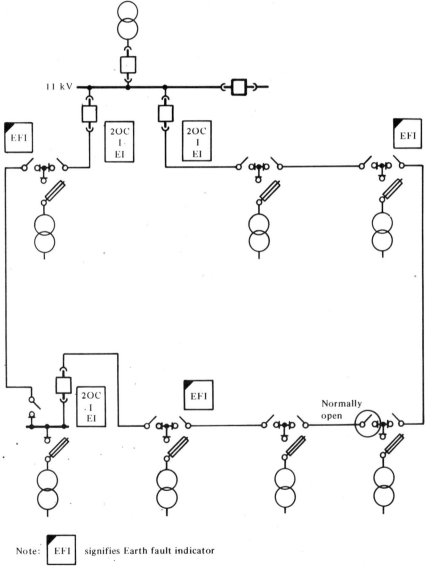

Note: EFI   signifies Earth fault indicator

Fig. 16.3.4A   *H.V. ring main system*

in outage time for h.v. faults.

When a fault occurs on an h.v. cable in a radially operated ring main system substations are shut down until the fault is located and supply is restored by resectioning.

The process of fault location is facilitated if earth-fault indicators are installed at appropriate points on the network as shown in Fig. 16.3.4A. The majority of faults are earth faults, or commence as earth faults before changing to phase faults, and as such can be detected by a core-balance current transformer fitted over the h.v. cable. The current transformer operates an attracted armature type relay having a manually reset flag indicator. Inspection of the indicators immediately after a fault enables the extent of the path of earth-fault current to be determined, leading to quicker identification of the faulty cable section. The relay has a brief time delay to prevent response to transient unbalance and is sensitive to earth fault currents of 50A or more in the main conductors. It is usually necessary to ensure that the flux due to earth-fault current in the phase conductor is not nullified by the return of the same current, in reverse direction, in the cable sheath. The electrical continuity of the cable sheath is therefore broken, usually at the point at which the current transformer is fitted. Successful use of this particular indicator is dependent upon all indicators being reset soon after the event in readiness for any future fault. An alternative type is available with an automatic voltage operated reset feature. The voltage source is the l.v. supply in the substation in which the device is installed and resetting therefore takes place at the instant when l.v. supplies are restored.

If it is essential to maintain a firm supply on a given busbar under fault conditions on one of the feeding circuits, two or more h.v. cables must be run in parallel to these busbars, each suitably equipped with protection to ensure discrimination and automatic isolation of the faulty cable. In general, the distances are short in urban networks, and therefore a unit protection scheme with pilot wires can be used.

An h.v. network which affords firm supplies to four substations in this way is shown in Fig. 16.3.4B. Each cable circuit is equipped with unit protection using a pilot wire system, thus there are a total of seven protected zones. A fault in any protected zone causes tripping of the circuit breakers at each end; the affected cable is lost but supply is maintained by the other cables. It is necessary to ensure that the different current distribution after a fault at any point on the network, does not give rise to overloads.

The method affords effective protection against cable faults but there are other effects which need to be taken into consideration. At each substation the protected zone extends only to the point on the main circuit conductors at which the current transformers are installed, so that the busbar, switchgear and most of its internal connections are outside the zone. There is a possibility of pilots being open-circuited, a trip circuit failure or failure of a circuit breaker to trip for mechanical reasons. A cable fault coupled with failure of the unit protection, or a switchgear fault, are similar in that they can only be cleared by circuit breakers further back in the system, resulting in the loss of all supplies to the network under consideration. Although this could be alleviated by the provision of additional safeguards, e.g.

directional protection, busbar protection, pilot-monitoring etc., the cost of such additional equipment is difficult to justify and the method usually adopted is to install overcurrent and earth fault i.d.m.t. relays at selected points to sectionalise the network and limit the extent of outage. In Fig. 16.3.4B, the i.d.m.t. relay

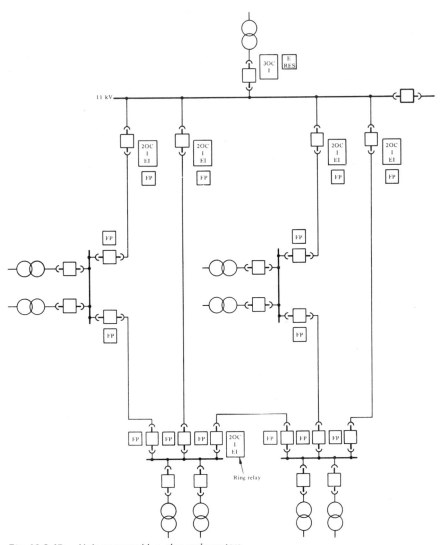

Fig. 16.3.4B   *Unit-protected h.v. ring main system*

installed in the ring separates the network into two groups each of two feeders and only one group is shut down for the type of fault under consideration.

The shut down of the group involves operation of a total of three relays, two on the feeders at the primary substation and the ring relay. Until the fault is cleared by operation of all three relays, fault current is sustained by the transformer at the primary substation which will be tripped if its relay operating time is exceeded. It is instructive to consider how faults at different positions affect the operating sequence of the three network relays and the total clearance time. If a fault occurs in a feeder cable-box at the primary substation virtually the whole of the fault current will flow directly through its own circuit breaker which trips at the relay setting. The fault current path is then via the other three circuits, feeding the fault from the remote end. The fault is now seen by a total of four relays, the three on the feeders plus the ring sectionalising relay. If the feeder impedances are roughly similar and the ring sectionalising relay has a lower time setting it will be the first to trip thus cutting off fault current in two feeders. The remaining feeder is the only circuit now feeding the fault and its relay operates to complete the fault clearing sequence. The total fault clearance time is therefore a combination of fully sequential and simultaneous relay operating times. By comparison, a fault at the remote end of the network, say on the busbars at a substation, produces significant current in all relays simultaneously. The ring sectionalising relay will be the first to operate thereby clearing the fault from two feeders and final clearance comes when the two remaining feeder relays have both operated. Under these circumstances the total clearance time will be different from the previous case and almost certainly shorter.

With paralleled feeder networks, therefore, the position of the fault has a pronounced effect upon the relay operating sequence and it is necessary to find the condition which gives the maximum total clearance time. This is done by selecting a fault position, performing network analysis to ascertain fault current distribution, calculating relay operating times to find the first relay to operate and how far the others have moved toward their operating points. The network condition after the first relay has operated is then analysed to ascertain the revised current distribution and relay calculations performed again to ascertain the next relay to operate and so on until the fault is cleared. The whole process is then repeated for faults at different positions until the maximum total clearance time has been established. The operating time of the transformer protection at the primary substation must then discriminate with the maximum total clearance time.

The calculations are not so onerous as would appear because the factors contributing towards the longest time become apparent after only a few fault positions have been tried. Overcurrent and earth fault relays need to be considered as two separate groups. Phase faults appear throughout the system as overcurrent and as a result all overcurrent relays are involved in the time grading considerations. The maximum time delay is fixed by protection considerations on the primary substation transformer and the minimum by the necessity to discriminate with protection on any distribution transformer. The preferred minimum discrimination interval of 0·4s between stages usually severely limits the number of stages that can be employed between the upper limit at the primary substation and the lower limit at the distribution substation. Because earth-fault current does not appear as such throughout the entire system there are usually fewer stages of earth-fault protection to be graded between upper and lower limits and no difficulties arise.

The method of affording firm supplies using unit protection by pilots with back-up overcurrent and earth-fault protection has the merit of relative simplicity and is economic if the pilots are laid with the main cables. A number of other arrangements have been used. Unit protection by pilots may be modified to include the switchgear busbars in the protected zone so that each successive protected zone overlaps the next to this extent. As a result back-up protection is no longer required to cope with busbar faults but other risks, such as pilot circuit failure, remain. Time graded directional schemes as described in Chapter 2 eliminate the pilot difficulty, are responsive to busbar faults and other failures but require a source of polarising voltage usually derived from voltage transformers which add to switchgear costs. Distance protection is inapplicable to high density urban distribution because of difficulty in achieving sensitivity to the short distances involved and again a voltage source is necessary.

16.3.5   Primary substations

Primary substations are the points in the system where supply is received at e.h.v., transformed to h.v. and fed via busbars and circuit breakers to the h.v. distribution network. The h.v. distribution voltage commonly in use in the United Kingdom is 11kV; at e.h.v. the voltages are typically 33kV, 66kV or 132kV, the trend being towards 132kV. There are usually two or more transformers ranging in size from about 5 MVA to 60 MVA, the very large transformers having double secondary windings to limit the fault level on the 11kV side and the normal current rating of the lower voltage switchgear to an economic value. In addition to the variety of voltages and transformer capacities in use there are variations in the method of neutral earthing, the arrangement of busbars and the facilities for voltage control. There may be local e.h.v. switchgear controlling the transformers and possibly other circuits or the transformers may be controlled by remote e.h.v. switchgear in which case each transformer and its associated e.h.v. cable is known as a transformer feeder. The running arrangement is usually with pairs of transformers in parallel to afford a firm supply to the 11kV busbar but schemes of separate transformer running arrangements exist under which loss of supply to a section of 11kV busbar is restored by coupling automatically to a healthy section.

The requirements of the protective gear are primarily:

(*a*)   to clear a faulty 11kV feeder from the system before higher level protection operates,

(*b*)   to clear a faulty transformer or transformer feeder before the protection of any parallel healthy circuit operates and before any higher level protection operates,

(*c*)   to limit the effect of busbar faults on other parts of the system.

In addition to these primary requirements there is a secondary requirement to limit the effect of the failure of a particular part of the protective system to operate.

Requirements (*a*) and (*b*) are clear cut, but (*c*) poses problems as to the extent of the provision to be made against busbar faults. At one extreme it may be argued that busbar faults are rare and that provided higher level outage is protected against then only a single busbar with a nonauto section switch between transformer positions, is justified. On the other hand the magnitude of an outage, with possibly lengthy restoration time may be considered as justifying a duplicate busbar arrangement with unit protected sections. As one might expect, an arrangement somewhere between these two extremes is usually adopted but the busbar arrangement may not rest on security considerations alone.

The various schemes of protection appropriate to primary substations are dealt with in detail in Chapters 12 and 13.

16.4   Distribution system protection – interconnected l.v. systems

Various interconnected l.v. systems are in use in large cities in this country and abroad and such systems involve protection considerations over and above those of a radial system.

Interconnected l.v. systems are particularly suited to city distribution because the l.v. cables required to supply the load naturally form a practically continuous grid over large areas. Thus the substations which supply such a network may easily be operated in parallel through the l.v. network via solid links or cartridge fuses. There are savings in both capital and running costs. The savings take place because, to a greater degree than on a radial network, an interconnected network couples

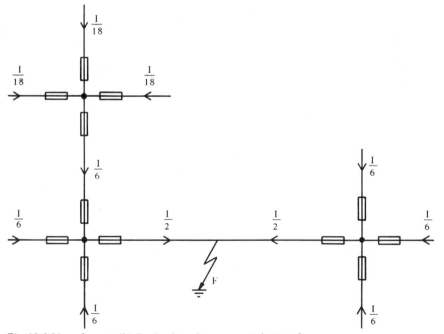

Fig. 16.4.1A   *Current distribution in an interconnected network*

together the loads virtually all of which have some diversity one with another. Thus the maximum demand supplied by the transformers is less and fewer are required or their capacity is less. The percentage loading of transformers tends to equalise because they are effectively in parallel, giving the condition for minimum copper loss and since the total transformer capacity is reduced the total iron loss is less. Losses in the l.v. network are also reduced because cables are fed from both ends and because the number of parallel paths is increased.

The other important feature of interconnected l.v. systems is the generally adopted practice of coupling together the l.v. networks supplied from substations on different h.v. feeders and arranging that the l.v. network is immune to the loss of a single h.v. feeder, the load being taken up on the remaining feeders in the same group. This is a valuable advantage because the greatest single cause of loss of supply to consumers is h.v. feeder faults.

16.4.1   The l.v. network

There are variations in the method of dealing with the l.v. network. Fig. 16.4.1A shows a fully fused arrangement, cartridge fuses being fitted in the phase conductors at all link boxes. If the fault current distribution followed the ideal pattern shown the fuses would discriminate and only those at each end of the faulty distributor would operate. In practice irregularities in the pattern of impedances between junctions upset the distribution of fault current and unwanted fuse operations takes place. This situation is complicated by a further effect which is that some faults clear themselves leaving fuses intact, particularly with the larger size of fuse. The form of construction of the cable, the conductor material and the prospective fault current all have a bearing upon the probability of fault self-clearance. If all these factors are favourable then very nearly all faults will clear which leads to the proposition that the fuses are unnecessary, or relatively so. On this basis some interconnected l.v. systems have operated with large blocks of load solidly interconnected, ultimate disconnection for a non self-clearing fault resting upon l.v. protective gear at the substations. A disadvantage of this degree of solid interconnection is that there are operational difficulties in restoration after a non-self-clearing fault. Between the two extremes of fully fused and solidly interconnected arrangements there are hybrid schemes which perform well.

16.4.2   Substations

In an interconnected l.v. system, the transformers are effectively connected in parallel across the h.v. and l.v. networks and any faulty unit is required to be rapidly isolated from both networks. The usual protection considerations for the parallel operation of transformers apply and it follows that protection is required to interrupt quickly the backfeed to a faulty transformer from the l.v. network. Although unit protection of the transformer could be employed, economic considerations favour the use of directional protection on the l.v. side because this protection is responsive also to the back-feed current from the l.v. network to an h.v. cable fault. L.V. protection for faults in the forward direction, e.g. on the l.v. network, is usually by direct-acting trips shunted by time fuses, the switchgear being in the form of an air circuit breaker.

Protection on the h.v. side of the transformer is required to respond to internal faults and faults on the h.v. and l.v. connections. This requirement may be met in different ways. If the loss of an h.v. feeder due to a transformer fault is an accepted risk then local protection can be omitted, reliance being placed upon the feeder protection at the primary substation to give fault clearance. With such an arrangement however there is difficulty in discriminating between the current due to heavy load on the feeder and that due to a fault on the l.v. side of a transformer. Local protection of the transformer overcomes this difficulty and at the same time enables sensitive earth-fault protection to be provided economically for the transformer primary. The switchgear is usually an oil circuit breaker and the protection is by direct acting trips with a time fuse delay for overcurrent faults and instantaneous operation for earth faults, the latter having a sufficiently low setting to protect the whole of the primary winding. An intertrip to the l.v. circuit breaker ensures that the l.v. back-feed is broken when the h.v. circuit breaker operates. H.V. fusegear is a possible alternative to the h.v. circuit breaker, again with an intertrip to the l.v. circuit breaker, but this does not provide the sensitive earth-fault protection.

16.4.3 The h.v. network

It is usual for the h.v. network supplying an interconnected l.v. network to comprise a group of from four to eight h.v. feeders, each feeder operated radially and supplying typically about ten 500kVA substations. There may be provision for coupling feeders together at their extremities and elsewhere to the extent that if a section of h.v. cables is lost due to fault, supply to all substations may be restored by switching. Alternatively, such coupling facilities may be absent in which case supply to an area which has suffered the loss of an h.v. feeder can only be maintained through the interconnected l.v. network. A disadvantage of this arrangement is that a fault at the primary substation end of a feeder may impose undue stress on the l.v. network since the latter is required to support the whole of the load of the feeder until the fault is located and repaired.

As an alternative to radial operation and at a rather higher capital cost, feeders may be equipped with unit protection and operated in parallel. Supply to substations is then firm against any single h.v. cable fault and under this condition load is not required to be supported through the l.v. network, other than that due to the loss of a substation transformer.

The h.v. network may be interleaved or blocked. In an ideal interleaved network, the h.v. cables are routed so that neighbouring substations are supplied from different feeders. In a blocked network one feeder supplies a number of neighbouring substations which is termed a block and this block adjoins blocks supplied by other feeders. If the number of substations in a block is small then typically the number of blocks is large and the blocks may be interleaved, giving a distributed block arrangement. Interleaving reduces the burden of current across the l.v. network which occurs under feeder outage conditions.

16.4.4   Protection on a distributed block l.v. interconnected system

Fig. 16.4.4A shows a distributed block system supplied from a group of four 11kV feeders fed from one section of busbar at a primary substation. Each feeder on leaving the primary substation supplies an l.v. interconnected block through four substations and this block is coupled to similar blocks on other feeders each by four sets of fuses, termed fringe fuses. The feeder then continues to a more remote area where it supplies another interconnected block similarly arranged. The diagram shows a totally symmetrical formation for simplicity of presentation but a number of variations are possible. For example, any feeder may supply more than two blocks and the number of transformers feeding a block may be more or less than four; this in turn affects the number of fringe fuses between blocks. The extent to which such variations may exist is determined by a full knowledge of how the network operates under various fault conditions but, in general, symmetry and uniformity ease protection discrimination considerations. Although not shown in the diagram the configuration of the l.v. network is frequently such as to allow direct fusing between diagonally opposite blocks, e.g. A1 and C1, thereby improving the uniformity of loading when a feeder is lost due to fault.

Three features of the way in which the network is required to operate under fault conditions may be noted at this stage. An l.v. network fault in an interconnected block, if it does not self-clear, results in shut-down of the block, clearance being obtained by operation of all the l.v. circuit breakers on transformers feeding that block and by operation of the fringe-fuses which connect it to other blocks. An h.v. cable phase fault is cleared by feeder protection at the primary substation and by reverse-power protection on the l.v. circuit breakers on all transformers supplied from that feeder. Both the near and remote blocks on the faulty feeder are therefore involved in this operation. An h.v. cable earth fault is cleared by feeder protection at the primary substation but the cable may remain alive back-fed from the l.v. network since the reverse-power protection will not necessarily operate under this condition. The cable can therefore, via the transformers connected to it, provide paths in parallel with l.v. cables and assist in the transfer of power across the supported l.v. blocks.

Fig. 16.4.4B shows the protection arrangements. The 11kV feeder protection is a two-pole overcurrent and single-pole earth-fault relay with a normally inverse characteristic on all elements.

The transformer h.v. circuit breaker in each substation is equipped with direct acting trips to give time fuse delayed overcurrent and instantaneous earth fault protection. An auxiliary switch intertrips the l.v. circuit breaker.

Protection associated with the l.v. circuit breaker is current-transformer operated and comprises direct-acting overcurrent trips with time fuses and a reverse-power

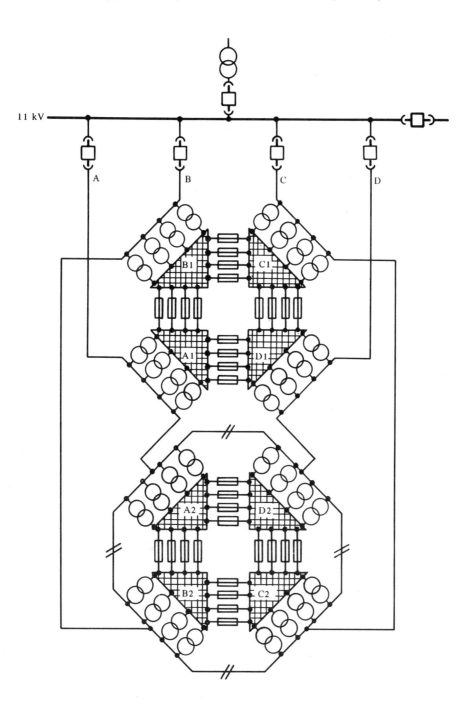

Fig. 16.4.4A   *Distributed block interconnected system*

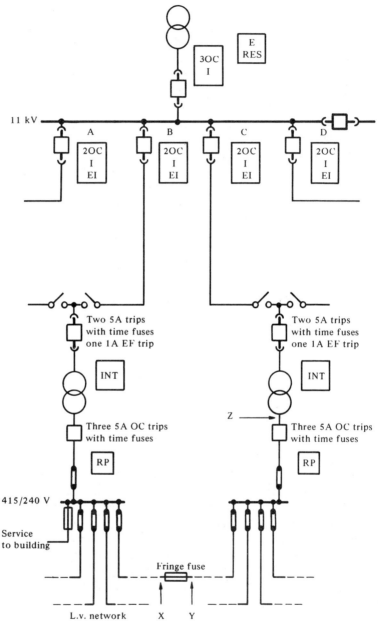

Fig. 16.4.4.B *Distributed block system protection*

relay operating a shunt trip. The shunt trip also responds to tripping current from the intertrip circuit and supply is taken via fuses, from the transformer l.v. connections. Supplies to the voltage coils of the reverse-power relay are afforded in a similar way.

The reverse-power relay has to satisfy a number of requirements. Because of transformer reactance in the fault path the power factor of the fault current is low and the relay is therefore designed to have its maximum sensitivity at about $55°$ lagging. Voltage depression may be considerable at the time when the relay is required to operate and the relay, together with the l.v. circuit breaker shunt trip coil, is designed for operation with the phase to neutral voltage reduced to 30V, to suit typical worst conditions. Rapid disconnection of an h.v. cable phase fault is necessary, otherwise fringe fuses will operate, and this gives a requirement for very fast operation, typically 30ms. Subject to fast operation and stability under transient conditions, the operating current is somewhat less critical, but 200% is a practical value. The relay must be stable for faults in the forward direction and a three-phase design rather than three separate single-phase elements overcomes the problem of incorrect response in one phase which occurs under certain asymmetrical fault conditions.

The characteristics of the fringe fuse used in the l.v. network is determined having regard to the fact that under h.v. fault conditions the current experienced by fringe fuses seldom exceeds 5 000A. In order to provide a 200ms delay at this current to ensure discrimination with the l.v. reverse-power protection (including circuit breaker operating time) a 400A fuse with a slightly modified characteristic is used.

Referring to Fig. 16.4.4B and considering the chain of protection from the primary substation down through feeder B to a single substation and thence to the l.v. network at point X, it is evident that discrimination is unlikely to present problems except possibly between the time fuses either side of the substation transformer. These fuses are effectively in series, however, so that correct discrimination serves only as a guide to fault conditions and the performance that may be obtained by grading the time fuses is adequate for this purpose. Correct discrimination may also be anticipated if consideration is extended to point Y on the other side of a fringe fuse and thence to point Z on the remote side of reverse-power protection at a substation on feeder C. The reverse protection at Z operates, all other protection protection on feeder B remaining stable. Correct discrimination at point Y is however dependent upon there being only one fringe fuse in the circuit and this gives rise to a fundamental principle which relates the number of fringe fuses between interconnected blocks to the total transformer capacity in the block. The relationship which has been established is that the number of fuses should not exceed one fuse per 750kWA of transformer capacity.

It is necessary to consider the stability of h.v. feeder overcurrent protection when an l.v. block supplied by the feeder experiences a non-self-clearing fault. At each substation supplying the faulty block the l.v. circuit breaker overcurrent protection is subject to that substation's individual contribution but the feeder overcurrent protection is subject to the sum of these contributions. In addition the feeder carries the load of a healthy block which it also supplies. There is in consequence a possibility of failure of discrimination between the feeder protection and the substation l.v. protection. If the feeder protection setting is determined by

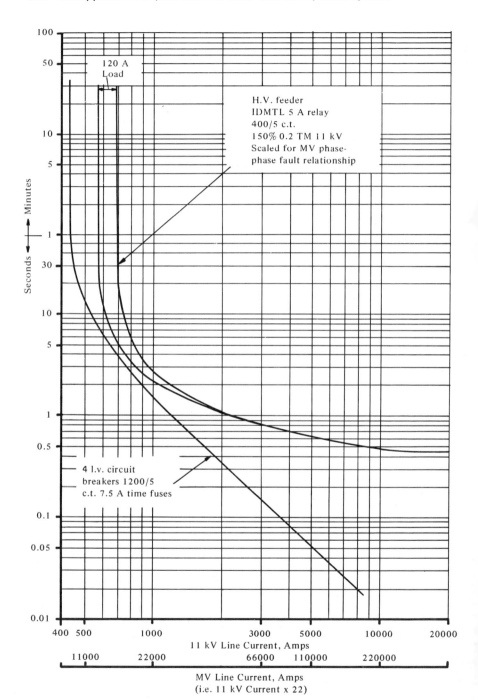

Fig. 16.4.4C   *Protection characteristics*
H.V. feeder and l.v. circuit breakers

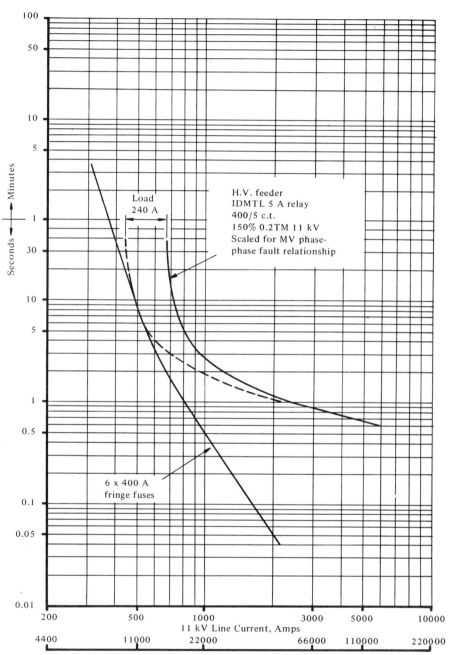

Fig. 16.4.4.D *Protection characteristics*
H.V. feeder and fringe fuses

other considerations, the need to maintain stability places an upper limit on the total capacity of substations which may be coupled together to form an interconnected block. The worst condition is for an l.v. phase/phase fault giving a 2:1:1 distribution of current in the h.v. phases under which the most heavily loaded phase has an effective transformation ratio of 1:22. Fig. 16.4.4C shows a comparison of the protection characteristic of the h.v. feeder protection adjusted for load on the healthy block against the characteristic of the l.v. overcurrent protection of four l.v. circuit breakers in parallel. The proximity of the curves indicates that the limit of feeder protection stability is reached with four l.v. circuit breakers fitted with 1200/5 current transformers and 7·5A time fuses. This protection is appropriate to a 750kVA transformer so that the upper limit of transformer capacity in an interconnected block is four 750kVA transformers.

In addition to the condition of feeder stability for a non-self-clearing fault in either block directly connected to the feeder it is necessary to consider the effect on stability when the fault is in a remote block under which condition fringe fuses are required to operate to isolate the faulty block. The feeder carries the load of its own two blocks plus the load due to the fault current in the fringe fuses. As in the previous case the worst condition is the l.v. phase/phase fault. Fig. 16.4.4D shows a comparison of the protection characteristic of the h.v. feeder protection adjusted for the load on its two blocks against the characteristic of six fringe fuses in parallel. It is seen that discrimination fails if the number of fringe fuses exceeds six.

The protection discrimination requirements described above are limiting conditions which apply to a theoretically regular network and they therefore afford a guide to design. Beneath these limits irregularities, which occur principally in the l.v. network, may impair current sharing and cause instability under fault or load current support conditions. In practice, these conditions are checked by a computer programme which by network reduction converts the numerous impedances making up the l.v. network into equivalent impedances between substations and fringe fuse positions. Currents are then calculated at these positions for three conditions:

(a)   Current flow in the l.v. network and transformers due to an h.v. feeder phase/phase fault, after the primary substation circuit breaker has opened.

(b)   The same condition but after reverse-power relays have operated, to determine the l.v. current flows to support the peak load in the blocks which have lost h.v. supply.

(c)   The support condition again but for an h.v. feeder phase/earth fault when the h.v. cable remains in circuit as a link between transformer primaries and forms a parallel connection across the supported blocks, giving a different distribution of l.v. current.

Under condition (a), current in the fringe fuses is checked against the 5000A limit at which discrimination with reverse-power relays fails. The l.v. phase/neutral voltage is checked to establish that a minimum of 30V phase to neutral is available for the operation of reverse-power relays. Under the two support conditions (b) and (*c*), the method of analysis simulates load current by the application of a limited fault of appropriate magnitude. The transformer and fringe fuse currents thus derived are subsequently superimposed upon the normal loads at these points to give a true representation of the condition, enabling points of excess loading to be identified. Since the h.v. system is arranged in the form of a ring main and supply to all substations may be restored, under single outage conditions, by switching, the safe loading is that which can be sustained until switching is complete, a period of, say, two hours.

Analysis of the network in the way described enables its performance under fault conditions to be determined with considerable accuracy and the few sources of instability which may exist are readily identified. They can usually be remedied by modifying the impedance pattern of the network, i.e. by changing fringe fuse positions or switching substations to other blocks. If this is not possible the procedure adopted is to forfeit some of the support capability of the network to ensure that the protection discrimination requirements are met under fault conditions.

16.4.5 Supply to large point loads

Large point loads due, for example, to major office premises frequently produce demands in excess of 1000kVA. Such loads may be supplied from substations incorporated in the normal way into a distributed block l.v. interconnected system but the arrangement tends to be uneconomic in respect of the aggregate capacity of connections to the l.v. network required to support the internal load of the premises when h.v. supply is lost. Also there may be difficulty in locating any nearby fringe fuses so as to avoid excess loading under the support condition. These drawbacks are overcome by installing two or more transformers each equipped with l.v. reverse power protection and supplied from a different h.v. feeder. Fig. 16.4.5A, shows such an arrangement using two 750kVA transformers and the protective gear is similar to that already discussed. It should be noted that the l.v. busbar forms a direct link between transformers on different feeders. Since this direct link exists in the position normally occupied by fringe fuses its presence may affect the number of fringe fuses permissible elsewhere between the same two feeders. Stability considerations may also limit the number of fuses that can be installed between the l.v. busbars and the external network.

Where a number of large point loads are grouped together the network may take the form shown in Fig. 16.4.5B. Small loads interposed between the major, directly fed, loads are supplied by single l.v. distributors laid from point to point and fused at each end. Ultimate clearance of an l.v. cable fault now rests on two fuses only and the feeder stability considerations which relate to a similar fault under the interconnected block condition no longer apply.

The electrical installations of large point loads may include plant driven by large induction motors. Voltage depression on the system supplying such motors causes the motors to act as generators, feeding into the system a current which decays

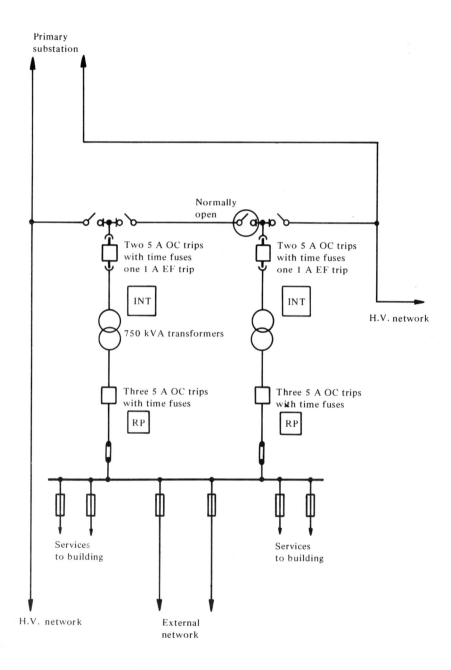

Fig. 16.4.5A *Method of supply to a point load*

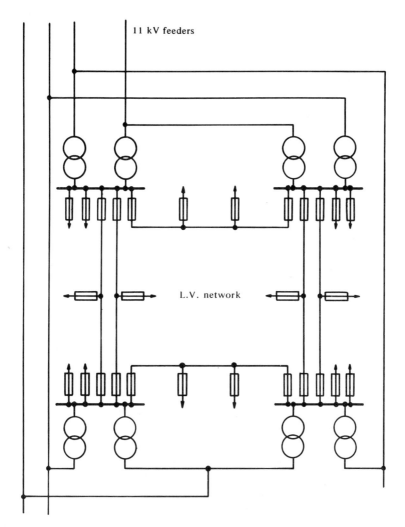

Fig. 16.4.5B   *Supply to a group of four point loads*
Note: h.v. and l.v. switchgear omitted for clarity

with time over several cycles. This current may cause unwanted operation of local reverse-power protection if the voltage depression is due to a fault on feeders other than those affording the supply. The effect is dependent upon both the size of the induction motor load and the characteristics of the reverse power relay and is unlikely to cause problems if the motor load is less than about 400 h.p. The characteristic of the relay may be compared with the calculated characteristic of the generated current and it is possible to determine the extent to which the relay needs to be delayed to prevent the effect from taking place. Alternatively, additional equipment may be installed to block relay operation while motor current persists. The additional delay which is introduced however is an undesirable feature in respect of a fault on one of the feeders affording supply, under which condition fast clearance is desirable for motor stability reasons.

16.4.6   Supply to h.v. consumers

If supply is afforded to a consumer at high voltage from a single h.v. feeder and the h.v. feeder suffers a phase fault, the feeder is shut down and the consumer loses supply; reverse-power relays in all substations connected to the feeder operate and isolate any back-feed from the l.v. network. If the fault is an earth fault, however, the reverse-power relays do not operate and the consumer's load is back-fed from the l.v. network. The load therefore appears as an additional commitment on the l.v. network and is supplied from a healthy source via fringe fuses. Additional fringe fuses to cater for this load cannot be provided because the total number of fringe fuses is limited by the number of transformers feeding the l.v. network, as previously discussed.

The difficulty may be overcome, at the same time affording a higher degree of security of supply to the consumer, by taking supply from two h.v. feeders and using directional protection. Fig. 16.4.6A shows such an arrangement. The i.d.m.t. relay is set to discriminate with similar relays at the primary substation and detects fault current in either direction corresponding to a fault on either feeder. The reverse-power relay which has a similar characteristic to the relay used with the interconnected l.v. systems detects the direction of fault current and its changeover contact directs tripping action to the circuit breaker facing a faulty h.v. cable. Thus the supply to the consumer is firm against an h.v. cable fault and the burden on the interconnected l.v. network is removed under feeder earth-fault conditions. It may be noted that a fault on the h.v. busbars supplying the consumer results in the opening of one local circuit breaker only, fault current is sustained on the other local circuit breaker but cleared by operation of the feeder switch at the primary substation end.

An alternative method of integrating the supplies to h.v. consumers with the h.v. network supplying an interconnected l.v. system is to supply the h.v. consumer or consumers from a unit protected h.v. network and to provide a spur feed to substations supplying the interconnected l.v. system from a circuit breaker fitted with i.d.m.t. protection.

16.5   Private generation

In systems which supply urban and metropolitan areas there may be consumers who operate private generating plant. The machines are usually of the synchronous type with capacities in the range 300 to 3000kW, the smaller sizes operating at 415/240V and the larger usually at 11kV. They may operate continuously in parallel with the public supply or as standby equipment with changeover or facilities for infrequent parallel operation. Since the consumer may be afforded supply at either voltage the layout of the consumer's installation in respect of the

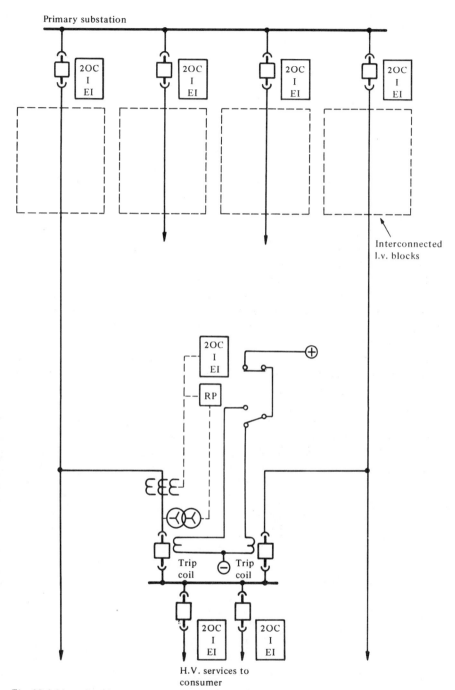

Fig. 16.4.6A *Supply to an h.v. consumer in a system which also supplies an interconnected l.v. network*

interface between the public supply and the generation may take a variety of different forms, too numerous for consideration here in detail. There are however protection problems peculiar to the interface which can be considered in general terms and which are separate from the specific generator protection considerations dealt with in Chaper 12.

It is important that the private generation should not jeopardise the public supply and equally that faults on the public supply should not interfere with the private generation. The presence of generation increases the fault level on the system and if generation is at high voltage this increase particularly affects the whole of the network on the primary substation concerned. Practically the whole of the generator's fault current contribution appears at the primary substation busbars with the result that this is usually the point of highest fault level on the h.v. system. The effect needs to be determined to ensure that the fault rating of switchgear throughout the system is not exceeded.

The neutral point of the consumer's system is required to be earthed. If the consumer's generation is at high voltage, the system earthing of the public supply is available during parallel operation but the consumer must provide his own earth for periods when independent operation is taking place. This may be by means of switched star point earthing but a preferable arrangement is the provision of an earthing transformer connected via a nonautomatic circuit breaker to the consumer's busbar and kept permanently in circuit. The transformer is required to have normal protection against internal faults under which condition isolation is by tripping the switches controlling sources of supply to the busbar to which it is connected. System earth faults may be detected by earth-fault protection in the connection between the transformer star point and earth. Normal overcurrent and earth-fault protection at the supply terminals is provided by i.d.m.t. relays to safeguard the public supply against faults on the consumer's installation. This will also respond to phase and possibly, earth faults, in the reverse direction, i.e. on the incoming public supply but may be supplemented with reverse-power protection, polarising voltage being obtained from the voltage transformer provided for synchronising purposes. The same source provides reference voltages for neutral voltage displacement protection which is the principal protection for earth faults on the incoming public supply. The objective in respect of faults on the incoming supply is to clear such faults without affecting the stability of supply to the consumer's load from his generation but problems may arise due to the protection being sensitive to voltage depression caused by unrelated faults on the public supply system.

Where generation is at low voltage the generator star point is connected directly with the consumer's earth electrode system and then to the earthing facility associated with the incoming supply. The latter normally has a direct connection with the star point of the secondary winding of the incoming supply transformer. With this arangement, restricted earth-fault protection may be applied to the generator itself but for faults outside the restricted zone and at the interface with the public supply, overcurrent protection by i.d.m.t. relay is usual. Where there is more than one generator three-wire machines may be used together with a static balancer connected to a busbar common to all machines, thereby providing a single star point which is earthed and effective for the complete system.

16.6   Future trends

In the application of protection techniques there is, in common with other aspects of electricity distribution, a need to practice due economy in affording a reliable supply to consumers.

Using data based upon comprehensive fault statistics available in the UK it is increasingly common practice to apply methods of cost benefit analysis and system reliability evaluation to system design and protection in order to meet this objective, and the trend can be expected to continue. Coupled with these processes exists the facility of carrying out analysis of networks for all types of faults using computer programmes which may be readily updated to suit changing network conditions. The precise requirements of protection schemes may therefore be determined and their performance predicted.

So far as equipment is concerned the present trend is towards the development of solid state devices which duplicate the performance of their electromechanical counterparts; a radical change is therefore taking place in equipment design, as distinct from its application. The solid state devices are more complicated and have more elements than their electromechanical equivalents but a particular feature is that their operating currents can be very much smaller. If advantage is to be taken of this feature then a reduction in the size of instrument transformers is a probable trend followed possibly by the introduction of new methods of detecting the magnitudes and phase angles of currents and voltages in the main conductors.

A logical extension of the application of solid-state techniques in complex systems could lead to substitution of individual solid-state relays by integrated systems which receive all necessary data and perform the appropriate protective functions and, in addition such functions as indication, alarm and metering.

16.7   Bibliography

Standards
ESI Standard 12-8: The application of fuse-links to 11kV and 6·6kV/415V distribution networks
ESI Standard 37-2: MV distribution fuseboards
ESI Standard 41-5: Indoor metalclad switchgear; ratings up to 250 MVA at 6·6kV and 350 MVA at 11kV
ESI Standard 41-12: Non-extensible ring main equipments incorporating an automatic fuse-switch and switches; ratings 250 MVA and 11kV and 150 MVA at 6·6kV
ESI Standard 48-2: Fault passage indicators for 6·6kV and 11kV underground and overhead distribution systems

Engineering Recommendation G26: The installation and operational aspects of private generating plant (The Electricity Council)

Article
'Application of test results to the calculation of short-circuit levels in large industrial systems with concentrated induction motor loads' by Cooper, Maclean and Williams *Proc. IEE,* 1969, **116**, (11)

Chapter 17

The application of protection to transmission systems

by J.C.Whittaker

17.1 General principles of application of protection to transmission systems

17.1.1 Introduction

This chapter describes the application to transmission systems of the various protection systems described in previous chapters, and gives the reasons for choosing a particular protection system for a given application. The chapter is based on the practice followed in the United Kingdom. This practice, which is constantly changing as new requirements arise and as new protection systems become available, is influenced not only by technical and economic considerations but also by historical factors; it is also based on the protection requirements for solidly earthed transmission systems, such as exist in the United Kingdom. The detailed protection requirements for other types of power system, for example for a transmission system earthed through arc suppression coils, would be appreciably different from those described in this chapter, although many of the basic requirements would be similar. Comparison of the practice in the United Kingdom with practice in other countries brings to light many interesting similarities and differences, but it is beyond the scope of this chapter to attempt to explain the reasons for the differences, or to describe in detail the many different techniques used overseas.

17.1.2 System design considerations

It is essential that there should be close liaison between the system design engineer and the protection engineer at a very early stage in the design of a power system. With high fault levels, for example 35 000 MVA at 400kV, one of the main limitations in system design is the speed at which faults, in particular three-phase faults, can be cleared from the system. This fault-clearance time governs the stability limit of the power system which in turn governs its design. For example, if there are teed feeder circuits, fault-clearance times may be appreciably increased, and the saving in the cost of circuit breakers as a result of tee-connecting circuits may have to be

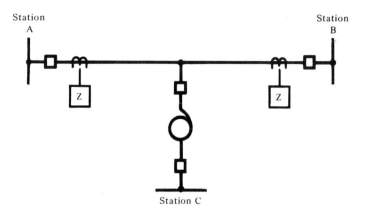

Fig. 17.1.2A *Transformer tee-connected via a circuit breaker to a feeder*

offset by the system design engineer against the cost of reinforcing the power system to ensure that it can withstand the longer fault-clearance times.

Normally, the system design engineer assumes that the operation of all protection on the system will be fully discriminative; but it is essential that he checks with the protection engineer that discrimination is feasible with the particular circuit configuration he proposes. The importance of any protection difficulties can then be assessed together with the cost of overcoming these difficulties. A simple example of this is a 120 MVA transformer tee-connected via a circuit breaker midway along a 257 kV line (Fig. 17.1.2A). As will be apparent later in this chapter, it can be very difficult and costly to provide a fully discriminative high speed fault clearance for such a circuit. The particular faults which are difficult to clear discriminatively are those occurring between the transformer h.v. circuit breaker and the transformer h.v. bushings, as these faults may be within the first zone reach of any accelerated distance protection installed at stations A and B.

17.1.3 Factors which influence the choice of protection

The following are some of the factors involved in choosing a suitable protection scheme for a given application.

17.1.3.1 Plant to be protected: The first factor to be considered in choosing a suitable protection scheme is the nature of the plant to be protected, for example generator, transformer, feeder etc.

The detailed characteristics of the plant to be protected must then be examined to determine if any special considerations apply in choosing a suitable protection scheme. As an example, a feeder may consist of a length of overhead line connected in series with an underground cable. Not all protection schemes suitable for protecting overhead lines are necessarily suitable for a combination of overhead line and cable, for example the relatively low impedance of the cable may be such that the effective length of the feeder is too short for the satisfactory employment of distance protection.

17.1.3.2 Probability of various types of fault: The various types of fault which may occur on the plant to be protected should next be considered, together with the probability of such faults occurring.

For example, on a transformer circuit the majority of faults within the transformer tank are earth faults, the risk of a phase-to-phase fault clear of earth within the tank being low. Breakdown of the transformer core insulation, and interturn faults also occasionally occur.

Earth-fault protection is therefore essential, and Buchholz protection is required to detect core faults and interturn faults which are clear of earth.

Fast and fully discriminative phase-fault protection, for example biased harmonic restrained overall differential protection, can often only be justified to provide phase-fault protection for the connections to a transformer. These connections, unless they are phase segregated, for example consisting of single-core cables rather than open copperwork, may present an appreciable phase fault risk.

Another example is on a generator not only can earth faults and phase faults occur, but the generator can be severely damaged by negative phase sequence currents. These currents arise from either uncleared unbalanced faults on the system or from single or two-phase open circuits. The latter may result from a circuit breaker failing to make or break on all its three phases, or from broken jumpers on a line. These risks, and their resultant effects on the generator, have to be assessed and it is usually found to be necessary to provide negative phase sequence protection for the generator.

17.1.3.3 Load and fault currents: The magnitude of the minimum and maximum fault currents at appropriate points on the system must be established in order to determine the sensitivity and stability requirements for the protection. The maximum expected possible continuous load current must also be known as this will determine the required continuous thermal rating of the protection. It may also affect the minimum permissible phase-fault setting, and the settings of any overcurrent, rate of change of current, or distance starting equipment.

The charging currents of overhead lines and cables must also be taken into account, as they may influence the minimum permissible protection settings.

17.1.3.4 Voltage and current ratings of protected plant: Not only should the normal continuous voltage and current ratings of the protected plant be taken into account in choosing the protection required, but any special requirements such as short time overload ratings, must be considered.

As an example, it may be permissible to overload a power transformer for a few minutes with safety, say to 50% overload, thus necessitating a minimum overcurrent protection setting greater than 150% of the rated current of the transformer.

Another example of a short-time overload rating required for a few minutes occurs in the case of certain overhead-line circuits where it is desirable to utilise the short-time thermal capability of the overhead line to enable quick starting gas-turbine or pumped-storage plant to relieve the overload condition.

For some unit systems of protection, particularly those utilising Post Office pilots, it is highly undesirable that continuous comparison of the currents at each end of the protected circuit be permitted under expected load conditions, otherwise a momentary interruption of the signalling channel may result in inadvertent tripping and starting (fault-detector) relays are therefore included to control transmission. For power line carrier systems the continuous transmission of carrier signals may also cause unacceptable interference to be radiated in frequency bands reserved for normally quiescent carrier. Furthermore, some power line carrier transmitters may have no continuous thermal rating but only a short-time rating of a few minutes.

In addition to the short-time overload rating, the protection system i.e. both the relays and associated current transformers, must be designed to withstand, both thermally and dynamically, the maximum fault current which can flow in the primary plant it is protecting. This short time fault current rating is normally for a 3 or 1s rated duration. The choice of time depends on the expected maximum fault clearance times. Where only 1s rated equipment is available, it may be necessary to investigate the thermal time constant of the protection bearing in mind that it is very unlikely that the magnitude of the fault current can in practice remain at its maximum value for the total duration of the fault.

17.1.3.5 Necessity or otherwise for high-speed operation: The maximum permissible duration of fault current is governed by two factors:

(*a*)   limitation of damage to plant
(*b*)   effect of long fault-clearance times on the system which is feeding the fault current.

The effects of long fault-clearance times must be assessed, not only with regard to the damage at the point of fault, for example an oil fire may be unnecessarily started in a faulted transformer, but the plant feeding the fault may also be damaged by the fault current, for example a cable through which the fault current passes may be damaged.

Fast fault-clearance times especially for three-phase faults may be essential to maintain system stability. On the British Supergrid system stability studies indicate that at some 400 kV stations system stability will be endangered if a close-up three-phase fault is allowed to persist for more than 80ms. Fast clearance times are also required on plant feeding large induction motor loads (e.g. at steelworks or oil refineries). The reason for this is that a prolonged dip in voltage may result in the induction motors slowing down to such an extent that, when the fault is cleared and normal voltage is restored, the motors draw such a high current attempting to accelerate that it produces a correspondingly large voltage drop between the supply and the motor terminals. This reduction in voltage may result in the motors being unable to produce enough torque to regain their normal operating speed.

On the other hand, unnecessarily fast protection should not be specified as, with certain exceptions, the faster schemes are more expensive, more complex and, in many cases, more liable to maloperate. For example, distance protection which has an operating time of under 10ms usually requires more faithful voltage inputs than are normally obtainable from most designs of capacitor voltage transformers.

In quoting protection operating times for assessing their effect on system performance it has to be borne in mind that the times quoted for a given protection system can usually only be approximate, as so many factors influence the actual operating time obtained on an individual fault.

Some of the principal factors involved are:

(a)   the magnitude of fault current (usually expressed as a multiple of the setting of the protection)
(b)   the type of fault, e.g. phase-to-earth, phase-to-phase or 3-phase
(c)   the ratio of the impedance of the source of the fault current to the impedance between the relaying point and the point of fault
(d)   the magnitude of the d.c. component present in the fault current, and the prefault magnetisation state of the current transformers
(e)   the magnitudes and phase angles of harmonic components and nonsinusoidal waveforms
(f)   the magnitude and direction of the load current flowing immediately prior to the fault
(g)   the resistance of the fault itself
(h)   the characteristics of any signalling channels used between the local and remote circuit breakers. The characteristics of the channel may be appreciably modified by transient electrical interference in the channel at the time of the fault, including interference from adjacent signalling channels.

With an increasing amount of generation being connected into the transmission system at higher voltages, i.e. the generator/transformers being switched at 400 and 275kV instead of 132 or 33kV, the ratio of reactance to resistance of the source impedance for faults on the transmission system is steadily increasing. This results in a higher probability of a large d.c. component in the fault current when the fault occurs at other than at the maximum point-on-wave of the voltage. Hence item (d) in the list is becoming of increasing importance because, if the main or interposing current transformers saturate, very long operating times may occur.

17.1.3.6 Importance of security of supply: To obtain fully discriminative protection for all types of fault may not always be economically justified, depending on the importance of the load being supplied. For example, in the arrangement shown in Fig. 17.1.3A, the l.v. busbars are supplied solely from the two transformers and the only form of phase fault protection is inverse definite minimum time (i.d.m.t.) overcurrent protection. If a phase-to-phase fault clear of earth occurs

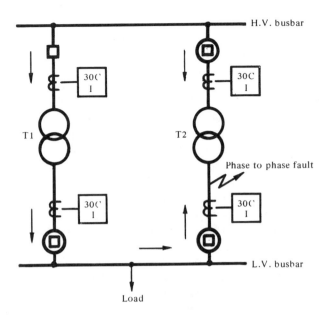

Fig. 17.1.3A   *Nondiscriminative tripping for transformer l.v. fault*

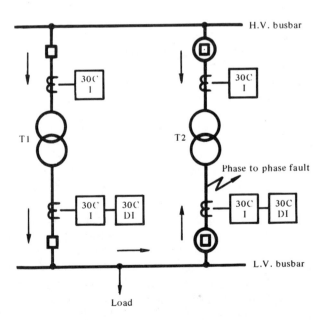

Fig. 17.1.3B   *Discriminative tripping for transformer l.v. fault*

on the l.v. connections of transformer 2, the fault current is supplied equally by both transformers and hence, neglecting load currents, the l.v. overcurrent relays on transformer 1 and transformer 2 will operate in the same nominal time, tripping the l.v. circuit breakers of both transformer 1 and transformer 2. Any load current will tend to cause transformer 1 relay to operate before transformer 2. In addition, the h.v. overcurrent protection will operate on transformer 2 thus clearing the fault. Any load connected to the l.v. busbar would thus lose its supply.

If, on the other hand, in addition to or in place of the l.v. inverse definite minimum time overcurrent protection, directional l.v. overcurrent protection or transformer overall differential protection were provided, either of these forms of protection would operate before the i.d.m.t. overcurrent protection and only the faulted transformer would be tripped, thereby maintaining the supply to the load (Fig. 17.1.3B).

17.1.3.7 Compatibility with existing protection: When choosing a protection scheme and its settings due regard must be paid to the characteristics of any existing protection on the power system. If the setting of a distance protection on the transmission system has to be such that it can 'see through' the step-down transformers and thus respond to faults on the distribution system, its time setting must be high enough to discriminate with the protection on the distribution system.

17.1.3.8 Availability of signalling channels: In transmission networks where substations are separated by only a few miles, as in London, the most satisfactory and economic protection for two-ended feeders is often to employ private pilot wire protection utilising pairs of wires in a network of private pilot cables. It is important to arrange that sufficient spare pairs are provided in the pilot cables when they are originally laid to ensure that an adequate number of pairs is available to meet all expected future needs.

Where private pilots are not available, it is usually economic in the UK to hire pilots from the Post Office for the protection of two-ended feeders. However, since 1978, the Post Office have in general withdrawn the facility for the hire of metallic circuits having maximum declared resistance and capacitance values. Hence many of the differential and phase-comparison protection systems designed to compare fundamental frequency quantities over Post Office metallic pilots are not suitable for most applications, and protection designed for use with voice frequency signalling systems is used in these cases. Power-line-carrier channels can often be economically justified, but the frequency bands available to the Supply Industry for this form of signalling, are rapidly used up and difficulty may often be experienced in allocating suitable frequencies without the risk of causing interference in adjacent channels, although better utilisation of the available frequency bands is achieved by installing carrier equipments which require narrower signalling bandwidths than hitherto. In allocating frequencies, not only must allowance be made for an adequate separation between signalling frequencies on lines at the same voltage, but cognisance must be taken of any mutual coupling of carrier signals between lines of different voltages, for example where carrier signalling is used on 275kV and 400kV lines which follow the same route.

Microwave signalling channels may be justified economically and technically, but the requirement for microwave links that repeater stations must be within line of sight of each other severely restricts their application. Even greater restrictions in the United Kingdom are the requirements to obtain a license to operate a microwave link and to obtain planning permission for the erection of microwave aerials and towers. The use of fibre-optic signalling channels, which incidentally are immune to electrical and magnetic interference problems, are likely to be used in future as protection signalling channels, particularly if the fibre-optic cable can be satisfactorily incorporated as part of the earthwire of an overhead-line circuit.

17.1.3.9 Cost: Where several protective schemes meet the specified requirements, the cheapest scheme which meets the specification would normally be chosen. In costing the schemes, care has to be taken to include all the relevant costs, for example capitalised costs of pilots, maintenance cost, etc. (See Section 17.5).

The cost of a particular scheme may be influenced by the need for other facilities such as control, metering or telecommunication requirements. The installation of private pilot cables for example, may not be economic for protection purposes only, but may be justified if also required for intertripping, control, metering and telephones.

17.2   Main and back-up protection and location of current transformers

17.2.1   Main and back-up protection

Main protection is defined as that protection which is normally expected to initiate, quickly and discriminatively, the tripping of appropriate circuit breakers to clear a fault from the system. Back-up protection is the protection which is intended to operate in the event of a failure or inability of any main protection to clear the fault.

The number and types of main and back-up protection systems to be installed on a given feeder or item of plant depends on technical and economic considerations. As an example, on the CEGB system it has been found, based on cost-benefit analyses, that the provision of some measure of redundancy for the main protection on the 400 and 275kV systems can be economically justified; but not, except in exceptional circumstances, for the 132kV system. These analyses take account of the estimated cost to the nation of a loss of supply, i.e. not only the loss to the supply authority of its sales revenue but also the cost to consumers. For protecting the CEGB 400 and 275kV systems the general principle adopted is that no credible defect in a single component or secondary circuit of the protection or tripping schemes should result in the nonclearance of a primary fault from the system.

Back-up protection for the 400, 275 and 132kV systems is usually of the non-unit type, e.g. definite minimum inverse time overcurrent or earth-fault protection, or sometimes in specific applications distance protection. In order to reduce appreciably the risk of the back-up protection being called on to operate a considerable measure of redundancy is provided in the main protection arrangements. Also most 400kV and 275kV circuit breakers are equipped with circuit-breaker fail protection.

17.2.1.1 Main protection: In order to ensure fast, discriminative and reliable main protection where more than one main protection system is provided they should be as dissimilar as possible.

For example, in the case of feeder protection:

(*a*)   The first and second main feeder protection, where practicable, should utilise entirely different principles, preferably a differential system and a distance system.

(*b*)   The first and second main protection should operate into independent tripping systems. (Fig. 17.2.1A).

(*c*)   If two distance protections are used, where possible one should be of the blocked type and the other should either accelerate or intertrip.

(*d*)   The first and second main protection should preferably employ different types of signalling channel, e.g. power-line-carrier and Post Office pilot, but where this is not possible and pilot circuits must be used, the two channels should be separately routed.

(*e*)   Two different manufacturers should provide the first and second main protection.

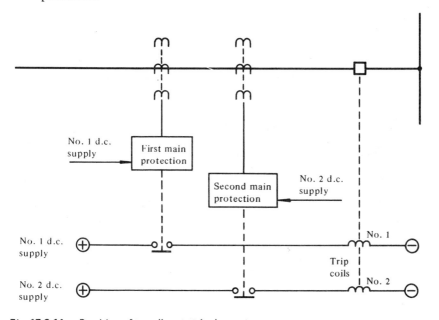

Fig. 17.2.1A   *Provision of two discrete tripping systems*

For main plant and its associated connections full duplication of the protection may not be technically or economically justifiable in which case, e.g. for transformers or generators, the protection of each item of plant can be grouped into two groups of duplicate or supplemental relays, each group being fed from separate d.c. supplies into two segregated tripping systems.

17.2.1.2 Back-up protection: Inverse definite minimum time overcurrent protection is usually provided as back-up protection for feeders, transformers and generators, but it suffers from the disadvantage of having relatively long operating times, which may be unacceptable from system stability or large induction motor load considerations. I.D.M.T. relays of electromechanical design are cheap, simple and reliable but relays of static design may have more flexible characteristics, e.g. a choice of various inverse time characteristics.

Fault clearance may also be nondiscriminative with back-up overcurrent protection. For example, Fig. 17.2.1B represents a small part of an interconnected network. In such a network, as the fault current may flow in any direction depending on the fault location, it is impossible to grade satisfactorily the back-up overcurrent protection settings on feeders, and it is usual, in the absence of specific operational requirements, to give the relays the same nominal settings.

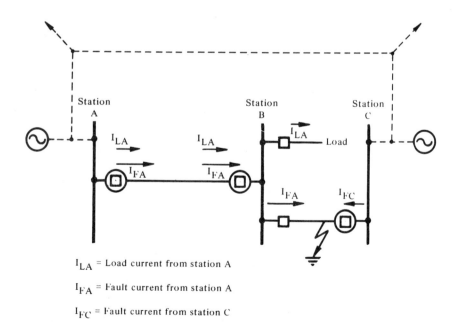

I_{LA} = Load current from station A

I_{FA} = Fault current from station A

I_{FC} = Fault current from station C

Fig. 17.2.1B   *Nondiscriminative clearance of fault by i.d.m.t. overcurrent protection*

Assume in the example chosen fault current can only be fed from stations A and C and an earth fault occurs on feeder BC close to end C. If the main protection on this feeder fails to operate, the back-up overcurrent relays at stations A, B, and C measure the following currents on the faulted phase:

At station A, feeder AB overcurrent relay measures fault current (I_{FA}) + load current fed from end $A(I_{LA})$.
At station B, feeder BA overcurrent relay measures fault current (I_{FA}) + load current fed from end $A(I_{LA})$.
At station B, feeder BC overcurrent relay measures fault current fed from end $A(I_{FA})$.
At station C, feeder CB overcurrent relay measures fault current fed from end $C(I_{FC})$.

It is apparent that the fault will be cleared at station C by the relay on feeder CB. It will also be cleared at station A or B, or both, by the relays on feeder AB. Both of these relays measure the same fault and load current and hence will have the same nominal operating times. There will therefore be a total loss of supply at station B.

The current setting on a back-up overcurrent relay is governed by

(*a*)   the minimum fault current for which the relay is required to operate
(*b*)   the maximum load current the circuit concerned is required to carry under emergency conditions.

It may happen that the setting required by condition (*b*) is greater than the setting required by condition (*a*), in which case the risks involved may have to be accepted.

In the United Kingdom the usual policy, in order to avoid the risk of cascade tripping in the transmission system, is that the overcurrent relays are set above the maximum load currents which are to be expected under emergency conditions.

One method of alleviating this limitation of overcurrent protection, at least as far as earth faults are concerned, is to connect residually one element of a three element overcurrent relay (Fig. 17.2.1C). This residually connected element can then be given a lower setting than the phase connected elements as it does not respond to balanced load currents. The choice of a suitable setting for the residually connected element is, however, difficult as the setting has to be graded not only with any other residually connected overcurrent relay elements on the system, but also with any distance protection on adjacent circuits. Furthermore, the minimum fault current to be measured by the relay may vary between wide limits over a period of 24h owing to changes in the system zero-sequence impedances. A common cause of these variations is the switching of generator transformers in and out of service at generating stations.

Distance protection with its 2nd zone and 3rd zone reaches inherently provides a back-up protection, but the effective reaches of the protection are much reduced

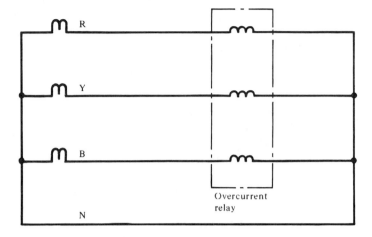

Normal 3 phase connection of 3 element overcurrent relay

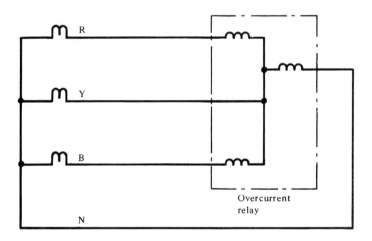

Residual connection of one element of 3 element overcurrent relay

Fig. 17.2.1C   *Overcurrent element connections*

by any fault current infeeds between the measuring point and the point of fault. Fig. 17.2.1D illustrates this effect. A fault in this typical example is assumed to have occurred near to station F on a feeder between stations E and F and the feeder circuit breaker at E has failed to trip. The apparent distance measured by the distance protection on the various feeders is indicated by the figures enclosed by boxes. It will be noted that on feeder D-E at station D the fault is apparently 376km instead of 91 + 12 = 103 km away, and at station A the fault is apparently 1195km

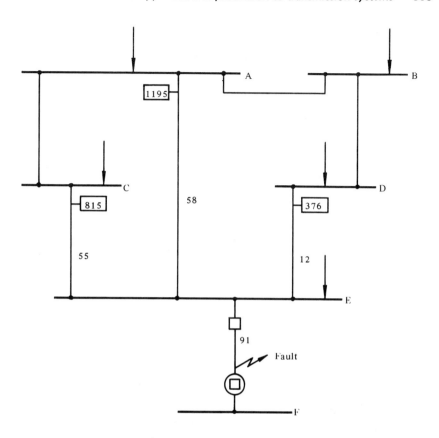

Fig. 17.2.1D   *Apparent fault distance as measured by remote distance protection*

away instead of 149km. In practice, more adverse situations can easily occur and in general distance protection is unlikely to provide any appreciable measure of back-up protection for the system when it has to measure beyond the busbars of a major power station or any other substation with a major infeed. Occasionally, distance protection has been installed as system back-up protection in its own right, in place of inverse-definite minimum time overcurrent protection but its predicted performance has not been satisfactory owing mainly to the reach shortening effect.

Another form of back-up protection applicable to resistance earthed systems is standby earth-fault protection. This protection system consists of a current transformer, the primary of which is connected in series with the neutral earthing resistor, and a relay which has a long operating time, usually up to 30s. The standby earth-fault protection operates in the event of any uncleared earth faults on the system and, where operationally advantageous, its tripping can be made in two stages. For example, the first stage trips the l.v. circuit breaker of the transformer, and if the fault current persists, the second stage, after a further time, trips the h.v. circuit breaker.

The maximum operating time of the standby earth-fault protection should be set below the rated time of the neutral earthing resistor.

It should be noted that the standby earth-fault protection should trip all the fault current infeeds to the affected part of the system, otherwise part of the system may be left still energised but without its neutral point earthed. The latter condition is liable to lead to 'arcing ground' conditions which may cause very severe damage to plant.

17.2.2 Effect of location of current transformers in determining protection to be provided

It is essential that there should be no plant or connections in the transmission system which are left entirely unprotected, and it is usual to ensure that the various zones of protection into which the system is divided overlap each other. To obtain the required overlapping without thereby introducing some lack of discrimination is impossible. In determining a protection scheme one of the most difficult tasks is to reduce this lack of discrimination to a minimum and to assess the extent to which a scheme should be complicated and money spent to cater for faults occurring on perhaps a few inches of connections between an open disconnector, or circuit breaker, and a current transformer housing. In this respect the location of the current transformers in the transmission system is of paramount importance, especially with regard to circuit breakers.

Considering first circuit breakers with current transformer accommodation in the bushings each side of the circuit breaker, e.g. dead tank bulk oil or SF_6 circuit breakers, it is easy to arrange that the zones of protection overlap within the circuit-breaker tank (Figs. 17.2.2A and 17.2.2B).

The risk of a fault occurring within the tank is very remote, and if such a fault should occur, from safety considerations it would normally be desirable to make both zones A and B dead. There is, therefore, little difficulty or disadvantage with this design of circuit breaker in arranging suitable overlapping of the protection zones.

With some forms of circuit breaker, e.g. live tank air-blast and SF_6 circuit breakers, for economic and technical reasons current transformers are often located on one side only of the circuit breaker (Figs. 17.2.2C and 17.2.2D). Arrangements to obtain discriminative tripping may become complex, and full consideration must be given to the risk of faults occurring between the circuit breaker contacts and the

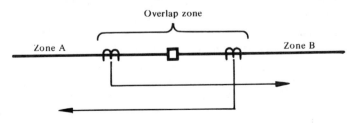

Fig. 17.2.2A   *Zones overlapping circuit breaker*

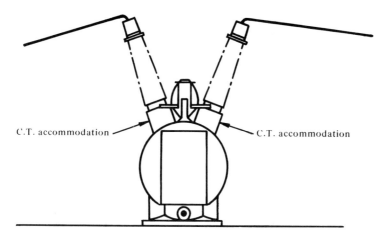

Fig. 17.2.2B *Dead tank circuit breaker*

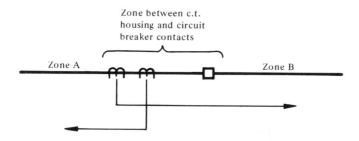

Fig. 17.2.2C *Zones not overlapping circuit breaker*

c.t. housing. The effects of such faults both on the plant itself and on the surrounding system must also be assessed. For example, in Fig. 17.2.2D the risk of a fault occurring at the insulator supporting the blast heads on outdoor switchgear is not negligible and measures must be taken for fast, and, as far as possible, discriminative clearance of such faults. It should be noted that such a fault (Fig. 17.2.2E) would still be fed from station B when the circuit breaker at station A and its associated busbar selectors were open, provided that the circuit disconnector were closed.

Usually at busbar stations, faults between the c.t. housing and the circuit-breaker contacts will be detected by the busbar protection, and cleared by the tripping of all the circuit breakers connected to the appropriate busbar and by the tripping of the circuit breaker at the remote end of the circuit concerned.

Various arrangements can be made for tripping the remote circuit breaker, the choice depending on the type of protection on the circuit and on the degree of discrimination required. The arrangement adopted also depends on the extent to which increases in the complexity and cost of the protective scheme are acceptable. Typical methods by which the remote circuit breaker may be tripped are:

(*a*)   by unstabilising unit forms of protection on the outgoing circuits, for example by contacts on the busbar protection trip relays. If a delay of approximately 0·15s is introduced before unstabilising the unit protection, thus enabling the circuit breaker at station A to open first, discriminative intertripping can usually be achieved.

(*b*)   by operation of the main or back-up protection at station B if this protection is of the non-unit type.

(*c*)   by means of an intertripping signal which is transmitted by a pilot wire or carrier current channel from station A to station B. This signal can be initiated by either the busbar protection trip relay or a fault-current detecting relay such as the current check relay in circuit-breaker fail protection.

The use of a current check relay has the advantage that the fault clearance is discriminative, but it has the disadvantage that the clearance is deliberately delayed and this delay may be unacceptable for fault-damage or stability reasons.

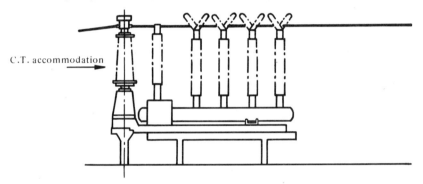

Fig. 17.2.2D   *Live tank air-blast circuit breaker*

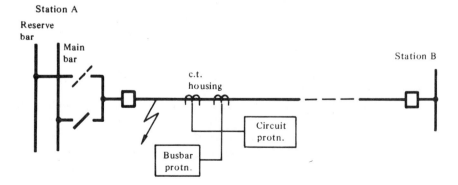

Fig. 17.2.2E   *Fault between c.t. housing and circuit breaker*

It would appear that there is a strong technical case for mounting current transformers on both sides of the circuit breaker. It must be borne in mind, however, that for circuit breakers of other than the dead tank type, mounting current transformers on both sides may entail having an undesirably large overlap zone. Furthermore, the insulation of busbars should be kept as reliable as possible and the introduction of current transformer housings may slightly increase the risk of busbar faults. The provision of room for c.t. housings on both sides of the circuit breaker may also increase the size of the switchgear bay and hence the size of the substation.

17.2.3 Two-stage overcurrent protection

If the main fault infeed is only from the h.v. side of the transformer, it is sometimes advantageous, both technically and economically, to replace the transformer l.v. overcurrent protection current transformers and the associated inverse definite minimum time relay by a two-stage relay comprising an inverse definite minimum time element, energised from c.t.s on the h.v. side of the transformer, and a d.c. timelag element (Fig. 17.2.3A). The first stage, the i.d.m.t. element, is arranged to trip the l.v. circuit breaker only, and the second stage, the d.c. timelag element, the h.v. circuit breaker. This two-stage relay enables faster discriminative overcurrent protection to be obtained for the transformer as the discriminating time can be reduced from the usual minimum time of 0·5s for grading two i.d.m.t. relays to a fixed time of, say, 0·2s, that is, the maximum circuit breaker tripping time plus a safety margin.

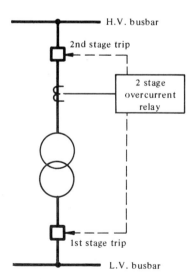

Fig. 17.2.3A   *Two-stage overcurrent protection*

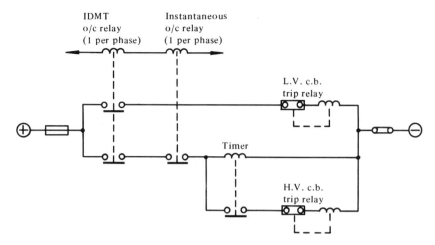

Fig. 17.2.3B *Two-stage overcurrent protection d.c. circuits*

Typical d.c. tripping circuits for a two-stage overcurrent protection are shown on Fig. 17.2.3B. Most i.d.m.t. relays, having operated, take an appreciable time (over 100 ms) for their contacts to disengage. Hence, if the tripping of the l.v. circuit breaker causes the cessation of fault current, there is a danger that, unless the timer is immediately de-energised, the timing relay will complete its operation, energise the h.v. circuit breaker trip relay, and the unnecessary tripping of the h.v. circuit breaker would result. For this reason, unless the i.d.m.t. relay contacts have a disengaging time of less than 100 ms, an instantaneous current relay is provided with contacts having a very fast disengaging time. The contacts are connected to open the coil circuit of the timing relay immediately the fault current ceases.

17.3   Intertripping and protection signalling

17.3.1   General

The various types of intertripping and protection signalling equipments and associated communication channels are described in detail in Chapter 7.

The choice of the method to be used for initiating the tripping of the remote circuit breakers usually lies between the following:

(*a*)   D.C. signalling, normally only used for intertripping, in which an uncoded d.c. signal is transmitted over privately owned pilots. The receive relay may or may not be surge-proofed, depending on the risk of appreciable induced a.c. in the pilot wires.

(*b*)   Voice-frequency signalling, in which a coded voice-frequency signal is transmitted, normally over a hired Post Office channel, but sometimes over private pilots or other types of channel.

(c) Carrier signalling, in which a carrier signal, normally coded, but may be uncoded for certain simple signalling applications, is transmitted over the conductors of the primary system.

(d) Fault throwing, in which a fault is deliberately initiated on the primary system by closing a fault throwing switch. The fault is detected by the protection at the remote station which in turn initiates tripping of the appropriate circuit breakers.

For a given application, in addition to technical considerations, the main factors which govern the choice of method of tripping the remote circuit breakers are the availability and cost of providing the signalling equipment and channels.

Where more than one intertripping or signalling channels are required for security of operation reasons they should be as diverse as possible with regard to both the design of the equipments and the types of communication channel used, as mentioned in Section 17.2.1.1.

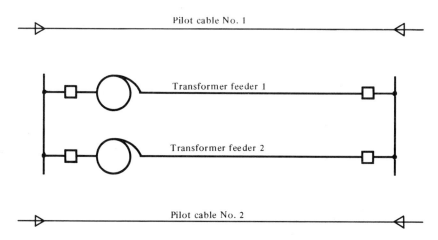

Fig. 17.3.1A *Routing of protection and intertripping channels for double-circuit transformer feeder*

Problems may arise, however, as a direct result of providing this diversity. For example, if it is assumed that the only communication channels which can be economically justified for the protection and intertripping for the double circuit transformer feeder shown in Fig. 17.3.1A are two separately routed private pilots, and it is also assumed that each feeder is equipped with two main protection systems and that the intertripping for each feeder is duplicated, then in order to increase the dependability, i.e. to reduce the risk of a failure to trip, it is evident that the first main protection for TF1 should be associated with pilot cable No. 1 and the second main protection with pilot cable No. 2. Similarly, the first intertripping channel for TF1 should be in cable No. 1 and the second intertripping channel for TF1 in cable No. 2.

However, some forms of main protection will maloperate on load or through fault current in the event of the conductors in the pilot cable becoming short circuited. Similarly, with a simple d.c. intertripping system a live conductor in the pilot may, through insulation breakdown, be inadvertently connected to another conductor resulting in maloperation of the intertripping equipment.

One of the main causes of damage to pilot cables, particularly in urban areas, is building or road construction work when, for example, sheet steel piling may accidentally result in severing with consequent short-circuiting of conductors in the pilot cable. In this case, in the event of the communication channels for TF1 and TF2 being routed in the manner described, both TF1 and TF2 might be inadvertently tripped. On the other hand if all the protection and intertripping associated with TF1 were routed in pilot cable No. 1 and that for TF2 were routed in pilot cable No. 2 the risk of inadvertent tripping would be confined to a single primary circuit.

Where the protection or intertripping for more than one primary circuit is routed in one pilot cable the risk of more than one circuit being tripped in the event of damage to that pilot can be reduced in various ways. For example, the use of starting relays for the protection will reduce the risk of protection maloperation and the risk of inadvertent maloperation of the intertripping can be eliminated by using a voice frequency intertripping system instead of a d.c. system.

In practice, an engineering assessment has to be made of the consequences of the loss of supply owing to damage to a pilot cable or equivalent signalling channel and, within the economic constraints, the appropriate measures taken to provide reliable high-speed fault clearance.

17.3.2   D.C. signalling

D.C. signalling, which utilises privately owned pilots between the stations concerned, has the great advantages of simplicity and reliability, but if surge-proof relays are used, the operating time may be unacceptably long (about 150 ms). The operating time may increase appreciably with some types of relay if induced voltages are present in the pilot wires. Where faster operating speeds are required a voice-frequency signalling system has to be used.

Where the pilot circuits are very long, it is advisable to use a separate insulated battery for energising the pilots for the following reasons:

(*a*)   With some designs of two-way two-core intertripping schemes, if the intertrip send relays are operated at both ends simultaneously, the station tripping batteries at the local and remote stations may be connected in parallel via the intertripping pilots. This can lead to difficulties if the normal voltages of the two batteries is appreciably different.

(*b*)   It is undesirable to increase appreciably the capacitance to earth connected to the station tripping battery; excessive capacitance of the d.c. wiring can cause relays to maloperate in the event of a single earth fault.

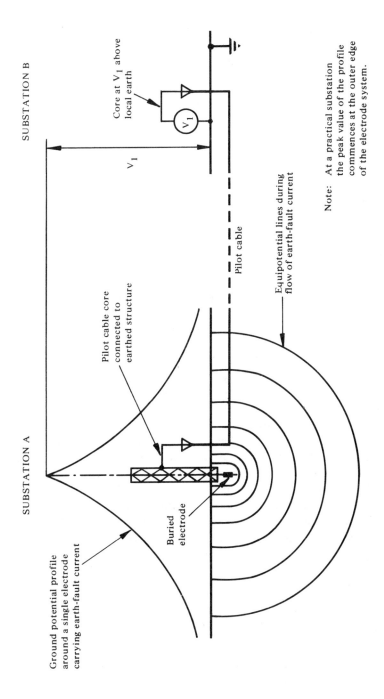

Fig. 17.3.2A   *Transferred potential*

(c)   A fault in the pilot circuit, which may not be detectable until a signal is sent, might affect the security of the battery supplies at the station from which the intertripping signal is being sent; for example, tripping of circuit breakers at that station may be delayed until the appropriate fuses have cleared the fault in the pilots and the tripping supply voltage has been restored.

(d)   Any rise in earth potential at the remote station due to the fault current may be transferred through the pilot circuit and imposed on the local station tripping battery, with resultant insulation failure (Fig. 17.3.2A). It is usual to provide 15 kV insulation to earth for batteries used to energise long pilot circuits.

17.3.3 Post Office signalling

When private pilots are not available voice frequency equipments are often used in conjunction with hired Post Office channels for protection signalling and for intertripping. Typical operating times for equipments at present in common use are between 25 and 40 ms.

The main disadvantages of using Post Office signalling channels are:

(a)   the equipment is complex and costly.

(b)   the hired pilots may be subjected to unauthorised human interference. They may also be out of service when a signal is required to be transmitted. In practice in the UK these risks have been low. However, the new designs of amplifiers and digital communication equipment incorporating solid-state devices may have to be protected by overvoltage protection with settings of a few hundred volts on their external terminals. There is therefore an increasing risk that the communication channel may be momentarily interrupted at the instant of fault by the effects of induction or rise of earth potential caused by primary system faults in the vicinity of the PO equipment. Also, although most Post Office equipment used on channels hired by the Electricity Supply Industry are independent of 240 V mains operated supplies and hence are not affected by voltage dips in that supply, in a few instances some are not and the changeover arrangements to a standby supply may not always be fast enough to ensure reliable protection and intertripping.

(c)   the signalling code may be simulated by disturbances in the hired circuits thus causing incorrect operation. Again this is a low risk, but the risk may increase appreciably if the Post Office transmission circuit includes carrier or microwave links, which may introduce unwanted frequency or phase changes in the received signal.

(d)   relatively frequent routine tests are required to prove the equipment is in proper working order.

(e)   the propagation time of the signal over a long Post Office link may be significant.

17.3.4   Carrier signalling

Carrier signalling is widely used where the cost of the power line coupling equipment can be justified. In the UK, its use is practically universal as one of the communication channels for the protection or intertripping of long feeders, unless technical restraints, e.g. a length of underground cable prevent its application. It is particularly useful as an alternative to Post Office signalling channels where the Post Office channels may be suspect, e.g. alternative routing for two independent channels may not be available, or where there has been a history of insulation problems due to flooding.

The main technical limitation in the application of carrier signalling is that in general it is unsuitable for circuits containing cable, owing to the loss of signal resulting from the mismatch in the characteristic impedances of the carrier frequency path at the cable sealing ends. Attenuation of the signal also occurs within a cable, the magnitude of the attentuation varying appreciably with cables of differing construction. These limitations can sometimes be overcome by providing line traps, or coupling equipment, or both, in the primary circuit at the appropriate points but it is rarely economic.

Another technical limitation in the application of carrier signalling is the attenuation of the carrier signal at any tee-points in the primary circuit. The resulting loss at the tee-point can normally be reduced to an acceptable value, typically 3·5 dB, by carefully matching the impedances of the coupling equipments at each end of the tee-connected circuit.

Carrier signalling has the advantage that the signalling channel, that is the power line itself, is not subject to unauthorised interference by human agencies in the same way as hired pilot circuits. On the other hand, carrier signals are liable to be severely attenuated under certain line icing and hoar frost conditions, and it is advisable on certain vital circuits to back up carrier signalling by Post Office signalling. Also, if the signal has to be transmitted along a power line which is faulted, satisfactory reception of the carrier signal cannot always be guaranteed. Carrier intertripping would therefore be unsatisfactory if total reliance had to be placed on it for the correct clearance of line faults.

Great care has to be taken in the design of a carrier signalling equipment to ensure that it will not maloperate when subjected to the severe interference by the opening and closing of disconnectors. This interference is particularly severe when disconnectors energise or de-energise conductors having a very small capacitance, for example short sections of busbar.

17.3.5   Fault throwing

Fault throwing, where the fault level permits, is a simple and reliable method of tripping remote circuit breakers. Fault throwing switches are at present available in

the UK for fault levels up to 3500 MVA at 132 kV.
The main disadvantages are:

(*a*)   when a fault throwing switch operates the system is subject to a disturbance.
(*b*)   the operating time of a fault throwing switch is long (approximately 0·3s) and may be influenced by weather conditions such as ice in the mechanism.
(*c*)   there is a risk of inadvertent operation.
(*d*)   when fault throwing switches are installed on transformer feeders directional overcurrent protection may have to be used to trip the transformer l.v. circuit breaker for feeder faults. The restrictive limitations in the application of directional overcurrent protection are given in Section 17.7.5.

17.4   Automatic switching

17.4.1   Design and application of automatic switching equipment

Insofar as this Section is concerned, the term automatic switching equipment refers to the equipment which initiates the post-fault automatic operation of circuit breakers and disconnectors in a prearranged sequence. The equipment initiates:

(*a*)   Permanent isolation from the system of any faulted plant which must not be re-energised, e.g. a faulted transformer.
(*b*)   Re-energisation of overhead lines and similar plant which may be only transiently faulted and which may be safely re-energised. If the fault on re-energisation is found to be permanent, the overhead line or similar plant may be automatically isolated to permit any banked or tee-connected healthy plant to be put back into service automatically.
(*c*)   Automatic reclosure of all circuit breakers which were closed prior to the fault and which may be safely reclosed.
(*d*)   The switching into service of standby plant, e.g. a transformer, which was not in service prior to the fault, because, for example, the associated switchgear fault current ratings would have been exceeded.

This Section deals only with the United Kingdom practice of three-pole tripping and reclosure of circuit breakers. Single-pole tripping and reclosure has not been installed in the United Kingdom because, in general, the transmission network is so strong and interconnected that little if any operational benefit would be gained by single-pole tripping and reclosure; hence the cost and complication of providing single-pole tripping and reclosure facilities would not be justified. It should be pointed out that, particularly with multiple earthed systems with double circuit lines and often using protection systems incorporating summation transformers, it may be difficult and costly to arrange for unambiguous identification of the faulted phase or phases. Also in the United Kingdom most circuit breakers at present installed on the transmission system have been electrically and mechanically designed solely for three pole operation.

17.4.2 High-speed automatic reclosing

Single-shot three-phase high-speed automatic reclosing of circuit breakers was widely applied in the 1950s to 275 kV feeder circuits. In this context 'high speed' implies reclosure of the circuit breaker within one second of it being tripped, typically in about 0·4s. In the event of reclosing onto a permanent fault initiation of further reclosures was prevented.

In a high-speed automatic reclosing sequence, once tripping has been initiated no time is available for subsequent checks to be made of the voltage conditions on the system. In fact, owing to the inertia of the circuit breaker's pneumatic or oil and mechanical systems, it is necessary to initiate reclosing before the tripping operation has been completed.

The permissible time for a successful high speed automatic reclosing operation is govered mainly by:

(*a*) A minimum time, dependent on the time taken to extinguish the arc at the point of fault and for any ionised particles at the point of fault to disperse.

(*b*) A maximum time, dependent on the rate at which the voltage vectors at the stations at each end of the circuit swing apart. This change in phase angle between the voltages is governed by many factors, such as duration, location and nature of the fault, the design of the system, in particular the impedance of the alternative routes between the stations concerned, the load on the system, the load on the feeder concerned immediately prior to the fault, the generator plant in service at the time of the fault and the transient character-istics of that plant.

It is apparent that in order to obtain the maximum circuit dead time for a mini-mum circuit reconnection time it is desirable that the circuit breakers at each end of the particular feeder should as far as possible trip simultaneously. Unit forms of protection are therefore ideal for feeders which are required to be equipped with high-speed automatic reclosing. Distance protection can however be used provided that sufficiently fast acceleration or blocking facilities are installed.

It was found during the 1960s that on many feeders the disturbance to the CEGB system which would result from high speed automatic reclosure on to a permanent fault was unacceptable, and for this and other reasons, such as the simplification of the design of circuit breakers, high-speed automatic reclosing was replaced by delayed automatic reclosing.

17.4.3 Delayed automatic reclosing

Delayed automatic reclosing, sometimes referred to as low speed automatic reclosing, can be defined as reclosure which is interlocked to ensure that specific switching and system conditions are satisfied before reclosure takes place in upwards of 2s from tripping. The minimum reclosure time is governed by the interlock system and by the design of the circuit breaker concerned; for example some types of oil circuit breaker should not be reclosed within 10s of tripping in order to enable the arc-control device to refill with oil, and any gas and carbonised oil to disperse.

The longer time taken to perform a delayed automatic reclosing operation, as compared with high speed automatic reclosing, permits checks to be made, after tripping has taken place, of such factors as whether the circuit concerned is dead, or, if it has been re-energised from a remote point, whether the voltages on each side of the circuit breaker which is to be reclosed are in synchronism or sufficiently close in phase and magnitude. In particular, delayed automatic reclosing has the advantage compared to high-speed automatic reclosing of enabling faulted plant to be isolated automatically before reclosure takes place. For example, in Fig. 17.4.3A a faulted transformer in a banked pair can be automatically isolated by operation of the motorised disconnector M, permitting the healthy transformer to be restored to service within a few seconds. Delayed automatic reclosing can also be applied to

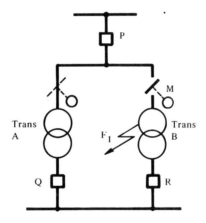

Fig. 17.4.3A   Automatic isolation of a faulty transformer in a banked pair

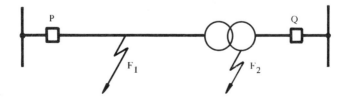

Fig. 17.4.3B   Faults on transformer feeder

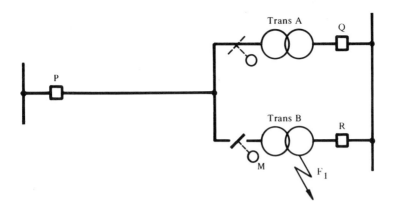

Fig. 17.4.3C *Fault on one transformer of a banked pair in a transformer feeder*

transformer feeder circuits as there is adequate time to determine, and to signal to each end, sufficient information concerning the fault to allow the correct action to be taken. For example, for the primary circuit shown in Fig. 17.4.3B if the fault occurs only on the line at F_1, the circuit breakers can be automatically reclosed, but in the event of simultaneous line and transformer faults $F_1 + F_2$, reclosure must not take place.

If two transformers are connected at the end of a transformer feeder (Fig. 17.4.3C) and a fault F_1 occurs on one of the transformers, reclosure can take place when the faulted transformer has been isolated.

Typical sequences for delayed automatic reclosing of circuit breakers are as follows:

(*a*)   A transformer fault on a banked pair of transformers (Fig. 17.4.3A).

Time s	Operation
0	Fault occurs on transformer B at F_1
0·2	Fault detected by transformer B protection and circuit breakers P, Q and R tripped
4·0	Automatic opening of the h.v. disconnector M for transformer B initiated
12+	Transformer B h.v. disconnector M fully opened
17+	Circuit breaker P reclosed thus re-energising transformer A
19+	Provided voltages across circuit breaker Q are in synchronism or if the busbar is dead, circuit breaker Q is reclosed

(*b*)   A line fault (but no transformer fault) on a transformer feeder (Fig. 17.4.3B).

Time s	Operation
0	Line fault at F_1 occurs
0·2	Fault detected by feeder protection and circuit breakers P and Q tripped
15	Circuit breaker P reclosed thus energising the line
15·2	If the fault is a permanent fault circuit breaker P trips and no further reclosure takes place
17+	Provided the line has remained energised for 2s, that is, the original fault was a transient fault, and if the voltages across circuit breaker Q are in synchronism or if the busbar is dead, circuit breaker Q is reclosed.

(*c*)   Simultaneous line and transformer faults on a transformer feeder (Fig. 17.4.3B).

Time s	Operation
0	Line and transformer faults $F_1 + F_2$ occur simultaneously
0·2	Faults detected by feeder and transformer protection and circuit breakers P and Q tripped. Automatic reclosing locked out by operation of transformer protection

(*d*)   A fault on one transformer of a banked pair at the end of a transformer feeder. (Fig. 17.4.3C).

Time s	Operation
0	Fault occurs on transformer B at F_1
0·2	Fault detected by transformer B protection and circuit breakers Q and R tripped. Circuit breaker P tripped by intertripping signal from transformer B protection.
4·0	Automatic opening of transformer B h.v. disconnector M initiated
15+	Transformer h.v. disconnector M fully opened. Intertripping signal removed, permitting automatic reclosing of circuit breaker P to proceed
17+	Circuit breaker P reclosed thus re-energising the line
19+	Provided voltages across circuit breaker Q are in synchronism or if the busbar is dead, circuit breaker Q is reclosed

17.4.4   Equipment design and programming

In the years prior to the late 1970s most automatic switching equipments consisted of electromechanical relays, mainly all-or-nothing relays and timers, mounted in relay cases with up to fifteen relays in each case. The relay cases were interconnected by panel wiring, as required, to provide the requisite facilities at a particular sub-station. Some of the relays were of standard design to provide, in conjunction with other relays, delayed automatic reclosing facilities for certain standard substation layouts, e.g. double busbar, four-switch mesh, three-switch and single-switch stations. There were, for example, groups of relays in one or more cases which comprised standard designs for 'mesh corner units', 'mesh circuit-breaker units' and 'transformer l.v. circuit-breaker units'.

With the increasingly high costs of switchgear in the 1970s, it was found more economical to depart from standard designs of substation, and to tee-connect or bank primary circuits in nonstandard configurations. This entailed designing the protection and automatic switching requirements very much on an individual circuit and substation basis, and the standard circuit diagrams for automatic switching schemes and equipment were no longer appliable, except possibly in the case of double busbar stations without tee-connected primary circuits. A typical example of a delayed automatic reclosing scheme for a double busbar station using electromechanical relays is given in Fig. 17.4.4A. This simple scheme is for the automatic reclosing of a feeder circuit breaker after a feeder fault. The corresponding sequence chart is given in Fig. 17.4.4B.

A further difficulty which arose from using standard designs of automatic reclosing equipments was that of modifying existing schemes to deal with the addition of new banked primary circuits at an existing station. Extensive changes in existing standard relays and panel wiring were involved which were both costly and time consuming.

Furthermore, the use of conventional electromechanical relays to perform a large number of simple logic and timing functions required a relay panel suite typically 4 m long for the relays associated with the automatic switching of the h.v. circuit breaker at a four switch mesh substation. This was reduced to about 2 m by using static relays.

Another problem which arises from the use of electromechanical relays is that some logic circuits require many relay contacts to be connected in series which, if not regularly maintained, introduce a risk that the scheme may fail to operate owing to contact failure. The risk of electromechanical equipments failing to operate when required to do so has been found in practice to be about 7% of the total number of required operations.

These problems can be overcome to some extent by installing suitable designs of sequence controllers using programmable wired logic arrangements, such as a diode matrix.

However, the logic requirements for automatic switching equipments have to take into account not only the conditions obtaining at the start of the automatic switching sequence but also any changes in these conditions whilst the sequence is in progress. As an example, if there is a thunderstorm in the vicinity of a substation with a complex primary circuit configuration, a line may be struck by lightning resulting in tripping of circuit breakers at that substation. If, before there is time to reclose the circuit breakers, another line into the substation is struck further circuit

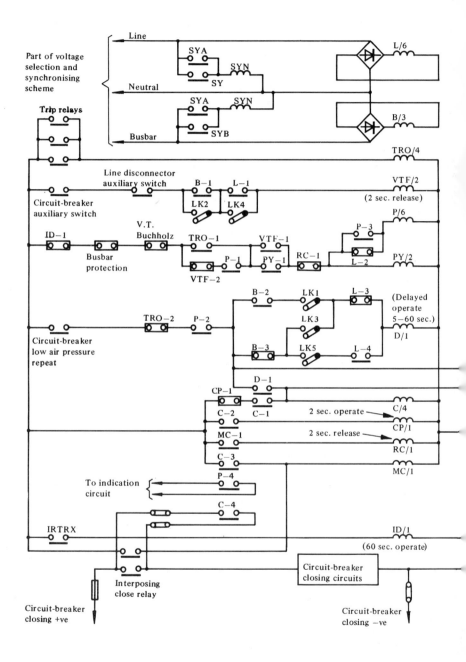

Fig. 17.4.4A   *Delayed autoreclosing* for feeder at a busbar station

KEY TO USE OF LINKS	1	2	3	4	5
1. Full synchronising facilities:					
1.1 Synchro. check only	O	O	O	O	O
1.2 Dead line charge or synchro. check	I	O	O	O	O
1.3 Dead bar charge or synchro. check	O	O	O	O	I
1.4 Dead line or bar charge or synchro. check.................	I	O	O	O	I
2. Limited voltage selection (synchro. check not available):					
2.1 No line reference v.t.					
2.1.1 Assumed dead line charge bar alive......................	I	O	O	I	O
2.2 No busbar reference v.t.					
2.2.1 Assumed dead bar charge line alive......................	O	I	O	O	I
2.2.2 Dead line charge bar assumed alive..................	O	I	I	O	O
O – Link out I – Link in					

Part of voltage
selection and
synchronising scheme

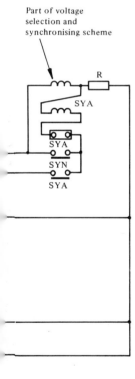

B   –   Busbar side voltage monitoring relay
C   –   Reclosing relay
CP   –   Close pulse timing relay
D   –   Dead line reclose timing relay
ID   –   Persistent intertrip detection timing relay
IRTRX –   Intertrip receive trip relay
L   –   Line side voltage monitoring relay
MC   –   Manual close repeat relay
P   –   Reclose start relay
PY   –   Line dead check start seal relay
RC   –   Reclose cancel relay
SY&SYB– Synchronising selection relays manual
SYA   –   Synchronising selection relay auto-reclose
SYN   –   Synchronising relay
TRO   –   Trip relay operated relay
VTF   –   V.T. monitoring and switchgear repeat relay

SEQUENCE CHART FOR DELAYED AUTOMATIC RECLOSING OF A FEEDER
CIRCUIT BREAKER AT A BUSBAR STATION

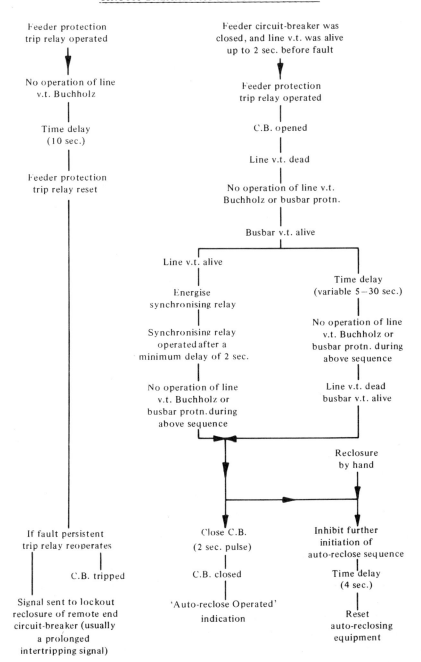

Fig. 17.4.4B

breakers will be tripped, necessitating in some cases a change in the sequence of the reclosure requirements. It is therefore essential that all the appropriate input data is scanned by the automatic switching equipment before each sequential step is taken. In practice, this results in relatively simple controllers such as are sometimes used for controlling simple sequential processes being unsuitable for automatic switching applications.

It also results in it being very difficult to prepare fully comprehensive sequence charts or flow diagrams to show all the logic requirements for complex automatic switching schemes, as so many options have to be shown. If such a chart or diagram is prepared it is essential that all the logic is included, i.e. the requirements for nonoperation as well as operation of the automatic switching equipment.

Another problem is to ensure that the various proposed sequence operating times are correct under unusual primary system switching conditions and that, when necessary, the times are automatically changed within the equipment.

In practice, these difficulties result not only in complex logic requirements for the automatic switching equipment but, equally important, the need for comprehensive testing facilities to enable the proposed requirements to be checked for various assumed fault locations and system switching conditions.

Dealing first with the automatic switching equipment itself for complex primary circuit configurations the interactive logic the equipment must provide has to be based on some form of computer technology, usually incorporating microprocessors in the design. A microprocessor can be defined as a digital processing unit constructed as one or more integrated circuits using large-scale integration (l.s.i.) manufacturing technology. It is an extremely compact programmable electronic component from which a digital computer can readily be constructed by the addition of memory, clock, input and output components. For an automatic switching equipment application suitable interfacing devices e.g. reed relays, opto-isolators etc., are required between the computer and the substation equipment.

A great advantage of a microprocessor based equipment is its flexibility. The hardware, can be ordered and installed largely independently of specifying the detailed requirements of the automatic switching scheme. This greatly eases construction problems. Furthermore, most changes in scheme requirements either before or after installation can be catered for by the relatively easy process of changing the software. The changes are usually accommodated by removal and replacement of the appropriate memory modules followed by the necessary retesting.

The microprocessor-based equipments are much smaller than their electromechanical relay predecessors, typically one 19 inch rack provides for a complete substation, most of the space being occupied by external cable terminations.

The equipments are also in practice more reliable than electromechanical equipments, particularly as by using suitable programs they can both monitor themselves continuously and check for discrepancies in the input information.

The main disadvantage of microprocessor-based equipments is that extensive precautions have to be taken to ensure that interference from the substation environment does not reach the integrated circuits. This interference can easily cause damage and malfunctioning unless the equipment is specifically designed to operate in a substation environment. One of the main sources of interference is caused by the opening and closing of disconnectors in the substation. These disconnectors can generate high energy interference over a very wide frequency band, in some instances up to tens of MHz, and the automatic switching equipment may itself be controlling the opening and closing of these disconnectors.

The preparation of the programme for the microprocessor-based equipment (the software) requires great care. One successful technique is to use in the design office a computer as a design aid and to program this computer in such a manner that it can satisfactorily simulate the input logic and also the equipment in the substation being controlled. In this way the proposed logic can be checked to prove its suitability under various system switching conditions for various assumed fault locations. It should be noted that the computer model of the substation and associated primary system must include simulation of remote substations and also of the relevant secondary equipment at those substations, e.g. intertripping send and receive equipments with their appropriate operating times. In addition, in order to follow and analyse the sequential operation of the proposed logic and of the simulated plant in the system model, all relevant changes in inputs, outputs and the necessary internal memories and timers have to be logged, as shown schematically in Fig. 17.4.4C.

Having proved the logic requirements for the automatic switching scheme, the next step is to program the automatic switching equipment in the required manner. For electromechanical and diode logic equipments this is a relatively easy task but for microprocessor based equipments the program has to be prepared in a suitable format by a computer and fed into the equipment by suitable programming devices e.g. for coupled-charge p.r.o.m.s (programmable read-only memory) components pulses of electrical energy for each bit of information.

A considerable amount of effort can be saved in programming microprocessor based equipment if the substation is split into defined functional groups of plant

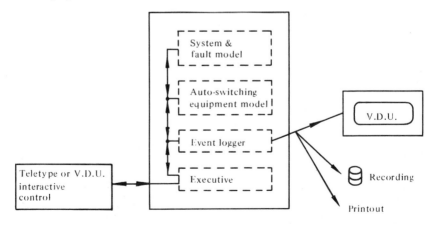

Fig. 17.4.4C   *Computer used for control logic design*

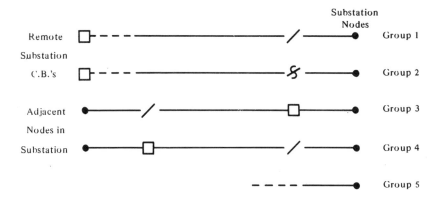

Groups for Assembly of Model

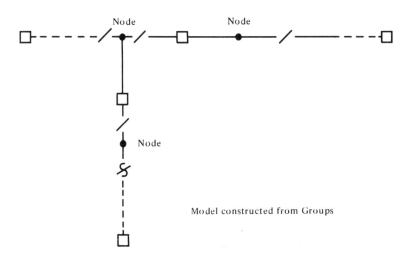

Fig. 17.4.4.D *Substation model*

(Fig. 17.4.4D) which can then be interconnected to form a substation and standard software designed to control these functional groups, in a standard manner e.g. 'This line has a persistent fault. Open the disconnector'.

Using a library of standard software modules, programs can be built up to perform standard automatic switching functions, e.g. 'After transformer fault on tee connected transformer feeder, open transformer disconnector and close line circuit breakers at mesh station'. This technique has not only the advantage that the program can be prepared quickly but also, once a standard module of software has been proven for a particular grouping of primary plant, the standard module can be confidently incorporated in programs for future substations, even though the automatic switching equipment may be of a different type.

Assemblies of the standard software modules can thus be used to simplify the determination of the logic requirements for a complex automatic switching scheme without the need to prepare complex sequence charts or flow diagrams. This results in considerable savings in engineering and drawing office manpower. It is, of course, essential that the program documentation incorporates the facility for 'plain language' comments on the tasks being accomplished at each step.

17.4.5   Commissioning

A major problem with complex automatic switching schemes is to commission the equipment once it is installed in the substation.

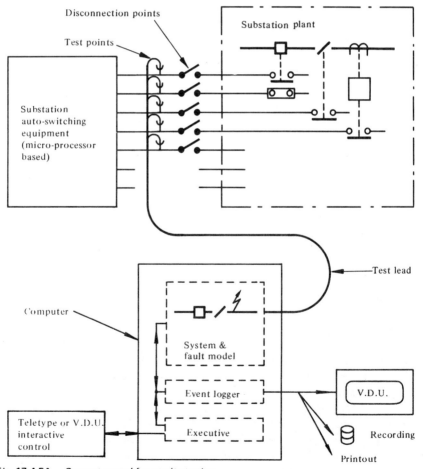

Fig. 17.4.5A   *Computer used for on-site testing*

Operation of the primary plant itself by the automatic switching equipment, apart from a few checking operations, is unacceptable from the point of view of requiring an unduly large number of operations of circuit breakers and disconnectors to prove all the required sequences. It would also be too costly in terms of the outage times which would be required.

With the growth in complexity of the schemes it is also found that adequate modelling of the substation plant by relays, switches and lamps becomes too difficult.

For complex schemes, a fairly elaborate model of the substation is required which can conveniently be provided by a transportable mini- or microcomputer programmed to simulate the substation concerned. In some cases it may be practicable, provided it is transportable, to use the same computer for the commissioning tests as used for programming the automatic equipment. An example of this technique is shown schematically in Fig. 17.4.5A.

17.5 Economic considerations

The cost of a protection system is influenced by such factors as:

(*a*) the complexity of the protection equipment,
(*b*) the voltage and current rating of the necessary ancillary equipment associated with the protection, for example current and voltage transformers, line traps, pilot cables, etc. The cost of these items may be very many times the cost of the associated protection relays,
(*c*) the development and engineering costs of the protection system,
(*d*) whether or not the protection equipment is being purchased in bulk, and
(*e*) the special requirements of individual purchasers.

It is therefore not possible to quote general prices for protection systems, but some indication of the relative costs of protection relays is given in Fig. 17.5A.

Type of relay	Relative cost
Single-pole instantaneous differential current	1·0
Three-pole i.d.m.t.	2·5
Three-pole directional i.d.m.t.	5·0
Pilot wire protection operating over metallic pilots with starting and supervision relays (per end)	12·0
Switched high-speed distance relay for phase and earth faults (per end)	20·0

Fig. 17.5A *Typical approximate relative costs of protection relays*

In costing any scheme, full account should be taken of all the relevant costs involved; for example, the capitalised cost of any hired pilots, the total installation costs, and the probable maintenance costs, including the cost of any necessary circuit outages.

The cost of the consequences of the proposed protection schemes failing to operate should also be assessed, e.g. the cost of any consequential interruption of supplies to consumers.

17.6   Typical protection applications in a major transmission system

In this Section, the factors involved in selecting protection systems for typical applications in a major transmission system are considered but, as it will be seen, in some cases the choice is not easy. The schemes described in this Section are those employed for protecting high-security transmission systems requiring fast fault clearance times for all fault locations. For less important transmission systems and e.h.v. distribution systems the requirements are not so onerous, and various economies and technical relaxations can be made; some of these are described in Section 17.7. It should be emphasised that the characteristics quoted for various types of protection refer to the protection systems at present available. New systems are continually being developed, and these developments modify some of the factors involved in choosing a suitable scheme.

For example, the recent development of very-high-speed protection systems measuring the direction of propagation of the step changes in current and voltage produced at the point of fault ('travelling-wave' protection) have recently been applied in some parts of the world.

17.6.1   Feeder protection

In order to provide fast and fully discriminative protection for feeders with the requisite degree of redundancy in operation and diversity of design (Section 17.2.1) two separate main feeder protection systems are normally provided. The back-up protection is usually definite minimum inverse-time overcurrent and earth-fault protection. In areas of exceptionally high earth resistivity a definite-time earth-fault protection may also be provided with a very high sensitivity to operate for high resistance earth faults.

17.6.1.1 Protection for a long overhead feeder: In this context a long overhead feeder implies a feeder over about 30 km long but under 200 km, with a negligible amount of cable in its route.

In order to obtain as much diversity in the protection as possible it is preferable to have a current differential system for one main protection and an accelerated distance protection for the other.

In view of the distance between the substations a power-line-carrier phase-comparison system is normally used for the differential system, although up to

40 km a voice frequency phase comparison system utilising a Post Office channel can be used. The latter is considerably cheaper than power-line-carrier protection, as no coupling equipment and line traps are required. It is probable however that the distance protection would normally use a Post Office channel for acceleration, and hence the desirable diversification of communication channels for the first and second main protection is lost.

(*a*)   *Carrier protection:* Practically all the power-line-carrier protection at present in service in the UK is static phase-comparison protection. This form of protection replaces older thermionic phase comparison protection and directional comparison protection.

The main advantages of phase comparison power line carrier protection are:

(i)   It provides fast and discriminative protection along the whole length of the protected feeder.

(ii)   It does not require a voltage input, hence it can operate correctly in the event of a voltage transformer associated with the other main protection on the feeder being defective.

(iii)   It is in general more sensitive than distance protection to high resistance earth faults (e.g. faults caused by ionised and polluted air from grass fires).

(iv)   The circuit breakers at each circuit end of the protected feeder are tripped within approximately 20 ms of each other, irrespective of the fault location. This feature is very important if high-speed automatic reclosing is provided; it is not important with delayed automatic reclosing.

The main disadvantages are:

(*a*)   high cost

(*b*)   possible difficulties in allocating frequencies in areas where an appreciable amount of carrier protection is installed

(*c*)   relatively complex commissioning, testing and maintenance procedures are required

(*d*)   under certain conductor icing conditions the carrier signal may be so attenuated that the protection has to be taken out of service to avoid the maloperation of the protection on through faults

(*e*)   normally even short lengths of cable cannot be inserted in the path of the h.f. signal. This limitation can be particularly difficult as it may not be known until a relatively late stage in the planning and construction of an overhead line, that for example for environmental reasons, a length of cable has to be inserted.

The early designs of phase comparison power line carrier protection were of the thermionic type and naturally required noninterrupted power supplies of many tens of VA. This necessitated in most cases the provision of large d.c. motor-generator sets driven from the 110 V station battery. Not only did these motor-generator sets require a considerable amount of maintenance and room to accommodate them in the substation buildings but, in order to provide as is customary 6 hours standby in the event of the l.v. a.c. supplies failing, a larger station battery was needed. With the advent of static phase-comparison protection and the replacement of thermionic protection, a considerable reduction in these auxiliary power supply requirements has occurred. Nevertheless, the provision of adequate non-interrupted power supplies for the phase-comparison protection is still necessary. The present practice is to use 48 V battery supplies for this purpose as they are subjected to much smaller voltage fluctuations in service than the 110 V battery used for closing and tripping circuit breakers.

(b) *Distance protection:* In UK applications the polar characteristics of distance protection are usually the conventional circular mho characteristics, although more complicated shaped characteristics are being introduced, where justified, to reduce the problem of setting the third zone so that it will not maloperate under emergency heavy load transfer conditions.

For both phase and earth faults separate or common measuring elements per phase are used for zones 1 and 2, and separate measuring elements for zone 3. It is considered that the extra reliability and speed obtainable with a multielement distance relay compared with a switched distance relay are justified for protecting feeders in a major transmission system.

Static designs of distance protection were introduced in mid 1960s and have steadily taken over from electromechanical designs. The main advantages of static distance relays are flexibility of characteristics, in particular the ability to shape the characteristic in the required manner, low VA consumption and high speed of operation.

The disadvantages of static distance relays are the need for auxiliary power supplies and the greater susceptibility of the relays to maloperate or be damaged by high frequency interference. The latter risks have in practice been reduced to a negligible magnitude by careful design and extensive type testing.

Recent designs of distance protection incorporate microprocessors as embedded components in their design. This has resulted in great flexibility in characteristics and logic sequences which can be easily changed without changing the design of the hardware. The characteristics themselves can also be improved, for example, the operating time can be made very fast (7 ms) provided there is no distortion in the input signals. In the presence of distortion the measuring time can be appropriately lengthened to ensure correct operation of the protection. Improved test facilities are also available if required, e.g. built-in on-line testing. The latter facility is included to improve the overall reliability of the protection in service.

If used in conjunction with phase comparison protection as the other main protection, for diversification reasons the distance protection should preferably be accelerated rather than blocked as phase-comparison protection is in this respect fundamentally similar to a blocking scheme, i.e. the local end must not be allowed to trip until it has waited to receive information from the remote end and that information has been compared with locally derived information regarding the current zero crossing points.

The main advantages of distance protection are:
(i) It provides fast and discriminative protection for all faults occurring on the feeder on which it is installed to within about 25% of the feeder length from the remote substation.
(ii) It provides some measure of back-up protection (zone 2 and zone 3) for other feeders and plant at remote stations and, often, on reverse reach of zone 3 at its own substation.
(iii) It does not necessarily need an incoming signal from a remote station in order to trip, even though the lack of an incoming signal may delay tripping.

The main disadvantages of distance protection are:
(a) It requires costly voltage transformers and if the protection is of the high speed type, e.g. under 10 ms, it normally requires voltage transformers with a high fidelity transient response; to obtain this response may be very costly.
(b) With some designs it may be difficult to obtain very fast clearance of close-up three-phase faults due to lack of polarising voltages.
(c) The protection may trip on load current in the absence of a voltage input, e.g. due to the voltage transformer fuses being inadvertently left out after line maintenance. To overcome this problem very-high-speed voltage transformer output monitoring relays may be installed to disconnect tripping before the protection can maloperate, but the cost and complexity of this monitoring equipment and the risk of the monitoring equipment maloperating and disconnecting tripping during a system fault has to be carefully assessed.

The available choice is between blocked or accelerated distance protection. Blocked distance protection has the advantage that when the remote end circuit breaker is open, faults are cleared quickly and discriminatively along the whole length of the protected feeder. On the other hand, for an accelerated protection with the remote circuit breaker open there is no operation of zone 1 protection at the end with the open circuit breaker and hence no acceleration signal is sent from that end. Faults on the feeder in zone 2, i.e. approximately 25% of the line length from the open circuit breaker are therefore only cleared in zone 2 time, which may be too long to be acceptable.

In the event of a known failure of the communication channel the blocked protection must be switched out of service as it would be unstable on a through fault.

An accelerated protection however has the advantage that in the event of a known loss of the communication channel the protection can remain in service, but faults occurring in zone 2 reach will only be cleared in zone 2 time instead of the faster accelerated time.

Various designs of blocking systems are available from manufacturers with differing performance characteristics and the most suitable system has to be chosen for a given application. Many of these systems include a first zone tripping facility independent of the receipt of any signal. The blocking or acceleration communication channel for the distance protection should ideally be of a different type from that used for other main protection on the feeder. On the other hand in the United Kingdom for a feeder, say, 30 km long using a voice-frequency phase-comparison protection over a Post Office channel for the first main protection, it might sometimes be difficult to justify the use of a carrier channel for blocking or acceleration of the second main distance protection. In fact, if a carrier channel could be economically justified it would normally be better to use the carrier channel for the phase-comparison protection (and thus eliminate the inherently long propagation time over a Post Office circuit of the complex phase comparison signal) and to use the Post Office channel for the simpler blocking or acceleration function. The latter proposal would not apply, however, where, for example due to a short length of cable in the carrier signal path, the attenuation by the cable and, more importantly, the reflections of the signal by the cable sealing ends result in a carrier signal which may be distorted and have an indeterminate effective phase shift in its propagation. In such a case it is preferred to transmit and receive the relatively simple blocking or acceleration signal over the carrier channel and rely on the PO channel to transmit the more phase sensitive phase-comparison protection signal.

Where a carrier channel cannot be used, e.g. lack of room in the available frequency spectrum or excessive attenuation due to a short length of cable in the middle of the long overhead feeder, double distance protection with PO signalling channels may have to be used. In this case, for diversity reasons, one of the main protections should preferably be of the blocked type and the other accelerated. This ensures that with a remote end circuit breaker open fast clearance times are provided by the blocked distance protection on the feeder. Also if all communication channels fail in an extreme emergency, e.g. due to widespread flooding of PO circuits, the three-zone feature of accelerated distance protection could still be used to provide discriminative protection for the feeder, albeit with some time delay.

In areas where high resistance earth faults are considered likely, the earth-fault distance protection can usefully be supplemented by a directional comparison earth fault protection module in order to provide the extra earth fault sensitivity; the separate signalling channel required for this facility would normally be over the same communication link which is provided for the associated distance protection.

7.6.1.2   Protection for a short overhead feeder: In this context, a shorter feeder is under 30 km long with a negligible amount of cable in its route length. A wider choice of protection is available than for long feeders since the use of private pilots as well as PO channels become economically feasible. Pilot wire systems and the factors which influence their application are described in detail in Chapter 10.

The choice of protection is largely governed, in particular for very short feeders a few kilometres long, by the cost of providing private pilot cables. As an extreme example for protecting an overhead line between two substations, say 4 km apart in a city area, it may be possible to utilise spare pairs in an existing pilot network at negligible cost. If, however, new pilot cables had to be laid, the cost of opening trenches, crossing and resurfacing roads etc., solely to provide pilot cables for protection could well be prohibitive. Overhead pilot cables suspended from the towers or embedded in the earthwire have rarely been used in the United Kingdom owing to unsatisfactory service experience. Fibre-optic cable embedded in the earthwire may in future provide a more satisfactory communication link.

Often underground pilot cables for protection and control purposes are installed in trenches on the same route as power cables, and hence are subject to induction and rise of earth potential effects in the event of faults on the power network. These induction problems can be one of the main limitations in using private pilots for protection. In a few cases it has even been found necessary to install isolation transformers every few kilometres in an existing pilot in order to reduce the induced voltages impressed on the pilot cores. Induced voltages, in addition to causing breakdown of the insulation of the pilot cable, in extreme cases may cause maloperation of the differential protection to which the pilot cores are connected. Details of the precautions which should be taken in choosing pilots are given in Chapter 7.

Where for the first and second main protection two physically segregated cables are not available for two private pilot protection systems, it is often economically justifiable to provide one private pilot wire protection as the first main protection and a Post Office pilot wire protection as the second main protection.

In the past, metallic pilots having known resistance and capacitance character-istics, have been rented from the Post Office which are suitable for a longitudinal differential protection system and these are likely to remain in use for many years, especially on very short routes. Where only voice frequency circuits can be rented from the Post Office a protection using a voice frequency signalling system can be used, such as voice-frequency phase-comparison protection or blocked distance protection.

Where no private pilots exist nor can be economically justified, one of the main protection systems may be a PO pilot system, and the other should preferably be of fundamentally different design such as distance or, for important circuits, power-line-carrier protection. The latter two types of protection are costly and in some cases cannot be justified; in this case two Post Office pilot protections with separ-ately routed pilots may be installed.

For very short overhead feeders, depending on the impedance of the source of fault current and the impedance of the circuit to be protected (i.e. the system impedance ratio) distance protection may be unsuitable; most distance protection systems have a maximum s.i.r. of about 50. In practice, most lines in a transmission system longer than about 6 km can be satisfactorily protected by distance protection, but it may have to be of the blocked type.

17.6.1.3 Protection for an underground feeder: Most of the considerations which apply to short overhead feeders apply equally to underground feeders. In view of the high capital cost of e.h.v. cables, these feeders are normally under 30 km. However, private pilots for protection purposes are much more likely to be available than for an overhead feeder as usually the cheapest way to provide the necessary communication channels between substations is to lay pilot cables on the same route as the e.h.v. cable, preferably in separate trenches to reduce induction problems. The latter particularly applies where individual e.h.v. cables are provided for each phase of the feeder.

On some feeders and networks, the high capacitance of the primary cables may require shunt reactors to be connected to the cable circuits either permanently or through a circuit breaker. This can lead to severe switchgear rating and protection problems related to the high charging current of the cables and to the interruption of highly inductive reactor currents. In general, separate fully discriminative protection systems are required for the cable and for any permanently connected shunt reactor to provide adequately sensitive protection for the reactor and to establish quickly which is the faulted item of plant.

The main problem in protecting cable circuits is the high charging current which may be an appreciable fraction of the load current; this limits the choice of minimum fault current setting for the protection. In fact, a maximum current setting of several times the steady state charging current depending on the manufacturer's recommendations may be necessary to ensure that the high transient discharging and charging currents in the primary cable circuit under external fault conditions do not cause the protection to maloperate. Similar transient currents flow when cable circuits are energised or de-energised. The frequency and magnitude of these transient currents depend not only on the parameters, i.e. capacitance, inductance and resistance of the primary circuit being energised, but also on the characteristics of the circuit breaker, e.g. the values of any switching resistors. These transient currents have, in practice, a frequency of the order of a few kilohertz, and in view of the low shunt impedance of the cable circuit at such frequencies appear as internal fault currents. The protection has to be designed to be sufficiently insensitive at these frequencies to prevent it from maloperating.

If distance protection is used for protecting the cable circuit the characteristic angle of the distance relays should preferably be approximately the same low angle as that of the cable circuit being protected in order to obtain optimum settings. The setting of distance protection on cable circuits with crossbonded sheaths presents a particularly difficult problem as the effective impedances of the cable circuit are dependent on the return paths of the fault current, and may vary over a wide range of values depending on the fault location, resistivity of the cable trench back-filling, etc.

As mentioned in Section 17.2.1.1, where more than one intertripping or signalling channels are required for dependability they should be as diverse as possible with regard both to the design of equipments installed and the types of communication channel used.

Problems may, however, arise as a direct result of providing this diversity. For example if it is assumed that the only communication channels which can be economically justified for the protection and intertripping of the double circuit transformer feeder shown in Fig. 17.3.1A are two separately routed private pilots, and that each feeder is equipped with two main protection systems with duplicate intertripping for each feeder, then in order to reduce the risk of a failure to trip it is evident that the first main protection for TF1 should be associated with pilot cable No. 1 and the second main protection associated with pilot cable No. 2. Similarly the first intertripping channel for TF1 should be in cable No. 1 and the second intertripping channel for TF1 in cable No. 2.

However, some forms of protection may maloperate on load or through fault currents in the event of the conductors in the pilot cable becoming short circuited. Also with a simple d.c. intertripping system a live conductor in the pilot may be inadvertently connected to another conductor through a short circuit, resulting in maloperation of the intertripping equipment.

One of the main causes of damage to pilot cables, particularly in urban areas, is building or road construction work where, for example, sheet piling may accidentally result in the severing and short circuiting of conductors in the pilot cable. In this event, if the communication channels for TF1 and TF2 were routed in the above manner, both TF1 and TF2 might be inadvertently tripped. On the other hand, if all the protection and intertripping associated with TF1 were routed in pilot cable No. 1 and that for TF2 were routed in pilot cable No. 2 the risk of inadvertent tripping would be confined to a single circuit.

Where the protection or intertripping for more than one primary circuit is routed in one pilot cable the risk of more than one primary circuit being inadvertently tripped can be reduced in various ways. For example, the use of starting relays for the protection will reduce the risk of protection maloperation and the risk of inadvertent maloperation of the intertripping can be practically eliminated by using a voice frequency intertripping system instead of a d.c. system.

In practice, an engineering assessment has to be made of the consequences of the loss of, or damage to a pilot cable or equivalent signalling channel and the appropriate measures taken within the economic constraints.

17.6.2   Protection for a transformer

Details of the protection systems available for protecting transformers are given in Chapter 11.

Transformers connected to a transmission system vary widely in size from several hundred MVA down to a few MVA, the latter being mainly for providing auxiliary supplies at small power stations. It is usual, at least as far as the high voltage connections are concerned, to provide similar protection for these small transformers to that provided for the larger transformers, as a slowly or incorrectly cleared fault on a small transformer may be as disastrous to the operation of the transmission system as a similarly cleared fault on a large transformer. Hence all transformers directly connected to a major transmission system require fast earth- and phase-fault protection, although the risk of phase faults clear of earth occurring inside a transformer tank is extremely low.

The risk of phase faults occurring on the h.v. or l.v. connections to a transformer is, however, not low, especially if open type connections are used. Flying debris can lodge on the connections although even if the connections are completely phase segregated, safety earths inadvertently left connected after maintenance work can result in three phase faults. As mentioned in Section 17.2.1, discriminative clearance of phase faults may be difficult if inverse definite minimum time overcurrent protection is the only phase fault connection provided for the transformer.

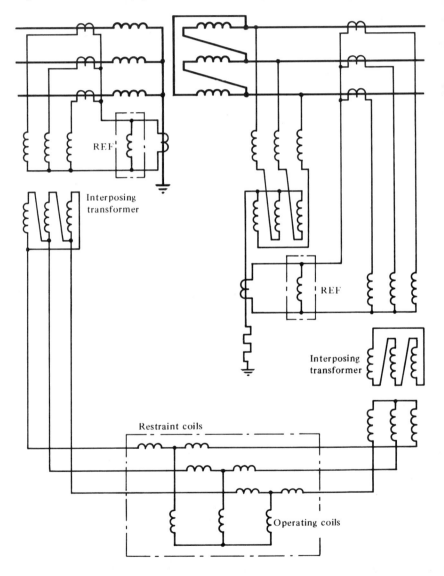

Fig. 17.6.2A   *Transformer overall differential protection*

With regard to the protection of the transformer itself, for double wound transformers fast earth-fault protection is usually obtained by unbiased differential protection separately covering the l.v. and h.v. windings, and fast phase-fault protection by a biased overall differential protection system (Fig. 17.6.2A). For economic reasons the earth- and phase-fault protection systems usually share the same current transformers. In addition to some form of inverse-time back-up overcurrent or earth-fault protection, Buchholz protection, and on some transformers other gas pressure operated devices, are provided. The Buchholz protection, as well as providing back-up protection for phase and earth faults on the transformer windings, also provides some measure of protection for interturn faults on the windings, and for core faults, i.e. failure of the lamination insulation resulting in high damaging circulating currents within the transformer core.

Most forms of transformer overall differential protection use a harmonic restraint feature to prevent the protection maloperating in the presence of

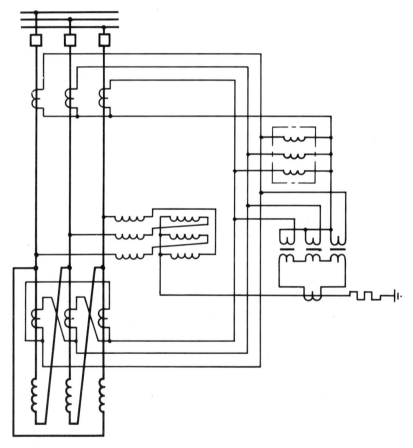

Fig. 17.6.2B   *Typical example of phase and earth-fault differential protection for individual winding of a transformer*

harmonics such as occur, for example, in the transformer magnetising inrush current. With loads having a very high harmonic content, e.g. arc furnace loads, this harmonic bias might result in very slow operation or even nonoperation of the transformer overall differential protection in the event of an internal fault occurring in the transformer. An alternative way of providing phase fault protection for such applications is shown in Fig. 17.6.2B where the protection for the l.v. windings only has been shown. Each winding is provided with a separate differential protection which avoids the transformer inrush and harmonic current problems but it requires current transformers to be mounted in the delta winding connections. This may be difficult and costly in practice and can rarely be justified, bearing in mind the very low risk of phase faults, clear of earth, occurring within the transformer tank. A typical protection scheme for a double-wound transformer is shown in Fig. 17.6.2C.

If the h.v. or l.v. connections are very short, the separate protection can be omitted, but the main reason for providing this protection is to give discriminative indication of the fault location which reduces appreciably the time required to establish the exact location of the fault. If, for example, the h.v. connection protection has operated and there is an insulation co-ordinating gap in the protection zone covered by the h.v. connection protection, there is a high probability that the fault was caused by the gap flashing over and that it is safe to restore the transformer to service without any tests being made. In some cases it is permissible to initiate automatic reclosing from the connection protection, arranging of course the prevention of automatic reclosing if the transformer differential protection has also operated.

For phase faults, the unbiased differential connection protection is also inherently faster than the biased differential transformer protection, thus providing faster clearance of phase faults than would be the case if the biased transformer differential protection zone embraced the transformer connections.

The high set overcurrent protection in Fig. 17.6.2C fed from the current transformers in the transformer h.v. bushings provides fast clearance of phase faults at the upper end of the transformer h.v. winding. It also backs up the transformer overall differential and restricted earth fault protection. The main difficulty when applying high set overcurrent protection is in establishing a suitable setting. The setting current must be sufficiently low to ensure that it will operate quickly with the minimum fault current available, yet it must not be so low that it will respond to faults on the l.v. side of the transformer or operate with transformer magnetising inrush currents which, for some types of transformer, may be as much as seven times the full load current.

The back-up inverse time overcurrent protection operates in two stages to provide discriminative clearance of faults beyond the transformer l.v. circuit breaker in the first stage, and faults within the transformer or on its l.v. connections in the second stage. Both the high-set and inverse-time overcurrent protection are often energised from current transformers in the individual transformer h.v. bushings to permit future banking of a second transformer without having to make

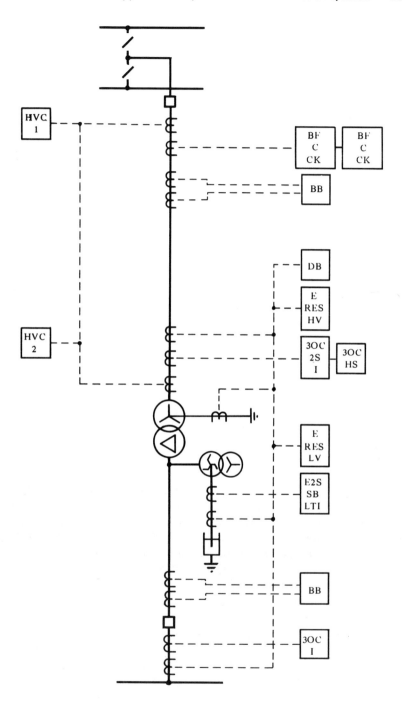

Fig. 17.6.2C *Protection scheme for a double wound transformer*

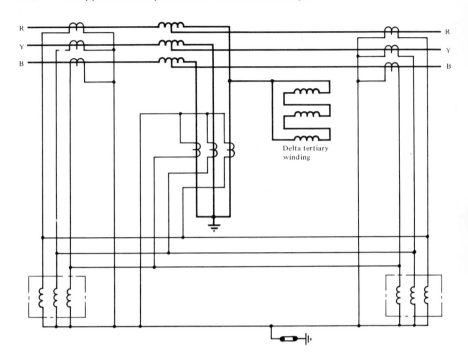

Fig. 17.6.2D   *Differential protection for an auto-transformer*

major changes in the protection of the existing transformer.

The unbiased differential protection of an auto-transformer is applied on a phase-by-phase basis as shown in Fig. 17.6.2D. The protection is equally fast and sensitive for phase and earth faults.

A typical protection system for an autotransformer and its connections is shown on Fig. 17.6.2E; it is basically similar to that for a double-wound transformer. One of the differences between Fig. 17.6.2C and 17.6.2E is that the l.v. side in Fig. 17.6.2C is assumed to be connected to a resistance earthed system (e.g. 33 kV) with only short connections between the transformer and the l.v. circuit breaker and hence the l.v. connection protection has been omitted. In Fig. 17.6.2E, the l.v. side is assumed to be solidly earthed (e.g. 275 or 132 kV) and there is separate protection for the l.v. connections.

The tertiary winding on an autotransformer may be used to provide, via a h.v./l.v. transformer, the l.v. a.c. supplies in a substation; it is also frequently the means adopted of coupling reactive compensation plant into the transmission system. A typical scheme for protecting such a primary circuit arrangement is shown in Fig. 17.6.2F. It should be noted that the tertiary winding, when not used for l.v. a.c. supplies or reactive compensation coupling, often has one corner of its winding solidly connected to the neutral of the autotransformer to ensure that it is properly earthed and also included in one of the autotransformer differential protection

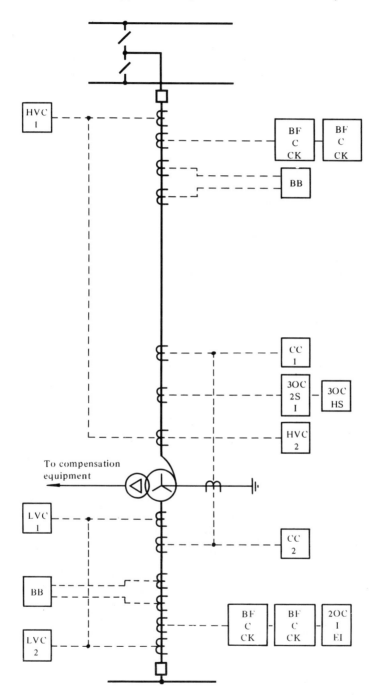

Fig. 17.6.2E   *Protection scheme for an autotransformer*

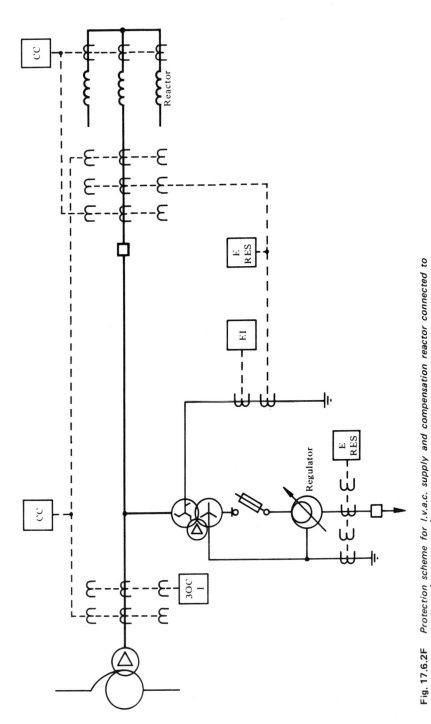

Fig. 17.6.2F Protection scheme for l.v.a.c. supply and compensation reactor connected to tertiary of an autotransformer

zones, (Fig. 17.6.2D). When the tertiary is connected to reactive compensation equipment and is earthed as shown in Fig. 17.6.2F, the earth connection on one corner of the delta tertiary must be removed to avoid multiple earthing, and the earth-fault protection for the tertiary winding is then provided by the differential earth-fault protection energised from the current transformers in the h.v. neutral of the earthing/l.v. a.c. supply transformer and in the bushings of the circuit breaker controlling the reactive compensation plant. Reliance is placed on Buchholz and back-up overcurrent protection for the very remote risk of a phase fault in the tertiary winding not involving earth.

It should be noted that, for economic reasons, there is no circuit breaker on the l.v. side of the l.v. a.c. supply transformer. The l.v. winding and connections of this transformer are protected by differential earth-fault protection, but fuses provide phase and earth-fault protection beyond the disconnector.

17.6.3   Protection for banked transformers

The protection requirements for banked transformers are influenced by:

(*a*)   the number and types of windings on the transformers to be banked, for example star/delta/star, interconnected star, or auto
(*b*)   whether the transformation ratio of each transformer in the bank is the same
(*c*)   the relative ratings and impedances of the two transformers
(*d*)   the extent to which each transformer is required, to have its own discriminative protection for operational and maintenance reasons.

If transformers of similar types are to be banked, and other factors permit, it may be permissible for a single transformer overall protection system to be shared between more than one transformer (Fig. 17.6.3A).

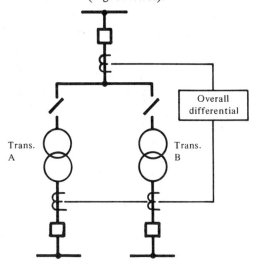

Fig. 17.6.3A   *Common overall differential protective system for banked transformers*

Care must be taken, however, to ensure, especially with biased transformer overall differential protection systems, that not too many current transformers are connected into the differential system, otherwise the c.t. magnetising currents may lead to an unacceptable increase in the setting of the protection. In general, for biased overall differential protection systems not more than two power transformers can be protected by a single system. It must also be borne in mind that with biased systems the bias is usually obtained solely from current flowing between the h.v. and l.v. current transformers, and if it is possible for high through-fault currents to flow between the l.v. current transformers, no bias will be available to ensure stability of the protection. In such an application it may be necessary to derive an additional bias feature from the l.v. c.t. currents.

If the banked transformers are of differing ratio it may be possible to employ a common overall differential system, but the magnetising currents of the additional main and interposing c.t.s, if any, may adversely affect the sensitivity and stability of the protection to an unacceptable extent. If a small transformer is banked with a much larger transformer, it is essential that a separate differential scheme be provided for the smaller transformer in order to obtain adequate settings for faults on the l.v. side of the smaller transformer. Alternatively, if the transformer is relatively very small indeed, for example, a 0·3 MVA 33/0·415 kV auxiliary transformer associated with a 90 MVA, 132/33 kV transformer, high breaking capacity fuses mounted as close as possible to the transformer 415 V winding would usually suffice. Faults in the auxiliary transformer which produce fault currents less than the setting of the overall differential protection will be detected by its Buchholz protection. However, for most transmission applications fully discriminative protection for each transformer and its associated connections is an operational requirement, any common connections having their own protection; an example is shown in Fig. 17.6.3B. It should be noted that very few changes are necessary to convert the protection arrangements shown for single transformers (Figs. 17.6.2C and 17.6 2E) into the arrangements for a banked pair.

Disconnector auxiliary switches are shown in the differential protection bus-wiring to enable the h.v. connection protection which is common to both transformers to remain safely in service when a transformer is out of service for maintenance and its h.v. disconnector is open. A separate differential protection relay energised from c.t.s in the transformer h.v. bushing which remains in service when the disconnector is open, may be provided, to protect the h.v. connections between the open disconnector and the transformer h.v. bushings, thus allowing the transformer to be energised from the l.v. side only. This mode of operation may be needed for example where reactive compensation plant is connected to the transformer tertiary windings and it is desired to retain this compensation plant in service when the transformer h.v. disconnector is open.

If certain limitations are acceptable an arrangement such as is shown in Fig. 17.6.3C may be permissible, in which there is a common protection system which initiates tripping, and tank earth-fault alarms indicate which of the transformers is faulty. The setting of the tank earth-fault indication relay has to be high enough to

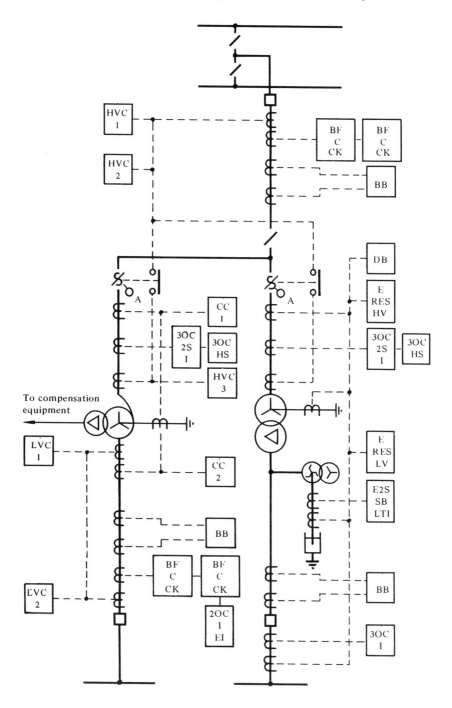

Fig. 17.6.3B   *Protection scheme for banked transformers*

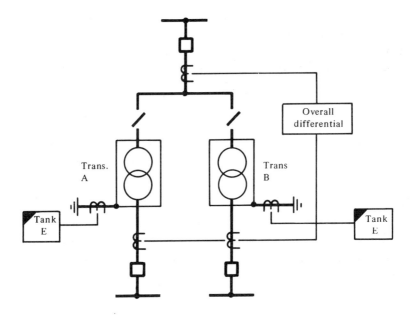

Fig. 17.6.3C   *Indication of faulty transformer by tank earth-fault relays*

ensure that transient currents which may flow through the capacitance of the transformer windings under external fault or switching conditions are insufficient to operate the relay. A typical setting used for a 275/132 kV 180 MVA transformer was 200 A. It should be noted that this arrangement does not permit discriminative indication of faults on the transformer connections and hence would not normally be acceptable for controlling automatic isolation of the faulted transformer. For this, and other maintenance and construction reasons this arrangement is now very rarely used. The arrangement may be acceptable if operating conditions permit a visual inspection of the transformer and its connections to be made prior to reclosure.

17.6.4   Protection for a teed feeder

Some of the most difficult problems the protection engineer has to solve are concerned with the protection of teed feeders. It is often very difficult to obtain fault-clearance times, sensitivity and stability comparable to those obtainable for two-ended feeders, and in rare cases it may even be impossible to provide a satisfactory protection scheme at all, thus necessitating a change in the design of the power system.

For many applications e.g. relatively short teed feeders, some form of differential or phase comparison protection system is preferred, using private pilots, power-line-carrier or microwave communication links. In present practice fast (under 40 ms) differential protection systems require a microwave link or similar wide bandwidth channel. Slower biased differential systems use private pilot wire circuits. In practice, in order to protect teed feeders especially if each leg is under 5 km in length, it is often necessary to split up the teed feeder into two or more protection zones by inserting current transformers at the tee point as illustrated in Fig. 17.6.4A.

In the scheme shown, there are three separate differential protection zones, and when a fault occurs in one of the zones the protection for that zone operates and in addition the operated protection is arranged to unstabilise the protection for the other two zones, thus initiating tripping at all three ends. Also, operation of any one protection system is usually arranged to initiate intertripping signals to all ends as the protection at the other ends may not operate even if unstabilised. Also direct intertripping of the circuit breaker is often a faster means of clearing the fault than waiting for operation of a local end of a protection system which has been unstabilised.

In addition to the relatively long fault clearance times obtained the scheme shown in Fig. 17.6.4A is very costly, especially if overhead lines have to be terminated in a compound solely to enable post-type current transformers to be installed at ground level.

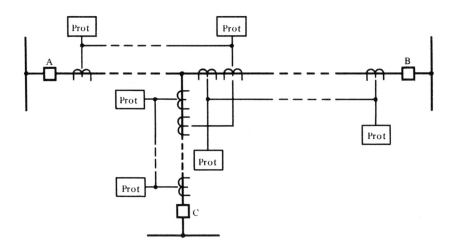

Fig. 17.6.4A *Protection of teed feeder with two sets of current transformers at tee-point*

One method of avoiding the need to install current transformers at the tee-point is to install a power directional comparison system in which the direction of power flow at each end of the protected feeder is measured and tripping is inhibited at all ends if the power flows out of the feeder at any one end (Chapter 10).

This system has occasionally been successfully applied but the following conditions must be met:

(*a*)   The system configurations and fault infeeds must be such that for all internal fault conditions fault current can never flow out of the protected feeder (Fig.

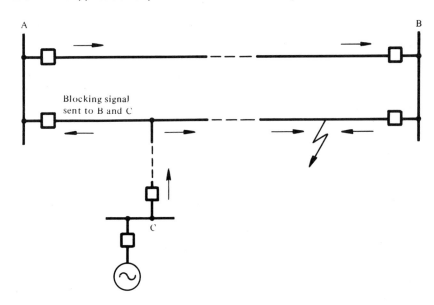

Fig. 17.6.4B   *Inhibition of tripping by false block*

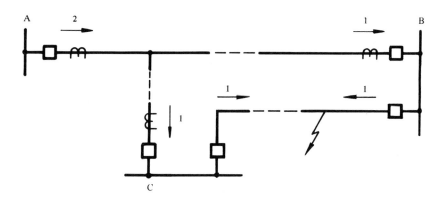

Fig. 17.6.4C   *Fault current distribution*

17.6.4B), otherwise the protection at the end where the fault current is flowing out of the feeder will send a blocking signal to the other two ends and thus inhibit tripping.

(b)   If overcurrent starting is used for the protection, the margin between the settings of the high set and low set relays must be large enough to ensure that, for an external fault, a high-set relay at one end cannot operate before a low-set relay at another end has operated, otherwise the protection will be unstable. If the through-fault current distribution is as shown in Fig. 17.6.4C, it will be seen that the high-set relay setting must be at least twice the low-set relay setting to ensure that a low-set relay at Station B or C operates before the high-set relay at Station A. To ensure that the low-set relays do not operate with normal load currents, a minimum fault setting of at least 200% of the maximum normal load current is necessary.

Often a more satisfactory form of protection for a teed feeder, particularly for a longer teed feeder, is accelerated or blocked distance protection. For diversity reasons one main protection should preferably be of the blocked type and the other accelerated, although it should be noted some modern systems use a mixture of acceleration and blocking for different measuring elements in the same distance protection.

There are very many factors to be considered in choosing the design and settings of distance protection for teed circuits.

One of the most important is the absolute and relative lengths, and hence impedances, of each leg of the teed circuit. The primary circuit configuration shown in Fig. 17.6.4D is for example much easier to protect than that shown in Fig. 17.6.4E as in the latter case the distance protections at stations A and C cannot be set to operate for faults near station B without responding to faults in or beyond stations C and A respectively.

Another important factor in choosing suitable forms of distance protection are the magnitudes and variations in the fault current infeeds at each end of the teed circuit. One aspect of this is illustrated in Fig. 17.6.4F. Assuming a fault occurs near station C, it is apparent that the distance protection at station A will see this fault further away than it actually is owing to the voltage being injected at the tee point from station B. Similarly, the distance protection at station B will see the

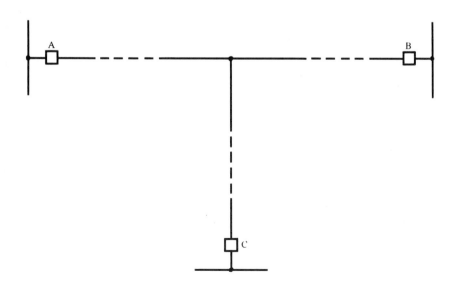

Fig. 17.6.4D *Symmetrical teed circuit*

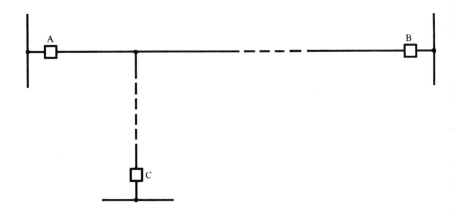

Fig. 17.6.4E   *Teed circuit with unequal legs*

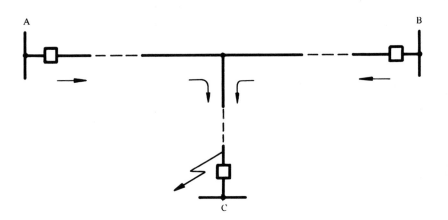

Fig. 17.6.4F   *Fault on a teed feeder*

fault further away owing to the fault current infeed from station A. The relays at stations A and B thus 'underreach' and, depending on the settings which can be given to these relays, they may or may not operate in their second or third zones. It is therefore frequently necessary to arrange on such a teed circuit that when the protection at station B operates it initiates the sending of intertripping signals to stations A and C. Incidentally, in general it is usually prudent even where it is not absolutely essential to arrange that the operation of the protection at any one station initiates the intertripping of the circuit breakers at all other stations on a teed circuit. Some of the parameters which have to be calculated and checked for a typical accelerated distance protection system applied to a teed circuit are:

(*a*)   maximum permissible zone 1 settings
(*b*)   minimum attainable zone 1 settings

(c) with all circuit breakers closed effective reach of relays at each end as a result of remote infeeds

(d) with one circuit breaker open, effective reach of relays

(e) with two circuit breakers open, effective reach of relays

(f) minimum zone 3 settings

(g) load transfer limitations.

The major underreach problem which occurs with an accelerated distance protection system can be reduced by using a blocked form of distance protection system for which the reach of the tripping zone can be appreciably increased.

However, choosing appropriate settings for the relays performing the blocking function can be difficult. Not only do the magnitudes of the phase and earth fault current infeeds affect the choice of setting but also the direction of the currents can affect operation as shown in Fig. 17.6.4B.

Some of the calculations and checks that have to be made for a typical blocked distance protection application are:

(a) Check that the minimum setting of the trip feature which is available after blocking has been removed reaches beyond the remote circuit end under the worst infeed conditions.

(b) Calculate the minimum setting for the block-remove feature.

(c) Check that the trip feature after blocking has been removed or the block-remove feature do not reach beyond the reverse reach of the remote-end block initiate feature.

(d) Check that the block-remove feature does not have a setting that will cause operation on reverse earth faults.

(e) Establish the load transfer limitations.

With some designs of complex blocked distance protection systems an assessment of its performance for varying fault locations and differing types of fault and system conditions can be very time consuming and a difficult task requiring extensive computation. In some cases in fact, the design of the protection system has to be tailored, with the aid of the manufacturer, to make it suitable for a particular teed circuit configuration, assuming certain maximum and minimum infeed conditions at each end of the teed feeder concerned and certain assumed ranges of positive, negative- and zero-sequence impedances for that part of the primary network which is effectively in parallel with the teed feeder to be protected.

After completing the calculations, checks or tests, it may well be found that the proposed teed circuit cannot be protected in a satisfactory manner to meet all operational conditions, load transfer restraints being a particularly common unacceptable limitation. The situation can be improved appreciably by inserting current transformers at the tee point as shown in Fig. 17.6.4A. A cheaper arrangement, by which acceptable performance may still be obtained is to insert post-type current

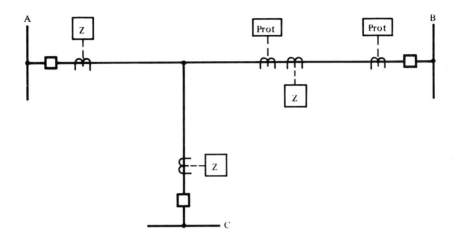

Fig. 17.6.4G *Protection of teed feeder with extra current transformers in one leg*

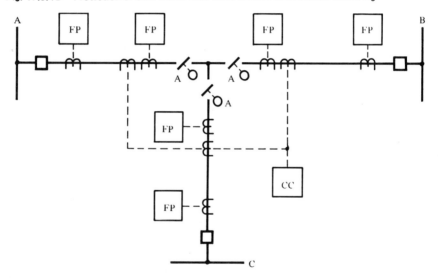

Fig. 17.6.4H *Protection of teed feeder with individual protection for each leg*

transformers in only one leg of the tee as shown in Fig. 17.6.4G; in this case it may be technically better and more cost effective to protect part of the teed feeder by a differential or phase-comparison protection.

If there is a requirement for automatic operation of disconnectors at the tee point to permit automatic restoration of the healthy part of a teed circuit, it is essential that each leg should be separately protected to enable the faulted leg to be identified and isolated as shown in Fig. 17.6.4H.

In spite of all the techniques mentioned above there are some arrangements of teed circuits which cannot be satisfactorily protected and the only option left is to rearrange the primary system.

17.6.5 Protection for a transformer-feeder

For very short transformer-feeders, less than approximately 2 km long, it may be technically possible, current transformer lead burdens permitting, to include the feeder in the associated transformer differential protection zone in which case the protection could be identical to that for a transformer. However, in order that a transformer-feeder may be switched back into service as soon as possible after a fault, it is necessary, for major transmission system applications, for the feeder and the associated transformer each to have its own individual discriminative protection.

The feeder section is in general protected in the same manner as described in Section 17.6.1, two main protection systems being provided for those transformer-feeders which form an important part of the transmission system.

The relatively high impedance of the transformer does, however, appreciably affect the application of any distance protection. The application of distance protection is eased where it can be set to look into the transformer winding, i.e. the impedance of the transformer can be used to enable the zone 1 reach setting to be longer than the feeder length, thereby permitting fast operation of the protection for all feeder faults between the transformer h.v. terminals and the h.v. circuit breaker. On the other hand, this advantage does not apply to any distance protection installed at the transformer end of the transformer feeder. Furthermore, the impedance of the transformer limits through fault currents to relatively low magnitudes which necessitates low settings for any blocking relays. The transformer is protected in the manner described in Section 17.6.2.

The transformer protection must trip both the h.v. and l.v. circuit breakers. Also the feeder protection at the transformer end may be very sluggish or even fail to operate if, as is often the case, the fault current infeed through the transformer is low, and hence two-way intertripping is normally required (Fig. 17.6.5A).

For very important transmission circuits, two independent intertripping systems are provided, normally employing voice frequency signalling over private or Post Office pilots. As mentioned in Section 17.6.1.3, for dependability reasons, the

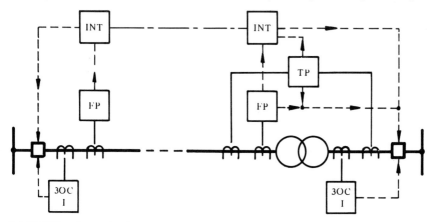

Fig. 17.6.5A *Protection for short transformer feeder*

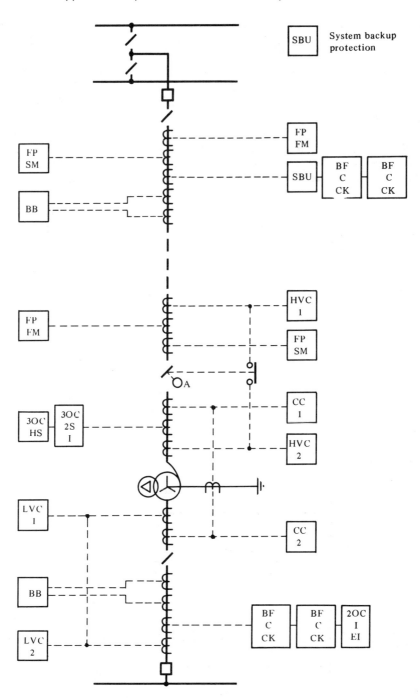

Fig. 17.6.5B   *Protection for transformer feeder forming part of a major transmission system*

intertripping and protection signalling equipments and communication channels should be as different as practicable. In addition, the intertripping is backed up by unstabilisation of any differential, phase-comparison or blocked distance feeder protection, and acceleration of accelerated distance protection. For less important transmission circuits, in view of the latter back up facilities, only one intertripping system may be provided. The reason for the provision of this considerable amount of redundancy is to reduce to a minimum, within economic constraints, the risk of an uncleared, or slowly cleared fault on the transformer or its associated l.v. connections. Severe and costly damage, particularly by fire, can result from slowly cleared faults on the transformer or its l.v. cables; this may result in a very long outage time before the transformer-feeder can be restored to operational service, with a consequent possible risk to continuity of supply to consumers.

A typical scheme for protecting a transformer-feeder forming part of a major transmission system is shown in Fig. 17.6.5B.

The protection arrangements for transformer-feeders not forming part of a major transmission system are described in Section 17.7.

17.6.6 Protection for a double-busbar station

Although the risk of a busbar fault occurring at most major transmission stations is

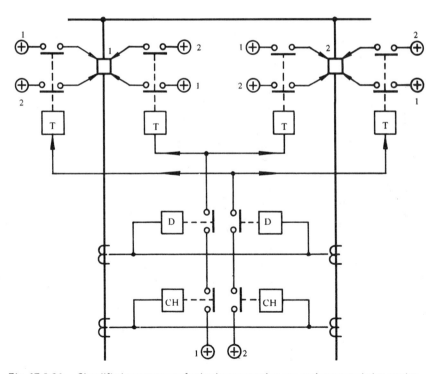

Fig. 17.6.6A   *Simplified arrangement for busbar protection at a major transmission station*

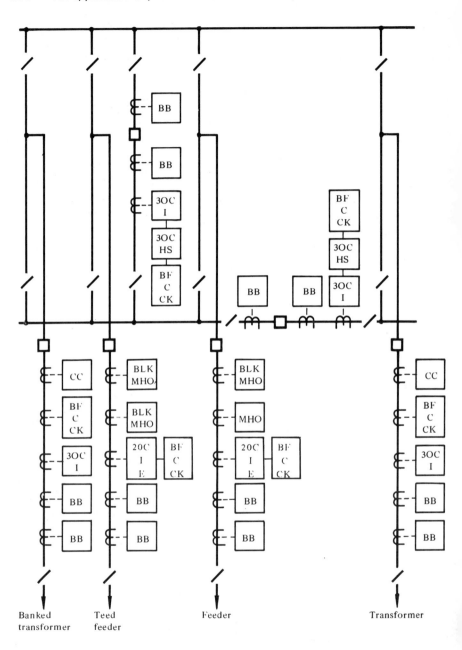

Fig. 17.6.6B   *Typical protection for part of a double busbar station*

extremely low, perhaps once in the life of the station, the consequences to the system of a slowly cleared busbar fault are so severe that the expenditure incurred in providing costly and complex busbar protection can be fully justified. A similar justification can be made for the provision of circuit-breaker fail protection at major transmission stations.

It is therefore usual practice at CEGB 400 and 275 kV stations to provide the busbar protection and breaker fail protection which is described in detail in Chapter 13.

It should be noted that at an important transmission station the design of the busbar protection should be such that the failure of any one relay to operate should not result in an uncleared busbar fault. It is therefore usual to provide some measure of redundancy in the 'two out of two' relay logic, e.g. extra per zone relays may be connected in parallel with both the check and discriminating relays as illustrated in Fig. 17.6.6A.

A typical example of the protection arrangements at a 400 kV double busbar station are shown on Fig. 17.6.6B.

17.6.7 Protection for mesh stations

The protection arrangements for a typical mesh type station are shown in Fig. 17.6.7A. The main differences between the protection arrangements at a mesh station compared to those at a double-busbar station concern the protection provided for the busbars. At a mesh station the number of circuit breakers required to be tripped in the event of a busbar fault is much smaller than at a double-busbar station and the operational consequences of an inadvertent operation of the busbar protection are very much less severe; hence there is no need for a 'two out of two' logic in the tripping sequence. The busbar protection at a mesh station is normally of the high impedance differential type and is arranged in a 'one out of two' logic.

Auxiliary switches on the feeder disconnector are arranged to disconnect the feeder current transformers and associated differential relay from the mesh corner protection buswiring when the feeder disconnector is open. Fast discriminative protection for the connection between the open feeder disconnector and the current transformer housing is thus provided when the feeder is energised or left in service from the remote end, e.g. for a teed feeder circuit.

17.6.8 Protection for complex primary circuit configurations

With the high cost of switchgear there has been an increasing tendency to design primary systems with the minimum number of circuit breakers, e.g. by banking and tee-connecting circuits. A relatively simple example is shown in Fig. 17.6.8A. It will be noted in this case that only a few changes are necessary to the protection arrangements shown in Fig. 17.6.3B. Nevertheless, for some primary circuit configurations the protection, and also the automatic switching arrangements can become very complex. An example is shown in Fig. 17.6.8B and the associated

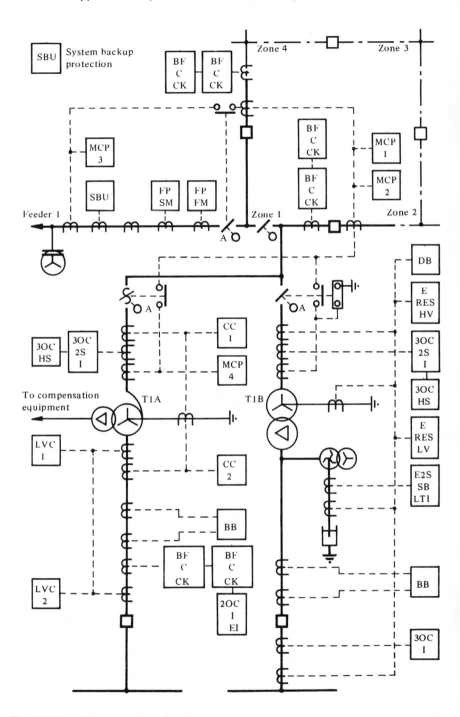

Fig. 17.6.7A   *Protection at a mesh station*

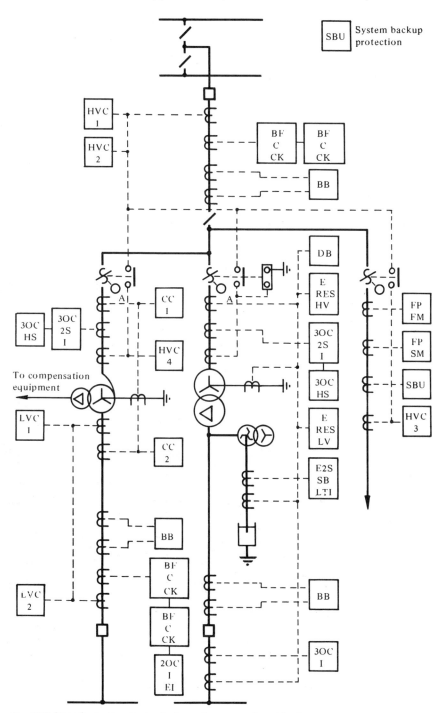

Fig. 17.6.8A *Protection for banked transformers and teed feeder*

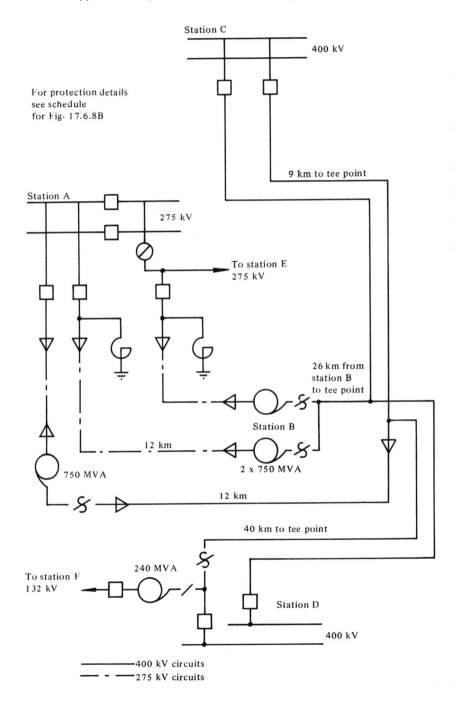

Fig. 17.6.8B   *Complex primary circuit configuration*

Protection and automatic switching scheme for feeders shown in Fig. 17.6.8B

Station	Voltage	Circuit	Protection
A	275	To stations C & D via station B	1st & 2nd Main: between stations A and B differential pilot wire feeder protection of two different types
A	400	To stations C & D via 275/400 kV transformer at station A	1st & 2nd Main: accelerated mho distance protection of two different types
B	275	To station A	1st & 2nd Main: differential private pilot wire feeder protection of two different types
B	400	To stations C & D	1st & 2nd Main: accelerated mho distance protection of two different types
C	400	To stations A & D	1st Main: mho blocked distance protection with PO signalling system to D 2nd Main: accelerated mho distance protection
C	400	To stations B & D	1st Main: mho blocked distance protection with PO signalling system to D 2nd Main: accelerated mho distance protection
D	400	To stations B & C	1st Main: mho blocked distance protection with PO signalling system to C 2nd Main: accelerated mho distance protection
D	400	To stations A & C	1st Main: mho blocked distance protection with v.h.s. PO signalling system to C 2nd Main: accelerated mho distance protection

Notes
1.   Stations C and D are major power stations whereas station A is a relatively weak infeed. The distance protection reaches from C and D are limited by the transformers at A and B and hence, there is no need to block the blocked mho distance protection from stations A and B. Furthermore, it was found that reliable blocking could not be initiated from stations A and B, if the circuit breakers at C or D were open.
2.   Intertripping is provided between all stations using a mixture of private and post office signalling channels diversely routed and cascaded where necessary. Operation of any protection intiates intertripping of all circuit breakers on circuit concerned.
3.   Automatic control facilities to avoid switching overvoltages and the effect of ferreresonance are arranged as follows:

(a) A-B-D circuits
Following the opening of the circuit breakers, the 400 kV switch disconnectors at B are opened automatically. The autoreclose sequence is as follows:
(i)   close D 400 kV circuit breaker to charge line
(ii) close B 400 kV switch disconnectors to charge transformers and A cables
(iii) check synchronise then close C 400 kV circuit breaker and A 275 kV circuit breakers.

(b) A-C-D circuits
Following the opening of the circuit breakers, the 400 kV switch disconnectors at A and D are opened automatically. The D switch disconnector may then be reclosed immediately. The autoreclose sequence is as follows:
(i)   close D 400 kV circuit breaker to charge line and D transformer
(ii) close A switch disconnector to energise transformer
(iii) check synchronise, then close C 400 kV circuit breaker, A 275 kV circuit breaker and D 132 kV circuit breaker.

The above closing sequences are also followed for manual operation.

schedule gives detailed protection arrangements for this particular primary system configuration.

With such complex primary circuits it is practically inevitable that, for protection and other reasons, there are operational limitations, e.g. some circuit breakers must not be left closed if certain other circuit breakers are open.

Also, the protection arrangements for such complex circuits inevitably result in longer fault clearance times than are attainable for simpler circuits and these longer times may not be acceptable as adjacent parts of the system are developed and faster fault clearance times are required. These complex configurations may, furthermore, necessitate complex logic for the automatic switching equipments to avoid switching overvoltages which might result from energising particular combinations of overhead lines and transformers.

Nevertheless, especially for transitional schemes, there are occasions when these complex primary circuits and their associated complex protection and automatic switching arrangements can be justified on economic grounds.

17.7   Typical protection applications in a minor transmission system or major distribution system

For less important transmission systems and major distribution systems where longer fault clearance times are permissible and where the dependability requirements for the protection are less severe major economies can justifiably be made in many cases by installing less elaborate protection schemes than those described in Section 17.6. On the other hand, in the growth of a power network in a country it is highly probable that a system which starts as a transmission system after several years or possibly decades will become part of a distribution system, and a cost-benefit analysis has then to be made of whether or not it is worthwhile to replace existing protection schemes on a part of the network by simpler schemes. Major factors in this analysis are the availability and cost of spares for the old protection and cost of maintaining it.

17.7.1   Protection for a feeder

In most applications, two main protection systems cannot be justified, and one main protection and overcurrent back-up protection is usually adequate. Similarly, duplication of protection signalling systems is rarely applicable; and for some feeders distance protection of the switched type without acceleration or blocking may well suffice. The same factors apply in choosing a suitable protection system as are described in Section 17.6.1 but for the majority of applications the cost of power-line-carrier protection may well be prohibitive, depending on the cost of the coupling equipment.

17.7.2 Protection for a transformer

The protection scheme is often basically the same as described in Section 17.6.2, but there may not be sufficient justification for providing overall differential protection in all applications; h.v. and l.v. differential earth fault protection, h.v. overcurrent protection, and l.v. overcurrent protection, often directional, may suffice.

17.7.3 Protection for banked transformers and dual secondary transformers

Some of the schemes described in the first part of Section 17.6.3 may be acceptable, using for example a common overall differential system for both transformers in a bank. In some substations dual secondary transformers, e.g. 132/11/11 kV may be installed and a typical protection scheme for such a transformer is shown at the transformer end of the transformer-feeder in Fig. 17.7.5B. It should be noted that in this scheme instead of attempting to provide transformer h.v. overcurrent protection at the transformer end, which would introduce discrimination problems, a relay is connected differentially with h.v. current transformers and current transformers in the l.v. circuit breakers to provide a plain balance scheme covering both transformers.

17.7.4 Protection for a teed feeder

Apart from there being no need for duplication of the main protection, the same considerations apply as described in Section 17.6.4. However, longer fault clearance times are often admissible in minor transmission systems and major distribution systems which, in general, eases the problem of protecting teed feeders.

17.7.5 Protection for a transformer feeder

Major economies can sometimes be made in the protection of transformer feeders compared to the schemes described in Section 17.6.5; longer fault clearance times are often permissible for feeder faults, and the cascade tripping situation illustrated in Fig. 17.7.5A may be acceptable. In this example, it is assumed that the limited fault current infeed at the transformer end is initially insufficient to operate the unit type feeder protection at that end. After the feeder protection at end A has operated and the circuit breaker Q has tripped, a higher voltage is available at station A busbars to drive an increased fault current through the transformers at station B, thus enabling the feeder protection at the transformer end to operate and initiate tripping of circuit breaker R. If the fault current infeed at station B for feeder faults is insufficient to operate the protection at that end and provided that the transformer feeder is unlikely to be energised or left energised from its l.v. side with the h.v. circuit breaker open intertripping can be provided to trip the l.v. circuit breakers. Alternatively, provided the fault current infeed at the h.v. end is

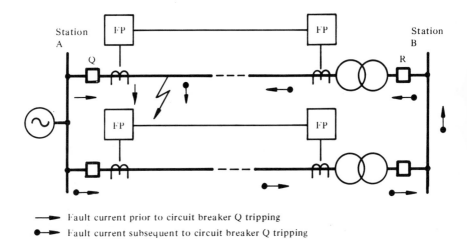

──▶ Fault current prior to circuit breaker Q tripping
●─▶ Fault current subsequent to circuit breaker Q tripping

Fig. 17.7.5A   *Sequential tripping*

high enough, some forms of differential and phase comparison feeder protection
have an inherent intertripping facility which may be sufficiently fast. If the transformer feeder is protected by distance protection at its h.v. end and the h.v. system
is solidly earthed directional overcurrent protection on the l.v. side of the
transformer can often provide adequate protection for feeder faults, thus saving, at
the transformer end, the cost of h.v. voltage transformers, current transformers and
a set of distance protection (see Fig. 17.7.5B).

The directional overcurrent protection must be set to discriminate between
faults on the h.v. system and faults on the transformer feeder (see Fig. 17.7.5C).

If fault current infeed through the transformer feeder l.v. circuit breaker is
significant for faults occurring beyond the h.v. circuit breaker, either the directional
overcurrent protection must have an operating time sufficiently long to obtain discriminative operation, or the directional overcurrent relay must be interlocked with
the distance protection at the h.v. circuit breaker end via a protection signalling
channel so that it cannot operate unless the distance protection has operated. This
is referred to as inhibited directional overcurrent protection.

If the fault current infeeds at the h.v. end of the transformer feeder are always
expected to remain within a restricted range, very simple and relatively cheap high
set overcurrent and restricted earth-fault protection may take the place of the h.v.
end distance protection as shown in Fig. 17.7.5D. (See Chapter 12, Section
12.9.2(*d*)). By choosing suitable settings for E1, E2 and the h.s.o.c. relays operation
of the protection can be restricted to faults occurring between the feeder protection
current transformers and the transformer h.v. neutral connection.

The high-set overcurrent must be set so as not to operate for faults on the l.v.
side of the transformer. The star/delta interposing current transformer eliminates
zero sequence currents from the inputs to the E2 relays; the setting of these E2
relays must however take into account, for faults on the h.v. system beyond the

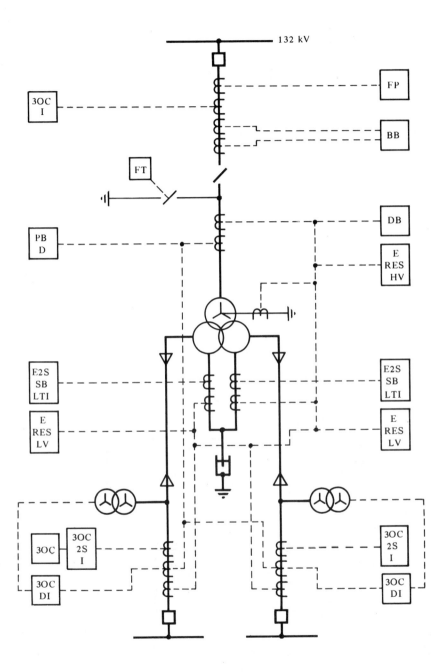

Fig. 17.7.5B *Protection scheme for transformer feeder with 132/11/11kV dual secondary transformer*

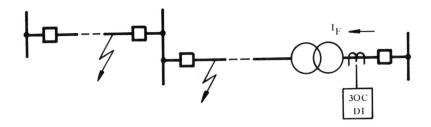

Fig. 17.7.5C   *Directional overcurrent protection on a transformer feeder*

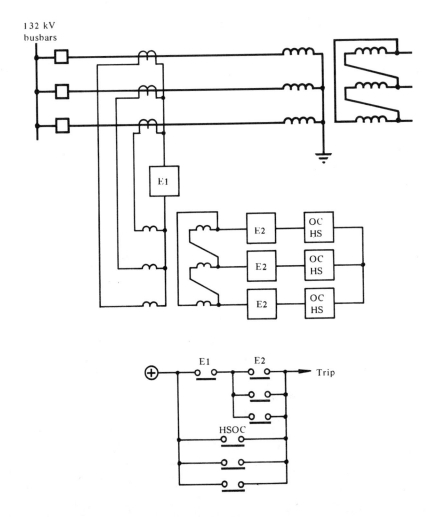

Fig. 17.7.5D   *High-set overcurrent with restricted earth-fault protection*

feeder protection c.t.s, any negative sequence current backfeed through the power transformer, including the backfeed from stored energy in any rotating plant on the l.v. network fed by the power transformer. Where necessary, the setting of both E1 and E2 must also take into account the current distribution when parallel transformer feeders supply a common l.v. busbar. The E1, E2 and h.s.o.c. relays should all be designed to be relatively immune to the effects of d.c. transients to avoid unwanted operation due to any d.c. component in the fault current and transformer magnetising inrush currents. To back up the intertripping on a transformer-feeder, it is often the practice for faults on the transformer or its associated l.v. connections to unstabilise any feeder unit protection or accelerate the h.v. end distance protection.

In some cases, to back up the intertripping, the transformer h.v. disconnector may be opened automatically after a suitable delay. In the event of the other means of tripping the remote circuit breaker having failed if the current is very low, e.g. from a Buchholz operation, the h.v. disconnector may successfully break the current. If it fails to break the current a local fault will be produced by the arcing at the disconnector which will result in operation of the feeder protection at the h.v. end. The philosophy of this technique is that the consequences of an uncleared fault on the transformer or its associated l.v. connections may be worse (e.g. a transformer fire) than if an attempt were not made to open the disconnector.

For many applications, particularly for long transformer-feeders, instead of providing hired or private pilot intertripping it may be cheaper and more dependable to install a fault-thrower. At 132 kV, the present design of fault throwers is limited to a maximum fault level of 2500 MVA. If fault throwers are installed, directional overcurrent protection is normally used to trip the l.v. circuit breaker for feeder faults.

17.7.6 Protection for a double busbar and mesh station

The protection for a double busbar and mesh station is usually identical to that described in Sections 17.6.6 and 17.6.7 except that the amount of redundancy can be reduced, e.g. there is in general no need for more than one discriminating zone relay and check zone relay to initiate tripping at a double busbar station, i.e. it can be a simple 'two out of two' relay logic scheme with no redundancy. For mesh stations a 'one out of one' relay logic scheme is normally adequate.

17.7.7 Protection for complex primary circuit configurations

The same considerations which are mentioned in Section 17.6.8 apply for choosing a protection scheme, but the longer permissible fault clearance times ease the problem. Also the need for high emergency load transfer capability is usually not as severe a problem as on a major transmission system.

17.8   Bibliography

General application

'Review of recent changes in protection requirements for the CEGB 400 and 275 kV systems' by J C Whittaker (IEE Conf. Publ. 125, 1975, pp.27-33)
'Recent developments in CEGB protection policy and practice' by J C Whittaker (IEE Conf. Publ. 185, 1980, Discussion Record, pp.1-4)
'Cost of power outages – the 1977 New York City Blackout' by W T Miles *et al.* (IEEE Industry Applications Society Annual Meeting, Seattle, 1979, pp.65-69)

Feeder protection

'Ultra high speed relay for EHV/UHV lines based on directional wave detection principles' by R P Carter (IEE Conf. Publ. 185, 1980, pp.166-170)
'The application of phase comparison protection to EHV transmission lines' by G Fielding *et al.* (UMIST Proc. of Internat. Conf. on Feeder Protection, 1979)
'Performance of distance fault detector relays' by W P Lewis (IEE Colloq. Dig. 1968/19, pp.239-249)
'Analysis of complex distance-relay characteristics taking load into account' by L P Cavero (IEE Conf. Publ. 185, 1980, pp.192-194)
'High speed protection for transformer feeders without pilot wires' by J Rushton (Electr. Energy, April 1958, p.132)
'Protection aspects of multi-terminal lines' (IEEE Special Publ. 79, TH0056-2-PWR)
'An evaluation of the comparative performance of distance and differential feeder protection systems' by W D Humpage and J Rushton (IEE Colloq. Dig. 1968/19, p.267)

Automatic switching

'A coherent scheme for the design and testing of automatic switching equipment' by C R Seymour (IEE Conf. Publ. 185, 1980 pp.69-73)

Chapter 18

Testing, commissioning and management of protection

by E.C.Smith, revised by D.Hay

18.1   Introduction

This chapter deals with protective gear throughout its life, from its being specified on a scheme, through the testing and commissioning stages into routine maintenance and fault investigation. The management of protective gear covers all those aspects and more; for example, keeping records, assessing performance, and the avoidance of mistakes in testing.

The chapter does not attempt to describe in detail how to commission any specific type of protection, but seeks to establish principles which apply to all schemes. Similarly the recommendations relate to the tests which need to be done, without specifying who shall do them.

18.2   Contractual obligations

There is little doubt that, where it is economically possible, it is better for the user of the equipment to commission it himself; by so doing he has a keen interest in the equipment right from the start and has the opportunity to get thoroughly familiar with it before it goes into commission. This knowledge will stand him in good stead during subsequent maintenance, and especially during fault investigation.

However, for various reasons it is customary to specify that the equipment shall be 'put to work' by the contractor. This immediately introduces such difficulties as 'marrying' extensions to existing schemes, and connecting d.c. and a.c. supplies to new equipment.

Such difficulties can arise even when one contractor is entirely responsible for all the new equipment; but the difficulties are worsened when several contractors are involved. For example, there may be different manufacturers for the h.v. switchgear, the l.v. switchgear, the transformers and the multicore cables. Each contractor is required to prove his own equipment, but he cannot always do so because of its interdependence with other equipment. During the commissioning tests something may fail to function; the cause of failure may not lie with that contractor's equipment but may be due to crossed multicores or wiring on associated equipment supplied on another contract. It is here that some co-ordinating influence is necessary.

This co-ordination can best be done by the user or the consulting engineers. Very often, in the interests of expediency, the user will investigate the trouble himself, but this is contractually wrong. If a contractor is responsible for setting his equipment to work, the user should refrain from sorting out his troubles for him. He should, as far as possible, require each contractor to prove his own equipment.

When several contractors are involved on a project it is advisable to have a group discussion beforehand to outline the tests which have to be done and to consider the effect of those tests on the equipment as a whole.

Although many tests may have to be done to prove a comprehensive scheme, some are usually more vital than others. The user may not be able to be represented at all the tests; he will have to decide which he must do himself, which he will participate in or closely supervise, which he will let the contractor do to a previously drawn-up programme (inspecting the test results afterwards), and which, if any, he will accept verbal assurance from the contractor as having been done by him.

Whether there is close participation or whether there is almost casual supervision, the user must remember one thing very clearly: he, and he alone, is responsible for ensuring that the new equipment has been correctly installed and that it can safely be connected to the system.

The contractor must satisfy the user of this. It is common practice, particularly for major installations, for the Board's specifications to call for 'testing and setting to work'; the specifications also require a 12-month maintenance period, during which any faults caused by poor design or bad workmanship are put right free of charge by the manufacturer.

18.3   The mental approach to commissioning tests

A fundamental thought should be kept in mind when approaching any commissioning test: the test is being done to prove the equipment is correctly installed. It may not be.

Throughout the tests, critical attention should be paid to all the aspects of the work; nothing should be 'glossed over' without a full explanation being sought. It is only by paying minute attention to detail that a high standard of performance can be achieved.

18.4   Commissioning tests

18.4.1   Reasons for commissioning tests

Commissioning tests are done to prove:

(a) That equipment has not been damaged in transit and that it can be safely and confidently connected to the system.

(b) That the specified equipment has been correctly installed.

(c) To prove characteristics of the protection which are based on calculations, for example the primary settings of high impedance protection systems.

(d) To obtain a set of test figures for future reference if and when necessary.

Commissioning tests, as well as covering protective gear, control and alarm circuits, also cover much of the primary plant with which such equipment is associated. Since, however, this book deals with power system protection, nothing more will be said of primary plant commissioning except that, on any primary circuit being commissioned, it is a good plan to consider it as being built of units such as busbars, busbar protection, circuit breakers, transformers, cables, disconnectors, protective gear, intertripping, and so on. Each such unit should be proved before attempting conjunctive tests on the complete circuit.

18.4.2 Planning of commissioning tests

It is desirable to plan commissioning tests in a logical order, ensuring that no equipment is overlooked and, once tested, is not unnecessarily disturbed, thus requiring a re-test. A commissioning programme should be planned as follows:

Study of Diagrams

(a) *Block diagrams:* It is helpful to have (or to prepare if none is available) a block diagram of a substation to show the lines, transformers and busbars and the c.t. and v.t. positions. The various types of protective gear may be indicated in block outline with thin solid lines between them and the c.t.s, and dotted lines between the relays and the circuit breakers they trip.

A block diagram of this kind (Fig. 18.4.2A) presents a very clear picture of the protection and control layout arrangements of a substation.

(b) *Circuit diagrams:* The manufacturers will often supply circuit diagrams, but if not they should be extracted from the main wiring diagrams. Separate circuit diagrams can be prepared for d.c. tripping, closing, alarm and indication circuits; and a.c. diagrams for various types of protection, voltage and synchronising circuits. Each class of circuit can be shown on a separate diagram so that each can be studied and tested without confusion. A typical circuit diagram is shown in Fig. 18.4.2B.

Two warnings are necessary with regard to the use of circuit diagrams; both warnings involve completeness of the diagram. If an engineer is extracting his own circuit diagram, he would be wise to make quite sure that he has included the whole of the circuits connected, say, between any given fuse and link; by doing a full diagram he can be confident that no possible 'sneak' circuits are overlooked. If using a manufacturer's diagram, he should satisfy himself that it is complete and

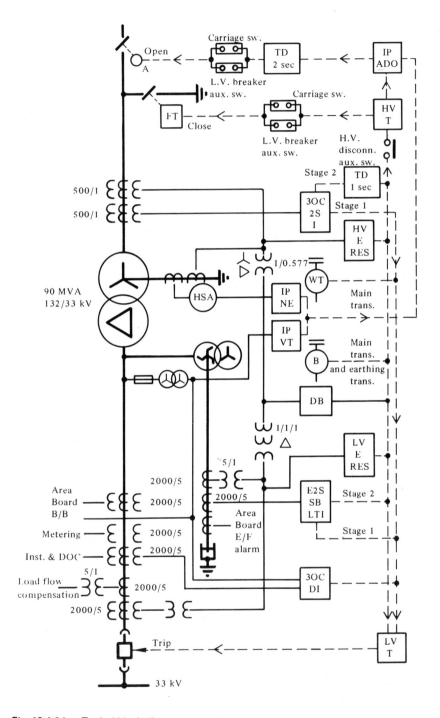

Fig. 18.4.2A   *Typical block diagram*

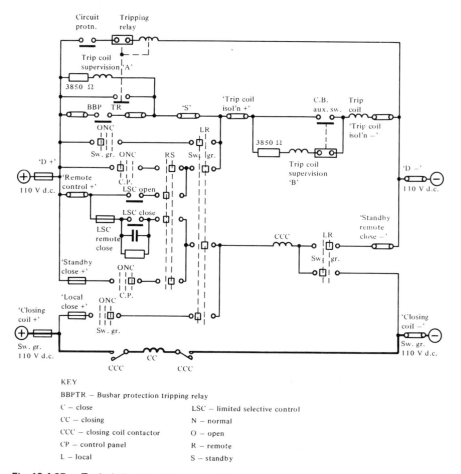

KEY

BBPTR — Busbar protection tripping relay

C — close	LSC — limited selective control
CC — closing	N — normal
CCC — closing coil contactor	O — open
CP — control panel	R — remote
L — local	S — standby

Fig. 18.4.2B *Typical circuit breaker control diagram*

that it shows every hazard in the circuit. For example, at one time o.c.b. rack-in plug and socket connections were not always shown on tripping and closing circuit diagrams. If circuit diagrams are being drawn by the user, he should make them as simple as possible, ignoring the physical layout of the equipment and making his diagram a pure electrical diagram, avoiding unnecessary crossovers and ensuring a smooth flow of the eye from side to side or top to bottom without any unnecessary 'to and fro' motion. Circuit diagrams of a semiphysical type, which are drawn so that the number of multicores necessary between two points can be readily assessed, are almost as difficult to follow as a wiring diagram, through various contacts and coils, until the circuit from positive to negative is complete, by which time (unless the engineer has an unusually retentive memory) a state of partial confusion will result.

Good circuit diagrams are invaluable during commissioning tests and fault investigations in that they permit the details of the circuit to be assimilated quickly.

From a circuit diagram it is often possible to diagnose the reason for a circuit fault before doing any confirmatory testing.

Planning the programme

(*a*)   *Overall review:* The equipment to be commissioned may vary from a single additional circuit connected to a low voltage busbar, to a complete 400 kV double-busbar substation with transformers, generators and lines.

In either case the method of approach should be the same. First of all, a list should be prepared itemising all the tests it is necessary to do; for example, insulation resistance, secondary injection, primary injection, control, indication, interlocks, alarms, tripping, end-to-end, auto-reclose, synchronising, on-load tests etc. In some cases it may be helpful to have sheets available headed, for example, 'disconnectors' or 'circuit breakers' or 'transformers', and on these sheets have a list of items that have to be inspected or tested before that particular piece of equipment can be said to have been checked.

Fig. 18.4.2C gives the schedules in rough outline of some of the tests usually done on different pieces of equipment. The schedule may be elaborated as necessary for a particular circuit configuration.

Fig. 18.4.2C   *Typical schedule of protection commissioning tests*

Inspection prior to detailed testing	*Voltage transformers* Ratio	*Tripping tests* Trip circuit supervision
Terminal tightness	Back-energising	Protection gear to tripping
Check of ferrule numbers	Phasing	relay
Insulation resistance tests		Trip interlocks
Examination of auxiliary	*Transformers*	Tripping relays to breakers
switches	Phasing at 415 v	Intertripping
	Winding temperature	Acceleration
Circuit breakers	indicators	Autoreclose
Timing tests	Buchholz device	
Check of c.t. positions		*Alarm scheme*
	Current transformers	Shorting of initiating
Disconnectors	Magnetic curves	contacts
Operating mechanism	Polarity	Proving from all initiating
Control circuits	Ratio	devices
Protection		
Secondary injection		
Primary injection		
On-load tests		

Whenever possible there should be a pattern in the approach to commissioning tests; for example, the a.c. circuits may be considered as feeding *into* the protective gear and the d.c. circuits as feeding *out from* the protective gear to the tripping relays and circuit breakers they trip. This method of working breaks the job up into easily manageable sections at an early stage and enables faults to be quickly cleared without the risk of losing track if a complete sequence of tests has been attempted altogether.

Having proved each section individually, tests to check the overall functioning can be done fairly quickly. The cause of any failure to operate satisfactorily can easily be pin-pointed, as the failure must be in the unproved connections between the already proved sections.

(*b*)   *The commissioning log:* A commissioning programme can be carried through more efficiently and effectively if proper records are kept. One convenient way is to make up a folder, sometimes called the commissioning log, containing stencilled sheets for recording:

the programme of tests
brief diary of day-to-day progress
the various test results
temporary conditions
outstanding items.

The commissioning log should also include copies of the circuit diagrams to be used during the tests, and any other sheets thought necessary.

Such a commissioning log enables a comprehensive record to be kept of the whole job, which will be of value not only during the testing programme but for any future fault investigation.

(*c*)   *Programming:* Tests need to be carefully programmed, not only to ensure that equipment is ready on time, but as regards plant outages, permits, allocation of staff, etc. The tests should also be programmed to take place in a logical and efficient order so that nothing already tested is disturbed during subsequent tests.

In preparing an overall programme of manufacturing time, delivery, erection, inspection, testing and commissioning, adequate time must be included for the last three items. Engineers engaged on the final commissioning tests are doing their part of the job after most of the other people have finished theirs; there is often impatience to get the new equipment into commission, and the commissioning engineers are liable (usually unjustifiably) to receive criticism for any delays in making alive, and are sometimes urged to cut short their tests. Commissioning tests may reveal several defects which need correcting, and a reasonable amount of time for such rectification should be included in the overall planned time.

18.4.3   Inspection prior to testing

The inspection tests can be itemised as follows:

(*a*)   Checking for tightness all connections in relay panels, control panels, marshalling kiosks, c.t. terminal boxes, etc.

(*b*)   Checking that fuses and links are properly wired. In the case of rewirable fuses, the wire should be tinned copper — *not* a soft lead compound which can deform and either blow at a current less than its rating or become loose after several weeks. The fuse wire should not be taut, as it is liable to break when the fuse is being inserted in its holder. Cartridge-type fuses should be inspected to ensure that the correct rating is used for the circuit.

If the links are of the type which are wired with stiff wire they should be inspected to ensure that the wire stiffness is not distorting the jaws and thus preventing adequate contact pressure.

(*c*)   Clearances should be checked between relay studs and the edges of the holes in the steel panel, making suitable allowance for possible dust accumulation over the years.

(*d*)   Ensure that all the secondary equipment in outdoor substations is weatherproof, but that there is provision for ventilation and heating (if required) to prevent condensation, in accordance with the Board's specification.

(*e*)   Particular attention should be paid to auxiliary switches. These appear in almost every circuit — for example, tripping, closing, indication, alarm, synchronising, autoreclose, electrical bolt interlocks, busbar protection, and occasionally in c.t. circuits other than busbar protection.

Points to look for are silver plating where specified, contact pressure, cleanliness, adequate 'wipe' and follow through. The drive should be examined to ensure that it is positive, not liable to jam or become disconnected from the main mechanism, and that its action corresponds with the main switch. On auxiliary switches used for busbar protection c.t. selection, it is essential that they are duplicated, and that the auxiliary switches make before and break after the associated primary contacts, so as to ensure that the secondary circuits are complete before any primary unbalance can occur due to pre-contact arcing or a high resistance in one part of the primary circuit. Tests should be devised to prove that the auxiliary switches meet this requirement. The importance of correct operation of auxiliary switches cannot be overemphasised, as failure of an auxiliary switch can defeat the best designed schemes.

(*f*)   Before energising new secondary wiring it should be checked as far as reasonably practicable that there are no bare, dangling, uncompleted leads anywhere on site which will be made alive at the same time as the equipment under test. Any such leads should be terminated, disconnected or (as an absolute minimum) well taped up.

18.4.4   The tests

We can assume that the tests to be done have already been scheduled, primary circuit by primary circuit, probably with target dates. Before beginning testing it should be confirmed that the particular part of the circuit under test is complete and that no one is likely to interfere with it. The tests to be done should be listed in chronological order together with any special precautions to be taken. The tests will fall under four broad headings:

(*a*)   Tests before making secondary equipment alive.
(*b*)   Tests before making primary equipment alive.
(*c*)   Synchronising tests where the new equipment is alive, but not yet in parallel with existing equipment.
(*d*)   On-load tests.

Schedules for recording test results should be compiled in advance, when preparations can be made at a time free from testing stress. The initial and comprehensive advance planning is a big help in making the tests run smoothly.

Below are listed some of the more usual tests, with comments.

(*a*)   *Insulation resistance tests:* These tests should be done with a 500 V Megger, care being taken that telephone type pilots are not included. To ensure that this voltage does not appear across rectifiers in the event of a wiring error, or across capacitors and solid state equipment, they should be shortened out until Megger tests are complete. Each circuit should be tested in turn whilst all the others are earthed to ensure that there is no connection between two supposedly separate circuits. This point is particularly important and needs stressing.

It is difficult to advise what value of insulation resistance should be obtained. On panel and other indoor wiring one would expect a figure in excess of 100 MΩ. On outdoor wiring in a medium-sized substation, 10 MΩ would be a fair figure; and on a very large substation, where wiring loops in to many auxiliary switches and junction boxes, 1 MΩ would not be unreasonable. The weather can also affect the results; a warm humid day tends to lower the value, whereas a cold dry day gives high values.

Often the Megger pointer will swing towards zero when meggering begins on a circuit. This is because the connected wiring has capacitance; the pointer will climb towards infinity as the wiring builds up its charge. It is advisable not to touch such wiring immediately after stopping winding!

(*b*)   *Secondary injection tests:* These tests consist of a.c. injection into the relay coils to prove that the relay calibration is correct. Even if the relays have been thoroughly tested in a laboratory or in the manufacturer's works, some kind of check should be made when they are mounted on the panel to ensure they have not been damaged in transit or by handling.

In general, high-accuracy secondary injection tests on site are not necessary. Laboratory standards are not being sought. What is needed is a set of figures, reproducible later from time to time on routine tests, which bear a known relationship to accurate figures previously obtained in a laboratory. If, however, the protective gear contains tuned circuits which have to be calibrated by secondary injection on commissioning, due regard should be paid to the frequency and wave shape of the test supply to ensure there are no harmonics present.

There are several types of relays, and these are discussed briefly under their appropriate headings.

(*i*)   *General:* Whatever type of relay is being tested, if it is fitted with a plug bridge the tests should be done on the lowest tap so that the whole of the coil is included. Calibration checks may be done on other taps if desired, but this should not be necessary. It is, however, wise to check the continuity of each coil tap. This can be done by moving the setting plug from tap to tap and checking that current flows when the test supply is switched on. The plug bridge shorting contact should be proved when the setting plug is withdrawn. This should be done with the test current switched on, and it should be observed that withdrawal of the plug does not open-circuit the relay coil.

Although the tests mentioned are of an electrical nature, due regard should be paid to the mechanical condition of the relay. Dust and other foreign bodies should be removed with a feather, or by a blower; *not* by the breath because this contains many droplets of moisture. The relay movement should be checked for clearance of gaps, contact alignment, and freedom of operation. If the relay is fitted with a mechanical flag, the flag should operate as, or just before, the contacts make, and the flag mechanism should not interfere with the operation of the relay.

(*ii*)   *Instantaneous relays:* These will be actuated by current or voltage and will usually be of the attracted-armature type. The current should be increased slowly until operation occurs. The current value immediately prior to operation should be noted because of the change in reluctance of the magnetic path of the relay (see Chapter 6). The current or voltage should then be decreased slowly, and the value recorded at which the relay resets.

(*iii*)   *Inverse definite minimum time (i.d.m.t.) relays:* It should be checked that the contact just makes on zero time multiplier (t.m.). Also the resetting time at t.m. 1·0 should be measured at zero current. For record purposes, the maximum current which will allow the relay to reset fully should be ascertained.

It should not be necessary to prove the relay curve, but at least two points should be checked on it; one to find the minimum current, with t.m. = 1·0, at which the relay will just operate (usually referred to as the creep value), and the other to check the timing at, say, four times current or voltage setting, and t.m. = 1·0.

(*iv*) *Biased relays:* Such relays have at least two coils; one tends to cause operation whilst the other(s) restrains. The method of test will vary with the relay type and application, but it is usual to check the bias curve by measuring the current needed in the operating coil to cause operation when different values of separately injected current are passed through the bias coil. Care should be taken not to overheat the relay by the fairly large operating current necessary to overcome a strong bias current. Only three or four points on the curve need be checked.

With some types of end-to-end protection, it may be necessary to carry out simultaneous injection tests at both ends to check, for example, the bias characteristics of a teed feeder pilot protection scheme. Several warnings should be issued here:

If the (dead) overhead line itself is used as part of the secondary injection equipment, the greatest care should be exercised with the equipment because of induced voltage from other lines on the same towers or in the vicinity. Such voltages can be dangerously high, and the protective equipment and 'live' parts of the secondary injection test equipment should not be touched unless temporarily earthed. Such work should only be carried out with the authority of a sanction-for-test card.

End-to-end tests using the primary line as an interconnector are deprecated because of the danger, but are mentioned here for the record.

If simultaneous secondary injection tests are to be done at the two ends using two sets of test equipment and separate supplies at each end, it is essential that the two supplies are in phase or in anti-phase, depending on the type of protection. If the phasing is known, well and good. If not, it will have to be established. Be careful not to rely too much on GPO pilots as a means of phasing out test supplies (which should, of course, be transformed to a safe voltage before applying them to the pilots), because the inductance and capacitance of the GPO pilots can introduce appreciable phase-shift. In one case, 30 V supplies at each end were phased out over a pair of GPO pilots by engineers who had not appreciated the possibility of phase-shift. Their results, when plotted out, indicated approximately $30°$ difference in phase between the supplies at the two ends. To compensate for this 'difference' the tests were done phase-to-neutral at one end and phase-to-phase at the other, when the two supplies were in fact in phase. Needless to say, most interesting results were obtained!

This problem of phase-shift in pilots can be overcome once it is known, but it is safer to phase out test supplies against a known voltage reference at each end.

With end-to-end injection there is wide scope for errors, and it is only too easy to overlook a $180°$ shift through a transformer.

End-to-end tests by secondary injection should not be relied on entirely for establishing protective gear polarity. At best, they are only a guide and the results should always be confirmed later by on-load tests.

If a biased relay is used for the overall protection of a power transformer it may have a harmonic-bias coil on it in addition to the load-bias coil. The harmonic-bias coil stabilises the relay against unwanted operation on magnetising inrush currents at the instant the power transformer is switched on to the system. The calibration of the tuned circuit associated with this coil should be proved, and here the frequency of the test supply should be confirmed as 50 Hz, otherwise inaccuracies may be present.

(*v*) *Distance protection relays:* Certain distance relays are of the d.c. permanent magnet moving coil type, in which the coil moves axially or radially. Sometimes the relay has only one coil fed from the d.c. bridge which compares the magnitudes of the current and voltage and so is a measure of the impedance to the fault. On another type the relay possesses two coils on the one former; one coil is fed from the rectified current and tends to cause operation, whilst the other coil is fed from the rectified voltage, thus tending to restrain.

In secondary injection tests on these relays, current and voltage of varying magnitude (to simulate different values of fault impedance) are fed into the protective gear to prove that the equipment is in calibration.

(*vi*) *Directional relays:* Directional relays are frequently of the induction type, where the disc or cup is acted upon by a current coil and a voltage coil. Depending on the phase angle between voltage and current, the relay will either operate to close its contact or remain with its contacts open.

Directional relays usually act in conjunction with other relays. For example, in a directional overcurrent relay the sensitive directional element controls the operation of a low-set overcurrent element. In many types of distance protection the directional relay acts as a starting relay and controls the operation of many auxiliary relays associated with the measuring elements.

In testing directional relays it is usual to prove that they will not operate or even creep in the presence of either actuating quantity alone. It is also necessary to find the phase angle between the current and applied voltage to give zero torque – that is, the point at which the relay changes direction. If the applied volts are then moved 90° from that position, maximum torque should be obtained. In that position figures may be taken of the minimum current required to cause operation at rated volts, and of the minimum voltage required to cause operation at rated current.

In the case of directional earth-fault relays, consider what happens when an earth fault occurs on a solidly earthed system. This condition is depicted vectorially in (*a*) of Fig. 18.4.4A in which a red phase-to-earth fault is assumed. The relay is fed with residual current and with a voltage derived from open-delta transformers: this is shown by V_{OD} in (*b*) and the fault current is shown by I_{RES}. The relays for this application are designed to operate with maximum torque when the applied current and voltage are in phase, and it is, therefore, necessary to move one vector or the other to achieve this in-phase condition under fault conditions. The voltage vector is the one most conveniently moved, and (*c*) and (*d*) show how the requisite amount of compensation is achieved. The angle of compensation is usually of the order of 60° to 70°.

Measurement of the compensation angle may be made by single-phase injection on, say, the red primary winding of the auxiliary v.t.s and by then measuring the open delta (V_{OD}), capacitor (V_C), and relay coil (V_{REL}) voltages.

The secondary injection tests on directional earth-fault relays should be carried out in a similar manner to the injection tests on directional overcurrent relays, due allowance being made for the difference in maximum torque angle and sensitivity.

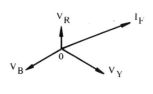

(a) Voltage and current phasors for Red phase earth fault on solidly-earthed system

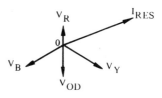

(b) Open-delta voltage and residual current in relay

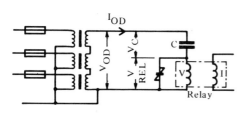

(c) Auxiliary v.t.'s, open-delta and voltage compensation circuit

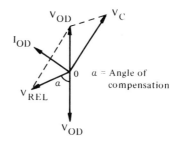

(d) Phasors showing angle of compensation

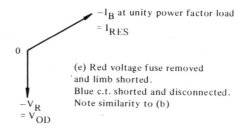

(e) Red voltage fuse removed and limb shorted.
Blue c.t. shorted and disconnected.
Note similarity to (b)

Fig. 18.4.4A *Proving of earth-fault directional relays*

(*c*) *Preliminary tests on current transformers:* Many things should be checked before the stage of heavy-current injection is reached. These are:

(*i*) *Overlap of c.t.s:* Where the c.t.s are arranged to overlap the circuit breaker so that a fault within the breaker is covered by both adjacent zones of protection, it should be proved conclusively that the c.t.s *do* overlap, otherwise a fault within

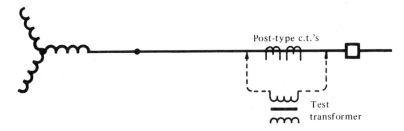

Heavy test current is possible

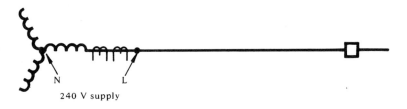

Test current severely limited by impedance of transformer

Fig. 18.4.4B   *Effect of c.t. position on magnitude of test current*

the breaker could not be cleared by either set of protection.

The proving may be done by visual inspection, thought being given to the ever present possibility of crossed ferrule numbers. If visual inspection is impossible or difficult, then a Megger of continuity indicator may be applied between the appropriate relay(s) and earth at the relay panels, whilst a roving earth is 'dabbed' on and off the secondary terminals at the c.t.s to prove they are on the correct side of the breaker.

(*ii*)   *The correct c.t.s:* Often there are several sets of c.t.s in the one bushing and it is vital to prove that these are respectively connected to the correct protection. Sometimes all the c.t.s will be of the same ratio but will have very different characteristics. At other times the c.t. ratio will be different but close enough to cause confusion unless great care is taken.

With post-type c.t.s or c.t.s in an o.c.b. bushing the proving of the correct c.t. ratio causes little difficulty because heavy test current can be passed through them; but where such c.t.s are in the bushings of a power transformer, the position is much more difficult because only small test currents can be passed. The two cases are indicated in Fig. 18.4.4B.

(*iii*)   *Magnetisation current tests:* These tests are done:

(*a*)   to prove there are no shorted turns in the c.t.,

(*b*)   to establish the knee point voltage (k.p.v.) of the c.t. (the knee point voltage is that point on the magnetisation curve where a 10% increase in applied voltage will result in a 50% increase in magnetising current),

(c) to establish the capability of the c.t.s. (This is allied to the point (c) (ii), page 412 and is a way of proving that the different types of c.t.s can be distinguished from each other.) Magnetisation curves are obtained by applying a *sinusoidal* voltage to the secondary winding of a c.t. and measuring the magnetising current flowing for different values of applied voltage. A typical curve is shown in Fig. 18.4.4C. There is no need to continue the test beyond the knee point. These tests must be made with the primary of the c.t. open-circuited. When carrying out magnetisation tests on c.t.s, it is most important that the applied voltage is progressively reduced to zero before interrupting the supply; otherwise the very high rate of change of flux may induce a voltage sufficient to damage the secondary insulation.

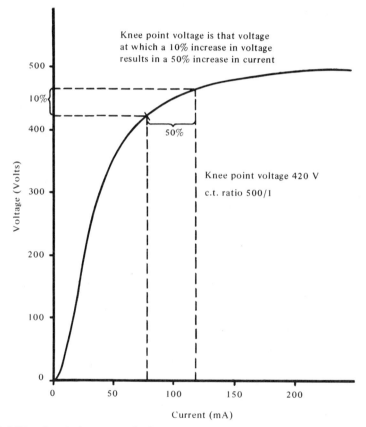

Fig. 18.4.4C   *A typical c.t. magnetisation curve*

(*iv*)   *Flick tests:* Much preliminary checking can be done with the aid of a 1·5 V battery and a voltmeter. All the c.t.s in a group can be checked in turn to prove that they are connected to the protection in the same polarity. A voltmeter, on a sensitive d.c. range, should be clipped across (and left across during the tests) the relay or c.t. secondary whilst the 1·5 V battery is touched across the bar primary of each c.t. in turn. Great care should be taken to ensure that the battery leads and voltmeter are applied in the same way each time. Fig. 18.4.4D shows the arrangement. It is important to note that the deflection of the voltmeter is the same each time the battery is connected, and each time it is disconnected.

A flick test can be done profitably with c.t.s in a transformer bushing, because the d.c. current can traverse the transformer windings with little opposition. It is even possible to do rough operation and stability tests by excluding or including the balancing neutral c.t. within the path of the battery current.

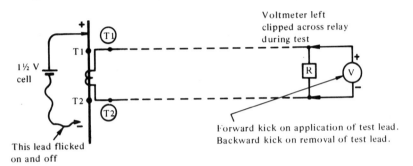

Fig. 18.4.4D   *Arrangements for flick tests*

(*d*)   *Primary injection tests:* Primary injection tests are required to prove that c.t.s are correctly connected to relays. These tests will usually include a check of the polarity of the three c.t.s in a group, and often the comparison of the group with another. The sensitivity of the protection, in terms of primary amps, may also be determined.

At this stage a simple diagram should be drawn (to form part of the commissioning log) showing c.t. locations, the testing transformer and the position of the test leads in the circuit for each test of operation, and stability, phase-to-phase, phase-to-earth, etc. Typical diagrams are shown in Figs. 18.4.4E, F, and G, but will be referred to again later.

Primary injection tests can be a prolific source of error. The following facts should be borne in mind:

(i)   The primary equipment must be dead. The engineer conducting the tests, although possibly not in charge of the safety aspects of the test, would be well advised to satisfy himself that all equipment to be worked on has been isolated and locked off from all live equipment.

(ii)   The work will probably have to be done under a sanction-for-test car.

(iii)   Safety earths may have to be removed.

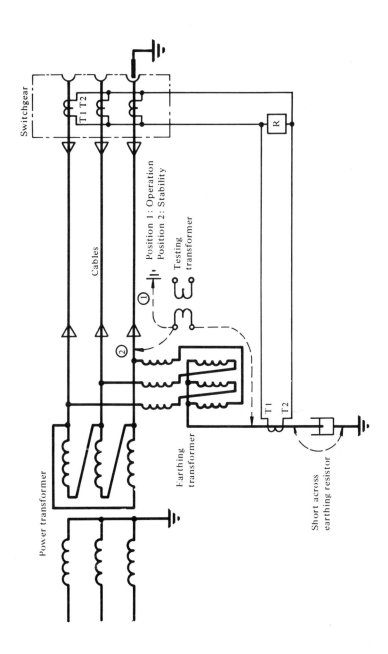

Fig. 18.4.4E   *Connections for primary injection tests on restricted earth-fault protection*

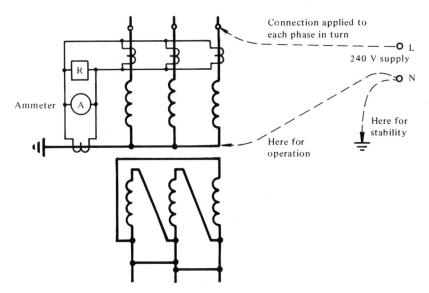

Fig. 18.4.4F   *Proving of c.t.s in transformer bushing by injection from 240V a.c. supply*

(iv) Test connections will have to be applied, and must make good contact in view of the low voltages and heavy currents which are used.

(v) The test current will sometimes flow through c.t.s other than the ones in which one is specifically interested at the time. Precautions will, therefore, be needed to prevent the tripping of adjacent circuits and the remote ends of circuits.

(vi) It is possible to produce what is thought to be an operating condition, whereas, in fact, the condition may be of one stability. This can occur by accidentally passing current in the wrong direction through the c.t.; the sketch of the c.t. positions and the test connections will help to prevent this.

(vii) Earth-fault relay coils, stabilising resistors, non-linear resistors and the like are often short-time rated and so may be damaged unless suitable precautions are taken.

(viii) Multipurpose instruments may be damaged unless they are on the correct range for the conditions being applied. Before switching on the test supply, think about the whole job and make sure that the necessary precautions have been taken. The precautions taken should be listed so that when the tests are complete everything can be restored to normal without the risk of anything being forgotten.

It is advisable to switch on at a low value of current and increase it slowly in case there are any c.t.s open-circuit or incorrectly connected. If the test results differ appreciably from those expected, reduce the current and switch off while the matter is investigated.

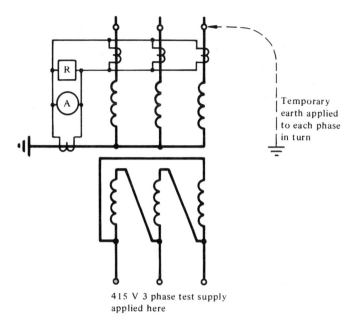

415 V 3 phase test supply
applied here

Fig. 18.4.4G *Proving of polarity of c.t.s. in transformer bushings by injection of 415V three-phase supply on l.v. side of power transformer*

A word of warning about the burdens of test instruments when connected in circuit on the milliamp range. On this range the instrument will have quite a high impedance, and this may affect the distribution of currents in the secondary circuit under test. This can be even more confusing if only one instrument is available and it has to be transferred from phase-to-phase.

It is wise to prove operation first – that is, prove that the protection will operate from at least one set of c.t.s. If the c.t.s are connected to form a circulating-current scheme, stability can be proved by going through the two sets of c.t.s in series. There should be no, or little, current in the relay.

Fig. 18.4.4H(*a*) shows some typical primary injection test equipment. The test current will usually be between 100 and 400 A. For the sake of clarity on the c.t. diagrams showing the different types of test, the injection equipment has not been drawn again, but the two heavy-current leads labelled (1) and (2) are temporarily connected to the c.t.s being tested.

Fig. 18.4.4H(*b*) shows three c.t.s residually connected to a relay. The ratio of the c.t.s must be proved, also the correct connections of the c.t.s in the group. If there is more than one group of c.t.s connected to a relay, as in busbar protection (Fig. 18.4.4H(*c*)), then not only must each group be proved as a group but each group must be balanced against the others.

Fig. 18.4.4H(*d*) shows how a ratio test is done. The test current is passed through one c.t. (say Red) and primary and secondary currents are measured. If the c.t. is correctly matched to the protection, the relationship between the two should confirm the c.t. ratio.

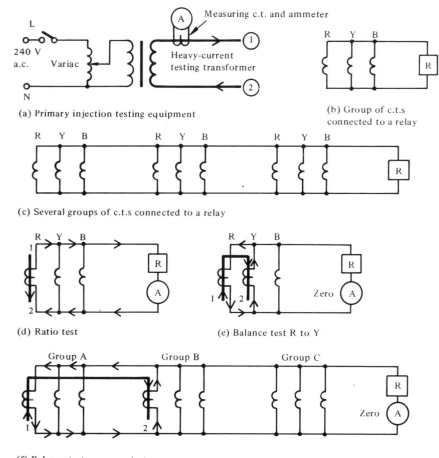

(a) Primary injection testing equipment

(b) Group of c.t.s connected to a relay

(c) Several groups of c.t.s connected to a relay

(d) Ratio test

(e) Balance test R to Y

(f) Balance test group against group

Fig. 18.4.4H   *Connections for primary injection tests*

To prove the c.t.s in the group, inject into the Red c.t. and out of the Yellow as shown in Fig. 18.4.4H(e). There should be little or no reading even though the same test current is flowing as before. If these conditions are satisfactorily achieved, current should be injected into Yellow and out of Blue, when similar results should be obtained. The correct balance of the c.t.s in the group has now been proved, as has also the ratio of all three.

Fig. 18.4.4H(f) shows several groups of c.t.s in parallel on a relay. One group must be proved for ratio and balance as already described, and the three c.t.s in each of all the groups must be balanced against each other. It is now only necessary to prove group against group. This can be done in several ways and one is described: test current is injected into (say) the Red c.t. of group A and out of the Red c.t. of group B. If the polarities and ratios are correct there should be little or no spill current in the ammeter. It has now been established that the ratio of the c.t.s in group B is the same as in group A; and since it has already been proved that the three c.t.s in each group balance, group A must balance group B. In a similar way group A (or group B) may be balanced against group C, etc. Where the relay is of the high impedance type, the test ammeter (A) in Figs. 18.4.4H(*d*), (*e*), and (*f*) should be connected in parallel with the relay instead of in series.

Reverting to c.t.s in transformer bushings where it is impossible to inject substantial test current, a test can be done by applying a 240 V a.c. lead to each h.v. bushing in turn whilst the l.v. side of the transformer has a three-phase short-circuit across it. If desired a 415 V three-phase supply can be applied to the three bushings but this will not prove the neutral c.t. as no current will flow through it. The use of the single-phase supply enables the neutral c.t. to be included in the test if desired as indicated in Fig. 18.4.4F. It will be appreciated that the primary currents flowing will be small so the secondary currents will only be of the order of milliamps. However, such a test can prove correct connections.

It is possible to obtain a larger test current by applying the three-phase 415 V supply to the l.v. side of the power transformer. This is shown in Fig. 18.4.4G, which also shows how a temporary short on the h.v. side can be applied in different positions to prove stability on each phase. Relay spill currents must be checked later when the transformer is on load.

Many transformers are protected by overall biased differential protection schemes incorporating h.v. and l.v. restricted earth-fault relays. Although heavy-current primary injection tests can be made from c.t.s to relays, it is difficult to prove the h.v. c.t.s against the l.v. c.t.s because of the phase shift through the transformer. Such balance can be proved when the transformer has gone on load, but a word of warning is necessary; if the transformer is fitted with a fault throwing switch, temporarily remove the tripping from the overall biased differential protection until the protection has been proved correct. A case is on record where the polarities were wrong, so the protection interpreted load current as an internal fault; the protection operated and closed the fault throwing switch on to the live 132 kV line.

On generator protection the zone of protection may include both the generator and its step-up transformer. The connections from all the c.t.s to the relays must be proved by primary injection, but the balance of the h.v. c.t.s with the l.v. c.t.s has to be proved when current is flowing through the generator and transformer. This is achieved by using the machine itself as a source of test current. Three-phase, phase-to-phase, and phase-to-earth temporary connections are applied in turn to the h.v. side of the transformer, and the machine is run on low excitation whilst correct behaviour of the protection is checked. These tests, in conjunction with the primary injection tests already done, prove the machine protection.

Because the generator transformer is fitted with tap changing gear, some spill current may appear in the overall protection when the machine is run on the external three-phase short-circuit. This test should, therefore, be done initially on the nominal-ratio tap of the transformer, and repeated on the two extreme tap positions. Because the primary currents are balanced in the three phases, there is no need for this part of the test to be hurried.

Unbalanced currents in a machine cause rotor heating, so care must be taken to ensure that this is not excessive. Before the unbalanced current is applied it is necessary to know the amount of unbalance, in order to determine for how long the unbalance can be tolerated, and what reading these conditions will give on the machine ammeters. As an example, consider the case of a 60 MW, 0·8 p.f., 11·8 kV generator connected to the 132 kV system through a 75 MVA delta/star transformer. On full load c.m.r. the 11·8 kV and 132 kV currents will be 3660 A and 327 A, respectively, and the currents in the delta windings of the transformer will be 2120 A. This is shown in Fig. 18.4.4I(*a*).

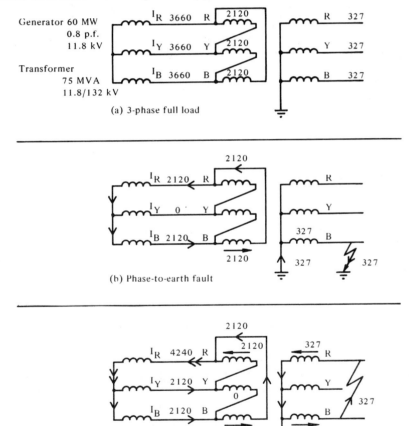

(a) 3-phase full load

(b) Phase-to-earth fault

(c) Phase-to-phase fault

Fig. 18.4.4I

If it is decided to pass the full load current of 327 A through to phase-to-earth 'short' on the 132 kV side of the transformer, the currents flowing in the three phases of the generator will be 2120 A, 0 A, and 2120 A as shown in Fig. 18.4.4I(*b*).

If the same current of 327 A is now passed through a phase-to-phase 'short' on the 132 kV side of the transformer, the currents flowing in the three phases of the generator will be 4240 A, 2120 A, and 2120 A as shown in Fig. 18.4.4I(*c*). To assess the effect of these unbalanced currents on the generator, reference should first be made to the sequence components shown in Fig. 18.4.4J. From this it will be seen that a phase-to-earth 'short' imposes a negative phase sequence condition of 57·7 per cent of c.m.r.

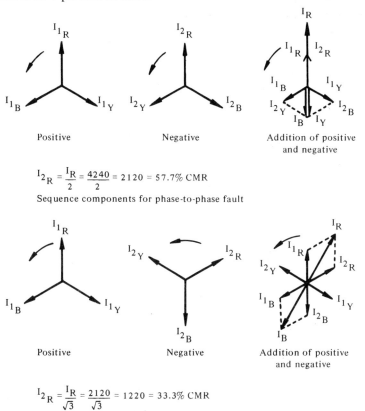

Positive   Negative   Addition of positive and negative

$$I_{2R} = \frac{I_R}{2} = \frac{4240}{2} = 2120 = 57.7\% \text{ CMR}$$

Sequence components for phase-to-phase fault

Positive   Negative   Addition of positive and negative

$$I_{2R} = \frac{I_R}{\sqrt{3}} = \frac{2120}{\sqrt{3}} = 1220 = 33.3\% \text{ CMR}$$

For phase-to-earth fault

Fig. 18.4.4J   *Sequence components of generator currents for faults on h.v.. side of generator*

Fig. 18.4.4K gives the n.p.s. withstand figures in percentage of c.m.r. rating for machines of various $I_2^2 t$ values. A machine with an $I_2^2 t$ value of 15 could withstand the earth-fault condition for 130s and the phase-fault condition for 47s, whereas a machine with an $I_2^2 t$ value of 7 could only withstand these conditons for 60s and 21s, respectively.

Reverting to the phase-to-phase fault condition which imposes currents of 4240 A, 2120 A, and 2120 A on the machine, the manufacturer may be unwilling to permit this slight overload on one phase (the c.m.r. rating is 3660A). If so, the test current would have to be kept lower, which would give a longer time for

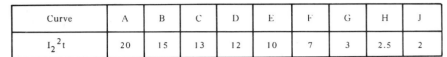

Curve	A	B	C	D	E	F	G	H	J
$I_2{}^2t$	20	15	13	12	10	7	3	2.5	2

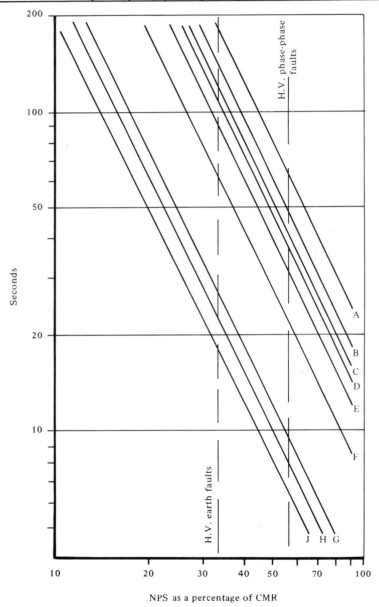

Fig. 18.4.4K

the readings to be taken. Whatever current value is taken and whatever the type of machine, reference to the appropriate curve will show for how long the condition can be withstood. It is then advisable to allow a factor of safety by halving these times.

(*e*) *Tests on commissioning of carrier protection (Refer also to Section 18.4.4(g)):* The band of frequencies at present employed in the UK for power-line-carrier signalling is 70-700 kHz, although certain parts of this band are not available for continuous carrier signalling. This restriction is necessary to avoid causing interference with radio service including those used for aeronautical and marine nagivation purposes. However, with the exception of a band designed to protect the international distress frequency, normally quiescent power-line-carrier systems may be used anywhere in the remaining available frequency range provided that test transmissions do not exceed two seconds and that there is an interval of at least two minutes between successive test transmissions. Carrier protection consists of the starting networks, the electronic equipment, the line coupling equipment and line traps, and the power supply unit and power packs. Tests are made to prove each of these items.

The starting networks can be checked by secondary injection. Before starting work on the electronic equipment the power supplies should be checked. These are usually provided by d.c./d.c. convertors which invert a battery supply to provide an a.c. supply which is then rectified and stabilised to provide the appropriate voltage level(s) required by the equipment. Arrangements vary with the type of equipment and the manufacturer's commissioning instructions should be consulted for detail, particular attention being paid to fuse ratings, polarity of supplies and voltage values.

Certain special test equipment is necessary for use on the electronic equipment and on the line coupling equipment. This test equipment comprises a cathode ray oscilloscope, a valve voltmeter, an oscillator and amplifier covering the range 70 to 700 kHz. The protection equipment consists of a transmitter and receiver at each end of the feeder, and tests have to be done on these to adjust the outputs and sensitivities and to check the performance of filters.

Line-coupling equipment provides a means of injecting h.f. carrier signals on to an h.v. power line and it prevents these signals being dissipated in the substation. A typical set of line-coupling equipment is shown in Fig. 18.4.4L. The equipment comprises a line trap and an h.v. capacitance stack, stack tuning coil ('series arm') and shunt arm associated with each of the two phases used for the transmission of carrier frequencies. The 'shunt arms' are connected across the earthy end of the series arms to provide a low impedance to earth for 50 Hz. The shunt and series arms constitute a bandpass filter. A number of standard bands are available, typical ones being shown in the table below.

On commissioning, the tuning of the line traps, the series arms and the shunt arm has to be adjusted or checked. The series and shunt arms should tune to the midband frequency, adjustment being provided on the series arm coils. The shunt arm should have been supplied already tuned to the midband frequency.

Band	Frequency range kHz	Midband (geometric mean) frequency kHz
1	70- 81	75
2	80- 95	87
3	90-110	99.5
4	100-125	112
5	110-140	125
6	120-158	138
7	130-175	151
8	150-214	179.5
9	180-280	225
10	250-500	354
11	350-700	495

The tuning of the line traps is achieved by suitable choice of shunt capacitor. One British manufacturer recommends tuning them to the carrier frequency, whereas another manufacturer recommends that they be tuned to the midband frequency. The *method* of tuning will be the same in both cases and is described below.

For these tests the oscillator, amplifier and valve voltmeter are used. Signal levels in excess of the maximum output normally given by test oscillators are required to mask possible interference, thus the amplifier should have an open-circuit output of about 50-100 V. For all tests the earthy side of the amplifier output and valve voltmeter should be connected to the station earth.

When checking the tuning of the various resonant circuits in the line coupling equipment, great care must be taken to see that electrical connections between units do not introduce capacitance in parallel with the unit under test. Stray capacitance should also be reduced to a minimum. With these points in view it is recommended that isolation of the line traps should be achieved by earthing the line traps on the line side with portable earths and disconnecting the copper connectors on the station side, the disconnection being made at the line trap end of the connectors. Reference should be made to Fig. 18.4.4M which shows the test connections required to tune the line traps, the series arms and the shunt arms.

Line traps: Because the line trap is a parallel-connected wide band resonant circuit with high impedance at resonance, the valve voltmeter reading will be a maximum over the bandwidth at resonance. To obtain good selectivity a high impedance source is required. This is achieved by connecting the live side of the amplifier output via a high resistance (a half-watt 30 kΩ carbon resistor is suitable) to the station side of the line trap. The valve voltmeter is connected with its live side to the line-trap side of the resistor.

Series arm: The series arm is a circuit with low impedance at resonance, and the valve voltmeter reading will be a minimum at the resonant frequency of the series arm.

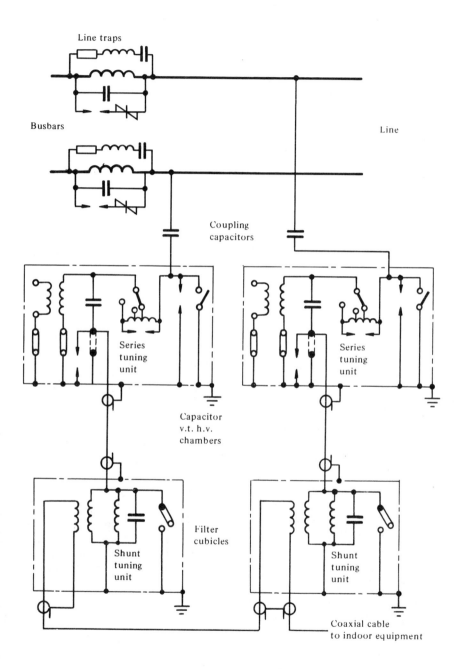

Fig. 18.4.4L   *Line coupling equipment*

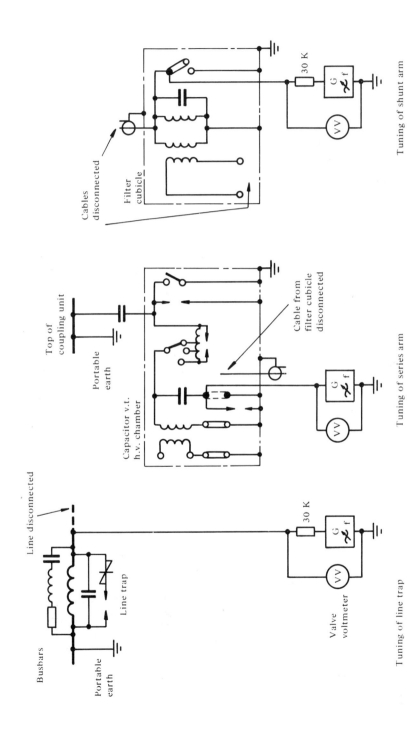

Fig. 18.4.4M

The lower end of the series arm should be isolated as it enters the capacitor v.t. h.v. chamber. On a combined coupling capacitor/capacitor v.t. assembly, the capacitor v.t. must be included in the circuit. To obtain good selectivity a low impedance source is required and an amplifier output impedance of 75 Ω is satisfactory. The live side of the amplifier and valve voltmeter are connected to the lower end of the series arm.

Shunt arm: The shunt arm is a parallel-connected resonant circuit. It should tune to the midband frequency of the coupling filter.

All connections should be removed from the unit and the live side of the amplifier should be connected to the unearthed side of the unit via a 30 kΩ resistor. The valve voltmeter reading will be a maximum at the resonant frequency of the shunt arm.

Since attenuation of the carrier signal occurs along the primary line an end-to-end measurement of this attentuation must be made. Again use is made of the oscillator and amplifier, which are connected to the h.f. cable at one end of the line whilst the received signal level is measured at the other. It is usual to make this test over a range of frequencies on either side of the intended working frequency. If possible three sets of tests should be done: one with the line dead and earthed on the station side of the line traps, one with the line unearthed, and one, later, after the line has been made alive and is carrying load. A curve of some typical results is illustrated in Fig. 18.4.4N.

Precommissioning tests of modern phase-comparison carrier protection should include tests on transmitter levels, receiver sensitivities and trip angle settings. These are best achieved by following the manufacturer's recommended commis-

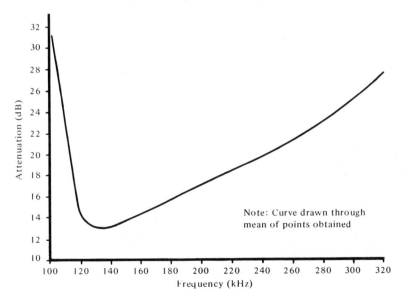

Fig. 18.4.4N   *On-load attenuation figures for 275 kV line; designed carrier frequency 132 kHz*

sioning instructions for the particular equipment, care being taken to ensure that adequate margin exists between alarm and trip level sensitivities. The built-in testing facilities which, by comparison of the injected currents at the two ends, permit routine stability and tripping tests to be carried out, should also be checked over and phased out.

The latest designs of normally quiescent power-line-carrier protection have had their built-in test facilities modified to comply with the permitted limits of carrier transmission time and are therefore capable of application throughout the band. However, during commissioning tests whenever carrier transmission to line is required care must be taken to comply with these conditions if operating at frequencies within the restricted bands. Individual manufacturer's commissioning instructions provide detailed information on this aspect specifically for their equipment.

To assist in checking the trip angle and sensitivity of the protection, facilities are provided for disconnecting the output to line and inserting a dummy load so that the equipment is terminated in 75Ω, thereby enabling these tests to be carried out without transmission of carrier to line.

When all these tests have been done satisfactorily the line may be put on load (see Sections 18.4.5 and 6) after which an end-to-end polarity test must be made. This can be done by the temporary disconnection and shorting of the same phase c.t.s at the two ends of the line to obtain an output. Operation of relays must be simulated if load current is below the setting of the equipment, and the phase of the carrier signals checked on the cathode ray oscilloscope. Fig. 18.4.40 shows the trip and stability zones of a typical phase-comparison equipment.

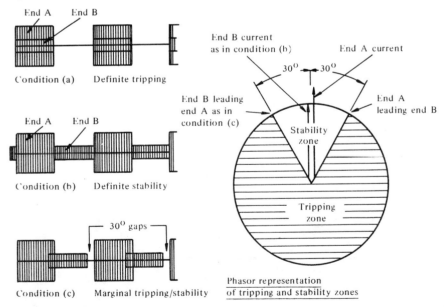

Fig. 18.4.40   Typical pictures from c.r.o

(*f*)   *Trip angle test unit:* One make of equipment has built-in facilities for checking the trip angle setting, but for another an external trip angle test unit is required. The fundamental requirement is to modulate the carrier frequency signal in order to produce variable gaps and so determine the trip angle setting.

This device produces pulses of variable duration which are used to modulate a constant carrier signal from the local oscillator in order to establish the shortest gap which will cause tripping.

D.C. pulses, adjustable in magnitude over the range 50 mV to 30 V and in duration from 20 to 75 electrical degrees are produced. Fixed duration pulses of 180 electrical degrees are also available by switch selection. Reference should be made to the manufacturer's instructions for suitable test points for connection of the test unit output.

Fig. 18.4.4P shows the circuit diagram of a trip angle test unit consisting of the following main parts:

(*i*)   *Power pack:* This is a simple full wave push-pull rectifier circuit producing approximately 30V across C1.

(*ii*)   *Phase shifter:* This is composed of a power transformer Tr1, resistors R1, VR1 and capacitor C2. Resistance R2 is high compared with R1 or VR1: consequently R1, VR1 and C2 can be considered to pass a common current and the voltage across R1 and VR1 will be 90 degrees in advance of that across C2. The vector relationship of these voltages is shown in Fig. 18.4.4Q from which it can be seen that the locus of the voltage at point D is equal in magnitude to one half of the secondary voltage of Tr1 while it advances in phase relative to that voltage as VR1 is reduced.

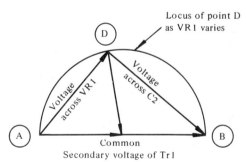

Fig. 18.4.4Q   *Voltage phasor relationship*

(*iii*)   *Phase comparator:* This is a logical NAND circuit, where the collectors of transistors T1 and T2 are both shorted to common if a positive voltage is present on either base. Therefore, as illustrated in Fig. 18.4.4R a pulse is produced on this common collector once per cycle, its duration being determined by the phase difference between the voltages at B and D (i.e. dependent upon the setting of VR1).

(*iv*)   *Current amplifier:* This is an emitter follower circuit, the output of which

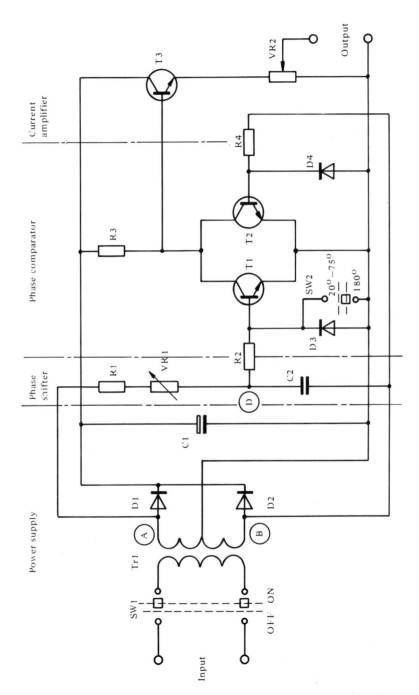

Fig. 18.4.4P   *Circuit diagram of carrier protection trip angle test unit*

is fed to the preset potentiometer VR2 which provides adjustment of the output voltage level.

(*v*) *Output switch:* In some cases it is necessary to have 180 degree pulses and these are obtained by removing the action of transistor T1 from the comparator circuit by shorting D3 via an output selector switch.

The components can be conveniently built into a small metal box with the potentiometer control and switches located on top for easy operation.

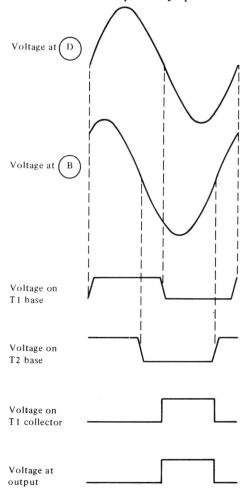

Fig. 18.4.4R   *Voltage waveforms*

(*g*) *Tripping and closing tests:* It is not possible to prove the trip and close wiring of a new circuit until the fuse and link have been inserted; yet if there is anything wrong with the wiring the battery may be short-circuited when this is done. As a precaution against anything untoward happening, it is wise to check with a voltmeter across the top and bottom jaws of the holder before the fuse is inserted, and again for the link. A zero reading on the meter proves that the fuse or link can confidently be inserted. A reading on the voltmeter is an indication that there is a path from positive to negative through the voltmeter and some part of the circuit. Such a voltage may be quite healthy – for example, there may be a path through some circuit supervision equipment or indicating lamp; but the reason for that path should be established before inserting the fuse or link.

As mentioned earlier, a copy of all extracted diagrams should be included in the commissioning log and as each contact, fuse, link, changeover switch etc., is proved, it should be ticked off on the appropriate diagram. If the same diagram is used for several circuits, differently coloured ticks may be used for the different circuits. If a relay has two separate contacts, one tripping a circuit breaker direct and the other tripping a tripping relay which then trips the circuit breaker, each should be checked separately.

Most present-day relays are fitted with mechanical flags, and it should be carefully checked that these are not likely to interfere with the operation of the relay element. If series electrical flags are employed it should be proved that two of them operate if their associated contacts are both closed in parallel. Under this condition the flag current will be roughly halved, and it is desirable to check that there is an adequate margin for operation.

Tripping tests should be proved at 100% and at least one lower value e.g. 60% battery volts. The latter is not an entirely theoretical test because if a circuit breaker is closed onto a fault requiring the breaker's immediate tripping, the volts available from the battery will be reduced by the drain of the closing solenoid. However, it should be noted that a requirement of British Standard Specification 5311 and 3659 is for the full fault breaking capability of circuit breakers to be available when the voltage at the trip coil is within the range 80-120% of nominal, and care should be taken in the design stage to ensure that 80% battery voltage is available at the trip coil under the most onerous conditions of operation.

Trip circuit supervision relays should be proved, and it should be checked that the alarm supply is not fed from the battery being supervised, otherwise no alarm could be given if the supervised supply failed. Trip-healthy lamps and resistors should be proved and the lamps should be shorted-out to prove that the series resistance is adequate to prevent tripping. In doing this test, it is advisable to short-out the lamp several times in quick succession whilst somebody listens adjacent to the switchgear to make sure that the associated trip coil plunger is not moving. A case has been experienced where the current passed by the resistor was sufficient to lift the plunger and move the tripping mechanism slightly but not enough to trip the breaker. After several operations, however, the tripping mechanism had 'inched' so far that tripping occurred.

If, during any of these tests, it has been necessary to disconnect the drives to banks of auxiliary switches to operate them in both positions, the drives must be reconnected after the tests and any split pins, circlips, etc., replaced.

(*h*) *Indications and alarms:* These tests involve checking that each indication and alarm functions correctly and they are largely self-explanatory. They are, however, important and the opportunity should be taken of instructing the operating staff in the functioning of the various controls and of giving them the opportunity of cancelling the alarms.

18.4.5 Phasing tests

It is necessary to prove correct phasing before a new piece of equipment can be put in parallel with existing equipment. For example, a 132/33 kV grid transformer is generally fitted with links in the 33 kV side which enable it to be connected to vector group Yd1 or Yd11, and tests should be done to establish that the new transformer phasing is the same as that with which it is to be connected in parallel.

This can be done before the transformer is made alive from the system by applying 415 V three-phase to the h.v. side, measuring voltages between the 132 kV and the 33 kV sides, and recording them in a schedule similar to the one below.

33kV Side   132 kV Side

R_1 Y_1 B_1

R_2···

Y_2·········· ····································

B_2··

Volts should be measured from R_1 to R_2, Y_2 and B_2, from Y_1 to R_2, Y_2 and B_2, and from B_1 to R_2, Y_2 and B_2. It is essential that the 132 kV and the 33 kV sides are temporarily commoned at some point for this test, otherwise misleading values will be obtained as there is no metallic return path for the voltmeter current. When the results have been obtained, the vectors can be plotted from which the phasing of the transformer can be established.

On lower voltage systems, for example up to 11 kV, it is possible to employ phasing sticks. These are insulated sticks which can safely be inserted into switchgear spouts and used in the same way as a voltmeter to phase out the R, Y and B phases of one circuit with the R, Y and B phases of a circuit already proved.

It is impracticable to use phasing sticks above this voltage, so for 33 kV, 66kV, 132 kV, 275 kV and 400 kV systems, phasing tests are usually carried out between the 110 V sides of voltage transformers connected to such systems. Phasing tests can, however, be done between a 110 V supply and one of 240 V or 415 V. Here again there must be a common point of reference between the voltage supplies which are to be compared. A 'null' method is insufficient — for example, if volts were only measured R–R, Y–Y and B–B, no reading would be obtained if the compared voltages were identical in magnitude and phase. Such a test could indicate perfect phasing; but it could also mean that the readings were not being

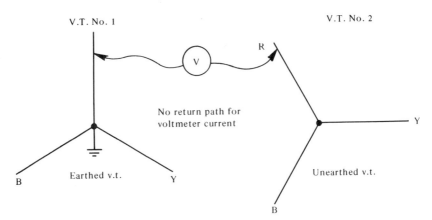

Fig. 18.4.5A   *Danger of 'null' method of phasing R-R, Y-Y, and B-B*

obtained because the two voltage supplies had no common point of reference. It would thus be possible for the supplies to be out-of-phase, yet no voltage reading would be obtained to indicate that fact. Fig. 18.4.5A illustrates this.

If the two supplies have no common reference point, one must be arranged either by temporarily earthing the unearthed supply on one phase or at the neutral, or by temporarily strapping the two systems together at one point.

To get a positive check, the red phase of one supply should be compared with red, yellow and blue of the other; then the yellow phase of the supply should be compared with the other three phases, and finally the blue. The results may be recorded on a schedule as shown in Fig. 18.4.5B.

Measured voltages			Phasors plotted	Actual phasing
Example 1				
	R_2	Y_2	B_2		
R_1	2	109	110		
Y_1	109	2	111		
B_1	110	111	1.5		
Example 2				
	R_2	Y_2	B_2		
R_1	34	90	123		
Y_1	124	33	90		
B_1	90	123	34		
Example 3				
	R_2	Y_2	B_2		
R_1	210	240	310		
Y_1	350	240	310		
B_1	210	240	130		

Fig. 18.4.5B   *Voltage measurement, plotting of phasors, and determination of phasing*

When a circuit is being paralleled for the first time, the v.t. associated with that circuit must be energised from a known source to prove that the v.t. connections are correct. After this has been done the voltmeter should be left connected, and then when the new v.t. is energised from an unknown source and synchronism is indicated, the two primary supplies must be in phase.

Although a phase rotation meter may be used in the case of a generator, it is a more definite check to employ two voltmeters connected red to red and blue to blue between the generator v.t. (already proved) and a v.t. on the system. The two voltmeter readings should beat up and down together at slip frequency, thus indicating that the phase rotation is correct, and they should both be at zero when the synchroscope needle is at 12 o'clock. Having checked this, the synchroscope can then be relied upon for closing in.

18.4.6   Closing up

The settings of overcurrent relays should be set down for paralleling or for switching in new equipment to ensure that if it is faulty, the fault will be disconnected with the minimum disturbance to the system. In this connection it is more important to set down the time multiplier than the plug setting. If the latter is set down then it must be restored to normal before load in excess of the temporary relay setting is picked up.

18.4.7   On-load tests

Having got the new equipment on load it is advisable to do certain tests. These have been touched on earlier, but are here given in more detail.

(*a*)   *Currents in relays:* A split plug and ammeter is a convenient way of checking currents in relays fitted with plug bridges. The ammeter must be on a suitable range and a split plug should be inserted on the same, or higher, tap as the relay setting — otherwise there is the possibility that the relay will operate if the circuit is heavily loaded.

It should be checked that there is negligible spill current in any residually-connected relays and in any protection working on the differential principle. Before measuring current in the c.t. circuits of differential relays it is advisable to remove the appropriate trip link.

Directional relays

(*b*)   *Phase-fault relays:* On-load tests of directional relays are required to prove the polarity of the v.t. connection with respect to the c.t. connection.

For these tests it cannot be stressed too strongly that the direction of the MW and MVArs must be positively known, also the power factor. Any load variation during the tests must be closely supervised — especially a change from a lagging to a leading power factor.

Primary injection tests and secondary wiring checks should already have established that the correct currents and voltages are associated with the appropriate elements. If proven instruments are already available on the primary circuit concerned, the load characteristics will be known; if not, it will be necessary to do 'wattmeter tests'. In these tests a set of vectors is plotted by which the position of the current relative to the voltage can be seen. A centre-zero wattmeter is used and the current-coil inserted in each phase in turn.

The wattful component of the red current is measured with R–N, Y–N and, for good measure, B–N volts. Some of the readings will be positive and some negative. These readings, plotted along the voltage vectors in the appropriate direction, will determine the position of the current vector. Fig. 18.4.7A shows a typical result.

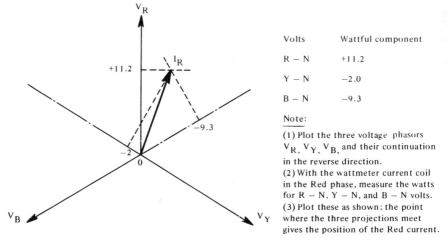

Volts	Wattful component
R – N	+11.2
Y – N	−2.0
B – N	−9.3

Note:

(1) Plot the three voltage phasors V_R, V_Y, V_B, and their continuation in the reverse direction.
(2) With the wattmeter current coil in the Red phase, measure the watts for R – N, Y – N, and B – N volts.
(3) Plot these as shown; the point where the three projections meet gives the position of the Red current.

Fig. 18.4.7A   *Wattmeter tests on directional relays to determine load and power factor*

All that now remains is to check that each phase-fault directional relay is behaving in the way it should. To check this it will be necessary to know the type of directional connection (30°, 90°, or 90° - 45°) applied to the relay. It will also be necessary to know the polar characteristics of the relay; if these have not been furnished by the manufacture they should have been obtained during secondary injection tests by applying to the relay voltages of varying phase angles relative to the injection current, and finding at what angle it has minimum torque.

Thus with all this information available, it will be possible to predict exactly what the directional relay should be doing for any load condition; and it must now be proved that it is doing the right thing for the particular load at the time. Normally a phase-fault directional relay is connected so that it will operate for a flow of fault power out from the busbar.

If separate phase-fault directional elements are used for each phase they should all behave in the same way under the same conditions, but if the three directional elements drive on to a common disc and spindle movement, each should be proved separately whilst the other two elements are temporarily disconnected.

It cannot be stressed too strongly that phase-fault directional relays have not been proved unless the following conditions have been satisfied:

(i)   The type of directional connection should be known.
(ii) The relay characteristics should be known – that is, its polar curve.
(iii) The direction and power factor of the load must be known without the slightest doubt.
(iv) Each phase-fault element in turn must then be seen to operate in the expected way for that load condition. This establishes that the c.t. and v.t. polarities are correct.

(*c*)   *Earth-fault directional relays:* Directional earth-fault elements are more difficult to prove in respect of c.t. and v.t. polarities because the polarising volts and amps will not be there under healthy load conditions. Fault conditions, therefore, have to be simulated.

On the load test it must first be checked that there is no open-delta voltage or residual current under this condition. The most convenient way of proving that a 70° relay will correctly respond to an earth fault on or beyond the protected line (as in (*b*) of Fig. 18.4.4A), is by short-circuiting and disconnecting the blue phase current transformer, removing the red phase v.t. fuse, and strapping the dead side of the fuse to the neutral connection. Section (*e*) of Fig. 18.4.4A indicates the resultant vectors and similarity to (*b*). The relay should operate for load-current phase-angles between about 90° lag and 60° lead.

It is not strictly necessary to make the test cyclically round the phases, since zero outputs for balanced input have already been checked; the other phases could, however, be proved for good measure.

18.4.8   Modifications to existing substations

All the tests so far enumerated have applied to new substations. Although possibly complex, the commissioning of a new substation is straightforward compared with major modifications to an existing site. In the latter case, much of the equipment has to be kept in commission during reconstruction which may involve reallocation of multicore cables, the connecting in or reconnecting of c.t.s and alterations to relay panels. Considerable ingenuity is needed here and much improvisation. Essential tripping and closing supplies have to be maintained during wholesale reorganisation, and much temporary cabling and wiring may have to be run to effect a smooth changeover.

It is impossible to stipulate any procedure for this class of work beyond stressing the need for particular care and advance planning.

18.5   Routine maintenance tests

Protective gear may stand quiescent for months and yet be required to operate with precision if a fault occurs on its associated primary equipment. Perhaps a more difficult requirement of the protection is that it must remain inoperative on nearby external faults. Routine maintenance tests on protective gear are done to ensure that the equipment is always ready to perform in a fully discriminative manner the duty required of it.

18.5.1 Causes and effects of deterioration

Protective gear does not normally deteriorate with usage, but can be harmed by adverse conditions. For example, a relay subjected to pronounced continuous vibration can suffer damage to its pivots or bearings; dampness in junction boxes and circuit-breaker kiosks can lower the insulation resistance of the multi-core cables and wiring; a polluted atmosphere may have a detrimental effect on relay ligaments, relay contacts and auxiliary switches; the heat produced by continuously-energised coils can often age the insulation; electrolysis may cause 'green spot', leading to open-circuited coils or contacts.

Measures to alleviate or prevent many of these causes are taken in the design stage of modern equipment. Outdoor terminal boxes are ventilated, heated, and proof against vermin. Access to terminal boxes is made easier by the provision of hinged or slide-off doors, instead of bolted covers; new relays are subjected to vibration type tests to prove that they will stand reasonably heavy ill-treatment without maloperation or damage; insulating materials are chosen to stand heat or damp without deterioration; and electrolytic corrosion can be prevented on d.c. circuits by using biasing equipment on the battery, thus keeping the whole of the d.c. wiring at a negative potential relative to earth.

18.5.2 Frequency of routine maintenance

When determining a programme, the frequency of routine maintenance inspections and tests will depend on the fault history and fault liability of the equipment. There is no point in overtesting equipment; the programme should be planned so that faults in the equipment are anticipated, not precipitated. The frequency of test will, however, vary widely with the type of equipment. Certain items are continuously monitored, some are checked several times a day, whilst others may be tested monthly, yearly or even every two years. Typical examples of the frequency and types of equipment are:

(*a*)   *Continuous monitoring*
Pilot supervision
Trip circuit supervision
Relay voltage supervision
Battery earth-fault supervision
Busbar protection c.t. circuit supervision

(*b*)   *Daily*
Relay flags inspected on every shift
Carrier protection tests - either manually every shift or by clock-test every 4 hours

(*c*)   *Monthly*
Water level of liquid earthing resistances

(*d*)   *Two-monthly*
Intertripping channel tests without tripping any switches

(*e*)   *Six-monthly*
Tripping tests

(*f*)   *Yearly*
Check operating levels, sensitivites, tripping angle and reflex test facilities of phase comparison carrier protection
Secondary injection on the more complex forms of protection
Insulation resistance tests
Check of battery biasing equipment
Injection of gas and oil actuated relays with air or oil
Calibration check on liquid earthing resistances

(*g*)   *Two-yearly*
Secondary injection tests on the more robust relays

18.5.3   Inspections and tests

The main features of the various inspections and tests are briefly indicated below:

(*a*)   *Inspections:* On outdoor equipment, check that heaters are on and that vents are not blocked. Check there is no evidence of vermin in relay panels and in switchgear terminal boxes; check relay settings against schedules or cards; inspect relay contacts and ligaments for correct positioning and corrosion; inspect relays for foreign bodies such as dust, specks of iron filing in magnet gaps, flaking of plated parts; voltmeter check to prove that battery biasing equipment is in order, etc.

(*b*)   *Intertripping tests:* These can be a prolific source of error especially on three- or four-point circuits. Particular care is needed to be on the correct panel. A detailed procedure should be established for carrying out these tests, the test links, if any, being changed over at all points of test before hand. Care must be taken to restore the links when the tests are completed.

(*c*)   *Tripping tests:* The complete sequence of tripping should be proved from the protective relays to the tripping of the circuit breaker. The relays are usually operated manually, but with particularly delicate relays there is some advantage in actuating them electrically. When relay covers are removed prior to these tests, any dust should be wiped off the top of the cover before removing it so that dust does not fall into the relay. The opportunity should be taken on these tests to prove that the relay contacts are clean and secure, and to observe the contact wipe. The flags should be checked for positive operation, and the appropriate alarms should be proved at the same time.

(*d*)   *Insulation resistance tests:* These may be done with a 500 V Megger, on one secondary circuit at a time with all the others earthed. The results obtained may vary with the weather, but it is the trend rather than the absolute value which is important.

(*e*)   *Secondary injection tests:* Any variation of operating or resetting times or value could indicate a cracked or sticking bearing. Before secondary injection maintenance on relays, the terminal boards and relay stems should be brushed down with an insulated brush or insulated vacuum cleaner nozzle.

(*f*)   *Recording of test results and progress:* It is important to keep a record of the progress of the results of routine maintenance tests. The methods adopted will vary to suit the particular organisation, but in principle should show the frequency of any test, when it is due, when it was done, and if it becomes overdue. The tests results can best be recorded on test sheets specifically made up for the different kinds of tests and protection. One method in use has a complete binder of such test sheets per station, and each sheet has enough spaces to cover several years' testing so that the results of past tests can be seen at a glance and compared. The test sheets are made out in schedule form, in such a way that the sheet is not only a record but a guide to what should be done on the tests. Any defects found in the equipment should be recorded. Defects of a design nature should be reported to the manufacturers so that they can improve their design.

(*g*)   *General.* In this section on routine maintenance tests, no attempt has been made to describe any test in detail; the philosophy of such tests has, however, been fully discussed. Several further important points can be made to conclude this section: one should be familiar with the equipment on which work is to be done, and full use should be made of appropriate diagrams and test schedules. It may be helpful to prepare a list of items disturbed during the tests so that the equipment can be quickly restored to normal without anything being overlooked. There is little point in maintaining equipment in perfect condition if it is put back into commission on the wrong setting or with a connection left off. In this respect, it should be noted that the disconnection points provided in certain wiring circuits are intended for special fault investigation purposes only and should not be used as isolation points during routine maintenance.

18.5.4   Maintenance of busbar protection, back-tripping and circuit-breaker fail protection at double-busbar type substations

The consequences of busbar protection failing to operate are very serious because clearance of the fault would then be dependent upon the operation of remote distance, overcurrent or earth-fault protection. These remote relays would be unable to discriminate between the healthy and faulty busbar sections resulting in complete disconnection of the substation with consequent disruption of the system. Not only would any generating plant at the faulted station be lost, but it is also possible that due to the long fault-clearance time involved other generators in the close vicinity would lose stability and that low-frequency protection would operate causing further interruption of supply. Therefore it is of paramount importance that busbar protection is maintained regularly to prove its integrity. Owing to difficulties involved in testing busbar protection, and the consequences of inadvertent operation during such testing, it has been the practice to take the protection out of service when carrying out maintenance. However, for the reasons stated above long outages of the protection can no longer be tolerated and techniques have been evolved for testing the protection in service except when checking insulation resistance of d.c. circuits.

From a study of Chapter 13 it will be seen that busbar protection, back-tripping and circuit-breaker fail protection are closely interrelated and test procedures must overlap all three facilities. It is usually permissible to take back tripping out of service to simplify test procedures, because the risks to the system are not so great as when busbar protection is out of service. Circuit-breaker fail protection can be tested when a circuit is out for routine maintenance.

The test procedures which follow are based upon the 400 kV busbar protection, back-tripping and circuit-breaker fail schemes shown in Chapter 13, but the principles demonstrated can be adapted to suit other protection arrangements as required.

(*a*)   *Basis of busbar protection & back tripping tests:* The basis of the testing procedure is to work on one zone of protection at a time relying upon the 2 out of 2 feature to prevent inadvertent tripping, and then ideally proving operation by simultaneous secondary injection of the check zone and a discriminating zone to trip each section of busbar in turn with its associated circuits. The trip outputs of the back-tripping receive trip relays must be isolated to ensure that the tripping is initiated from the circuit busbar protection relays and not from the zone relays via the back-tripping system. Operation of the back-tripping system up to the trip relay contacts is proved at this time and then the circuits are selected to the opposite busbar and the zone relays manually operated to prove the correct selection of the back tripping system via the busbar selector auxiliary switches.

If system conditions are such that it is not acceptable to trip a section of busbar together with its associated circuits a possible alternative is to trip only bus-coupler and bus-section circuit breakers leaving the circuits connected to an isolated section of busbar. As in the ideal method described in the previous paragraph all circuit back tripping relays should be operated via both busbar isolators to prove the complete scheme. For this test procedure tripping, intertripping and protection unstabilisation or acceleration from the circuit busbar protection trip relays, and interlocked current trip relays, must also be removed. Tripping of individual circuits can then be proved by manual operation of the latching type circuit trip relays during individual circuit maintenance.

In carrying out the tests it is recommended that the following precautions should be observed:

  (i)   No switching, earthing or similar work should be allowed within the station for the duration of the tests.
 (ii)   Weather conditions should be good at outdoor type substations.
(iii)   An agreed testing schedule should be prepared and adhered to.
 (iv)   A minimum of two engineers experienced in the protection should carry out the tests and each should check the action of the other.
  (v)   Autoreclose equipment at the remote feeder ends should be taken out of service.
 (vi)   Test points should be clearly identified and caution notices displayed on equipment not under test.
(vii)   The test supply source should be isolated, earth free and of high impedance with a substantial two pole switch between the injection supply and the test point.

(b)   *Test procedures for busbar protection and back tripping*

(i) *Insulation resistance:* Insulation resistance to earth of the current transformer circuits should be measured using a 500 V megger. The instrument should be applied across the appropriate earth links before they are opened and should not be removed until the earth link is reclosed. The insulation resistance of d.c. circuits must be measured with the appropriate supply links and fuses withdrawn and tripping circuits isolated. Wiring associated with individual circuits should be tested during routine circuit outages.

(ii) *Secondary injection:* All a.c. and d.c. tripping relays should be visually checked to ascertain that they have reset before and after injection of each a.c. relay. Injection tests should be carried out on only one phase of a discriminating or check zone at a time, increasing in small voltage steps and recording operating values of supervision, circuit and zone relays in turn noting also that only the relays associated with the injected phase and zone operate. The duration of current injection should be kept to a minimum to prevent damage to relays and equipment. It is not necessary to repeat these tests with the circuits connected to the opposite busbar to prove correct selection of a.c. wiring via busbar selector auxiliary switches, as these are monitored by the a.c. supervision relays.

(iii) *Tripping tests:* The protection should be operated for each busbar zone in turn, thereby tripping the associated circuits and operating the back tripping receive trip relays. Operation should be by simultaneous a.c. injection of the appropriate discriminating and check zone relays. The injected voltage should be approximately 150% of the setting value obtained in the earlier tests. It is not adequate to operate the a.c. zone relays manually for these tests as the manual effort achieved may exceed the electrical energy available for operation. This procedure will have established correct operation of the busbar protection but the circuits should be connected to the opposite busbar and the zone busbar protection a.c. relays operated manually, to prove correct selection of the back tripping receive trip relays by the busbar selector auxiliary switches which are not monitored. Tripping of the circuit breakers from their back tripping receive trip relays can be proved during circuit maintenance by manual operation of the latching type relays.

(c)   *Basic test procedure for circuit breaker fail protection:* As described in Chapter 13, circuit-breaker fail protection opens, via the back tripping system all the circuit breakers selected to the same busbar as the stuck circuit breaker. After proving the back tripping system by the test described in Section 18.5.4(*b*) the circuit-breaker fail protection can be tested during individual circuit maintenance, without risk to other circuits, by removing the links which isolate individual circuits from the back tripping bus wires. With these links removed the circuit-breaker fail protection can be tested down to its own back tripping receive trip relay. The tests should include insulation resistance, a.c. secondary injection of current check relays, d.c. sequence and timing tests.

18.5.5   Maintenance and testing of intertripping and protection signalling equipment

Type T40 intertripping and T15 protection signalling equipment (see Chapter 7) have achieved their fast operating times at the expense of simplicity, many more components being used than in earlier equipments: the circuitry also is much more complex. The quest for higher speed has also meant that the circuitry is much more susceptible to air-borne or cable-borne interference and precautions have to be taken to ensure that interference does not produce maloperation or inhibit or delay tripping.

Although all modern equipments are not necessarily to T40 or T15 specifications they tend to be based on the same design using similar techniques and requiring the same precautions against interference.

(a)   *Commissioning:* A full list of commissioning checks will usually be given in the manufacturer's hand book but the following aspects, which may not be included, should also be checked to ensure that:

(i)   the equipment is bolted down and securely earthed to the station earth bar

(ii)   all connections are tight and of the correct polarity

(iii)   the cabling is of the correct size, and that twisted pairs are used if specified

(iv)   there are no spurious earths on the cabling, or on the cubicle battery supply leads

(v)   the intertrip send relay does not operate with less than the specified minimum operate current

(vi)   the equipment, including modules, has no dry soldered joints

(vii)   the electrical noise fed back to the battery from the equipment is within the specification limit. A typical value for this is one not greater than 5 mV peak to peak over the bandwidth d.c. − 1 MHz. It is important to realise that such noise on the battery can adversely affect equipment connected to it, d.c.-d.c. power supply units being the most usual source of noise

(viii)   if Post Office line isolation is required this has been fitted and has not in any way been bypassed.

(ix)   no spurious tripping operations occur when withdrawing or inserting the power supply fuses. This should be checked by using a device which can respond to pulses as short as 1-2 ms and a suitable device using a reed relay is described in Section 18.5.5(*d*)

(x)   the output relay operation is as specified for the protection scheme; for instance is the delayed autoreclose facility required? Check also that the relay is operated for the minimum specified time, irrespective of the duration of operation of the sending relay

(xi)   end-to-end signalling times are in accordance with the specification. It is important to follow the setting up procedure as given in the manufacturer's handbook for the commissioning tests. End-to-end tripping tests should be carried out first with the battery voltage normal and then with it at the specified extremes, i.e. typically on the 48 V battery at 44 and 56 V, including tests with high volts at one end and low volts at the other.

(*b*)   *Routine maintenance and testing:* The equipment handbooks give advice on the frequency and type of routine tests but the recommended frequency of testing varies between equipment types. For some equipments even weekly tests are suggested, albeit level tests carried out with the equipment remaining in service. In practice the frequency of testing is very much a compromise between the economic use of resources and the need to keep the probability of an undetected fault as low as possible.

A commonly accepted maintenance programme is for the equipment to be subjected to routine tests every two months. However, if the increased reliability anticipated from the more modern equipment materialises it should be possible to extend the period between routine tests to six months without detriment. The recommended programme would then be for routine tests to be carried out at the end of the first, second, fourth and sixth months after commissioning and thereafter at intervals not greater than six months.

The types of tests to be carried out vary between the different forms of equipment but in any case are detailed in the manufacturers' handbooks. They cover such items as the checking and adjustment of power supply voltages, oscillator frequencies, monostable timers, signal levels at various test points etc. Finally the equipment should be end-to-end tested and timed.

Signal transmission time is critically important for intertripping and protection signalling equipment. For example when protection signalling equipment is used for blocking, on the occurrence of a through fault a signal must be received from the remote end in about 20 milliseconds from the detection of the fault, otherwise the protection will maloperate. Consequently, it is recommended that the equipment is timed during routine maintenance periods. Push button testing, whereby the send button is operated and the received signal observed at the remote end, does not give a real indication of signal transmission time.

Timing can most easily be achieved by a 'reflex' or 'round-the-loop' test. In this, the send relay at end A is operated by a push key, a contact of which also starts a digital timer. At the remote end B, the receive contacts are arranged to operate the send relay and return the signal to end A, the receipt of which stops the timer. The test is comparatively simple if switches are specially provided for this facility on the intertripping/protection signalling equipment or on the relay panel. Absence of such switching arrangements would make the test more difficult and entail the disconnection of pilot cores from the equipment terminals.

The time recorded for the test is the total for the signal transmission in both directions: half this time is normally a satisfactory estimate of the time for each channel. If the recorded time is outside the equipment specification further investigation is required to locate the trouble. It should be remembered that the measured time also includes the line transmission time but this is unlikely to be greater than about 1 ms for 22 km of cable length, which is the time for signal propagation along standard loaded cable. The propagation time for carrier routes should be much less.

(*c*)   *Fault investigation:* The recommended fault investigation procedures for solid state equipment as outlined in Section 18.6.3 are applicable to these types of equipment.

(*d*)   *Trip monitor device:* This device mentioned in Section 18.5.5(*a*)(ix) may be used during the commissioning and testing of intertripping equipments, and is easily constructed. The circuit diagram is shown in Fig. 18.5.5A.

The trip receive contacts which can either be clean i.e. clear of power supply, or supplied from 48 (or 110) V d.c. batteries are connected to terminals A-B. A 48 V power supply is connected to terminals C-D. (In either case the polarity is immaterial because of diode bridges D1-D4 and D5-D8). If the trip relay contacts are connected to a battery then key switch KA should be selected to the position shown in the diagram. When the trip receive relay operates, relay RA is energised and locks in over its own contact to the second coil. The audible alarm is given and the light emitting diode (LED) is lit. When the trip contacts have reset the alarm can be reset by momentarily operating the reset key.

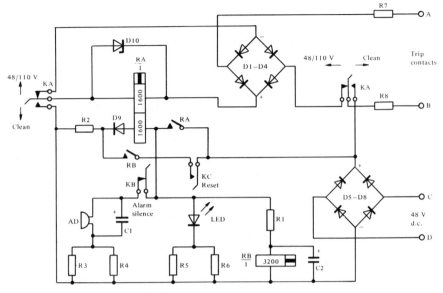

Fig. 18.5.5A   *Trip monitor device*

If long term supervision of a trip is required the alarm silence key can be operated to disconnect the audible alarm: a trip receive will still be indicated on the LED.

If the reset key is changed to the operated position, the alarm will automatically reset when the trip contacts restore. With fleeting trip conditions the audible alarm sounds and the l.e.d. lights only during the slow operate time of relay RB.

When the trip contacts are clean, key KA should be operated. The circuit to operate RA is then: positive terminal C or D; diode bridge D5-D8; key KA operated; terminal B; trip contacts; terminal A; diode bridge D1-D4; RA coil; key KA operated; negative via diode bridge D5-D8 to terminal C or D.

The equipment is compact and can be fitted in a box typically 110 x 90 x 55mm.

18.6   Fault investigation

Fault investigation falls under two main headings: the investigation of primary faults and the investigation of faults on the protective equipment.

18.6.1   Primary faults

In this context the cause of primary faults is ignored, and only the effects of that fault on the protective gear and secondary equipment are considered.

Faults which are cleared correctly by the protective gear normally need little investigation. The protective gear engineer should, however, satisfy himself that the protective gear operations are commensurate with the nature of the primary trouble. If there is any doubt he should also satisfy himself that the protective gear has not been damaged in any way by the fault conditions to which it has been subjected.

A suspected maloperation of protective gear should, however, be investigated in the greatest detail.

Greatest care should be taken to collect and consider all the relevant evidence and to assess it objectively.

Much can be gleaned from recording voltmeters and ammeters, stopped clocks, automatic fault-recording oscillographs, reports of flashes, vibration, noises, alarms, and dips on the lights.

18.6.2 Faults on the protective equipment

Many faults on protective equipment are simple and self-evident, such as low insulation resistance, badly adjusted flags, and relays out of calibration. Intermittent faults, or failure of a switch to trip when tripping tests are being done are often more difficult to diagnose.

It is important that the investigation of the fault should be carried out in such a way as not to destroy any evidence.

The most likely sources of trouble should be looked for first. In the case of a circuit breaker failing to trip, these should include low battery voltage, faulty plug and socket connectors, auxiliary switches, burnt-out trip coils, local/remote selectors in the wrong position, and some kind of mechanical failure. If a quick visual inspection reveals none of these failures, then electrical tests should be made. Such tests should cover checks of the trip supply, fuses and links and the contact resistance of the auxiliary switch and the local/remote selector, and the continuity of the trip coil circuit. These points should be methodically checked with an ohmmeter or voltmeter – *not* by pulling out fuses or disturbing any contacts. By checking through the circuit with an ohmmeter or voltmeter the faulty part can be identified with certainty. The trouble can then be remedied, and one is then certain that the reason for the failure has been found and cleared.

Sometimes the investigation may be lengthy and involved. In this case keep a chronological note of the items or parts of circuit tested and the conditions applying at the time those tests were done. This will help to avoid the confusion of thinking that a different result was obtained an hour earlier when the 'same' tests were done. In fact, an auxiliary switch, selector switch, or indicating lamp may now be in a different position from what it was before, thus altering the conditions completely.

18.6.3 Faults on solid-state equipment

The procedures previously described for commissioning and routine maintenance of conventional equipment are, in the main, also applicable to solid-state protection but the following additional points should be borne in mind.

(*a*)   Insulation resistance tests should not be carried out at a voltage in excess of 500 V.

(*b*)   During such tests diodes and transistors which might sustain damage should be shorted out.

Failures in solid-state equipment can usually be traced to a particular printed circuit card or module with the aid of the manufacturer's test procedures. Replacement of a faulty card or module, which usually has plug connectors, enables the equipment to be restored to service with a minimum of delay. Tracing and replacement of faulty components on the printed circuit card requires specialist knowledge and equipment and is best carried out at a central depot or at the manufacturer's works. Owing to difficulties in proving the card after repair unless a complete equipment identical to the one from which the faulted card originated is available, the latter course is to be preferred. A further point in its favour is that replacement components used by manufacturers will usually have been selected by a process of soak and heat tests before use. These tests eliminate most early failures and hence improve the subsequent reliability of the equipment. If in an emergency components from local suppliers are used they should be replaced by components supplied by the equipment manufacturer at the earliest opportunity.

In order to achieve quick restoration to service of faulted equipment, a suitable stock of spare cards and modules should be available. Holding such spares is expensive and this prohibits their provision at each equipment location. An economical arrangement is to hold spares at a central location to serve a particular area. As a general principle an overall spares holding, based on population, of 10% or one of each item whichever is the greater should prove adequate to meet most situations. This will obviously be subject to some variation in the knowledge of experience with particular equipments. Certain cards and modules are frequency conscious and in some cases it would be very difficult to justify holding one of each item. In such circumstances, consideration should be given to holding stocks of components to permit the adaptation of cards for a variety of frequencies.

18.7   The avoidance of errors when testing

18.7.1   General

The greatest care is necessary when making tests on site to ensure safety to life and security of supply. Every effort must be made to avoid testing errors, but the list of precautions can never be complete.

(*a*)   *The correct equipment:* Make sure that the correct equipment is approached. This sounds very easy, but on suites of panels or on panels which are badly laid out it is quite possible to become confused. A common cause of error is for the correct panel to be identified on the front, and the wrong one on the back; or vice-versa.

Ways of preventing such errors are the use of temporary screens or rope barriers,

PROTECTIVE & CONTROL GEAR TESTS ON SITE

REMINDER SHEET

Station : .... Equipment : .... Date : ....

Brief Description of Work : ....

Reason for test : .... Engineer in charge of test : ....

A tick should be placed against the items disturbed

EQUIPMENT	Disturbed	NOTES	Restored
Trip Link or Fuse			
Intertrip Test Links			
G.P.O. Pilot Links			
Battery Biasing Link			
C.T. or Terminal Board Links			
Voltage Fuses			
Test Switches			
Wiring : (a) Leads off			
(b) Test leads on			
(c) Temporary Straps			
Relays : (a) Settings			
(b) Wedges			
(c) Coils Shorted			
(d) Stabilising Resistances			
(e) Metrosils			
Auto Reclose			
Automatic Voltage Control			
Local/Remote Selectors			
Standby/Remote Selectors			
Busbar Protection (a) Discriminating Zones			
(b) Check Zone(s)			
Adjacent Circuits ?			
Remote Substations ?			

GENERAL TESTING HINTS

Identify correct equipment

Instructions - clear and concise

Diagrams up to date ?

Special vigilance if programme is changed

Check separately and independently

Test leads (a) Continuous (b) Well-insulated

Care with multi-range instruments

Danger of "un-programmed extra"

THINK before taking action

Final check-up after tests

FURTHER DETAILS OF ABNORMALITIES MAY BE WRITTEN OVERLEAF

Fig. 18.7.1A   *Reminder sheet*

the application of warning labels to be panels (back and front), on either side of the panel to be worked on, and the locking of those relay cubicles not being worked on.

(b)   *List of abnormalities:* A list should be made of all things disturbed during testing, such as wiring disconnected, test leads applied, relay settings altered, paper wedges in relays, trip links removed, voltage fuses removed, and so on. Such a list helps restoration to normal to be made quickly and ensures that nothing is overlooked. A standard form can be used for this purpose, a typical form being shown in Fig. 18.7.1A.

(c)   *Primary injection tests:* During primary injection tests:

(i)   It must be ensured that the primary equipment is dead and safe to work upon.
(ii)   The diagrams should be studied and c.t.s through which primary current will be passed should be noted. The necessary precautions should be taken to safeguard the security of adjacent circuits (see section relating to primary injection tests).
(iii) List any abnormalities as in (b) above.
(iv)   Ensure that no c.t.s are open-circuited.
(v)   Check that the test ammeters are on the correct ranges.
(vi)   After tests are completed, check that all test leads are removed and that everything is back to normal.

(d)   *Relay wedges:* During tests it is often necessary to wedge relays in the operated or non-operated position. In induction disc relays such wedges should be placed under the disc (so as not to apply excessive pressure to the bottom bearing). They should be conspicuous so that their presence cannot be overlooked.

(e)   *Test leads and clips:* Test leads should be periodically checked for insulation and continuity so that no mishaps occur due to faulty leads.

Test clips of the type which have a relatively large amount of bare metal exposed should not be used in congested locations where one clip could short across two relay studs.

(f)   *Instructions:* Where it is necessary during tests to pass instructions from one to the other, either directly or by telephone, care should be taken to ensure that such messages are thoroughly understood. A telephoned instruction in particular should be repeated by the recipient to make sure that the message has been properly received and understood.

(g)   *Responsibility for tests:* Where it is necessary for two or more engineers to work together on a series of tests, it must be agreed beforehand who is in charge. No action should be taken without the knowledge of that person.

(h)   *Multipurpose instruments:* If a multipurpose instrument is being used, great care should be taken to ensure that it is on the correct range for the measurements being made. Failure to do this may result in a c.t. being effectively open-circuited, or in an internal flashover which may wreck the instrument and injure the user.

(i)   *One source of supply:* No work should be done on any equipment which controls the only source of supply to consumers.

(*j*) *Final check:* Before leaving the site get into the habit of having a careful look round. Think back over the work that has been done to make sure that everything has been restored to normal. Although advice can be proffered and various devices used on site to reduce the chances of error, it is the continual practising of self-discipline that will do most to keep testing errors to a minimum.

18.8   The test equipment

Provided one is prepared to operate relays manually on a tripping test, no equipment is required for such a test. Only a megger is required for insulation resistance tests. Secondary injection tests, however, are in a different category, and opinions differ as to the best selection of equipment required for such tests.

Much can be done with a slider type resistor, an ammeter, a transformer, a switch and a stop-watch. The assembly of these, however, possibly several times a week, is tedious and inefficient and it is desirable to have such portable equipment already assembled in boxes to which external connections only need be made.

The design of such a test set depends on the type of protection for which it is needed, but considerable flexibility should be built into it to cater for all types of protection and current ranges.

One principle should be kept firmly in mind; one is not trying to set up a standardising laboratory on site, nor trying to reproduce the type approval tests.

The purpose of portable secondary injection equipment is to confirm as far as is practicable that the protection is in order and that it keeps in calibration within limits during the years which follow commissioning.

A supply is needed and a means of connecting that supply to the test equipment. A supply may also be required for a hand lamp, soldering iron or an oscilloscope, so some thought should be given to the provision of a test supply box to which one supply can be fed but from which a number of supplies can be taken.

In the test equipment some current control is necessary, the ranges usually being from 0 to 3 A on 'mains direct' or from 0 to 20 A through a transformer. Some instrumentation is needed, together with switches for controlling the supply; and a timing device to measure speed of operation. For distance protection or directional relays a voltage supply is also necessary, again controllable. The secondary injection test equipment is then completed by sundry test leads, alligator clips, split plugs and a pear switch. Each assembly should be portable, stackable and free from excrescences, and the requirements are discussed in more detail under the appropriate headings below.

(*a*) *Test supply:* For full flexibility this should be three-phase, four-wire, 415 volts of a sinusoidal waveshape and adequately protected. The greatest care must be taken when connecting to that supply to ensure that it is not accidentally earthed or short-circuited.

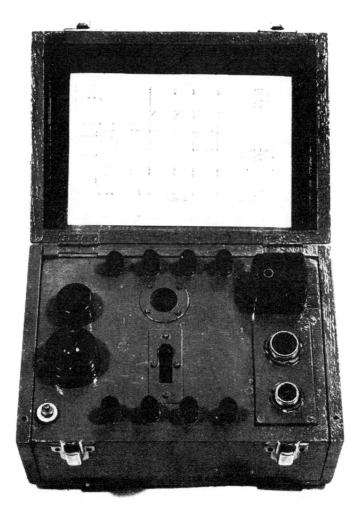

Fig. 18.8A   *Test gear — test supply box*

A three-pole and neutral switch specially and permanently allocated for test supplies should be provided in each relay room. Leads pushed into sockets and wedged in by match sticks are strongly deprecated.

(*b*)   *Test supply lead:* This should preferably be four-core flexible t.r.s or p.v.c. cable of ample length to connect from the supply to the test supply box located at the point of test.

The connection of the cable on the test supply box should be designed to prevent strain on the terminations.

The cable may be accommodated in a reel for easy unwinding and winding.

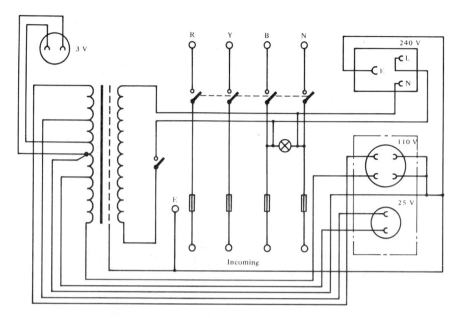

Fig. 18.8B *Test gear — test supply box*

(c)   *Test supply box:* The 415 V, three-phase, four-wire supply entering the test supply box is fused on entry and connects a four-pole main switch to four insulated output terminals. The box also contains a 240 V pilot lamp (connected between one phase and neutral), a 240 V 5 A socket, a 240/110/25/3 V transformer, and sockets for a hand lamp and a soldering iron. A two-pin socket is provided for connecting a 3 V lamp used for relay inspection. A photograph of one such box is given in Fig. 18.8A, and Fig. 18.8B shows its connections.

(d)   *Current box:* The current box derives its supply from the test supply box; this is achieved by an insulated bar containing four slotted brass 'spades' feeding a length of four-core cable running to the current box. The slotted brass spades easily slip under the insulated terminals on the output side of the test supply box.

Only one phase is used in the current box, but all three phases are brought to an arrangement of three sockets to provide selection of the phase required. The voltage box, described later, obtains its supply from the three phases of the current box. The selected single-phase supply is fed through a switch or contactor to a resistor/ potentiometer network and thence through a 'fine control' resistor to the output terminals for the 0-3A range. A two-way switch on the output side of the 'fine control' resistor enables the supply to be switched to 'mains direct' or alternatively to the primary of an external 240/30 V 20 A transformer. A pear switch on the end of a long lead enables the current to be switched whilst a relay high up on a panel is observed or timed. The current box is shown in Fig. 18.8C and a diagram of its connections in Fig. 18.8D.

When using the 240/30 V transformer to test relays, it will be appreciated that

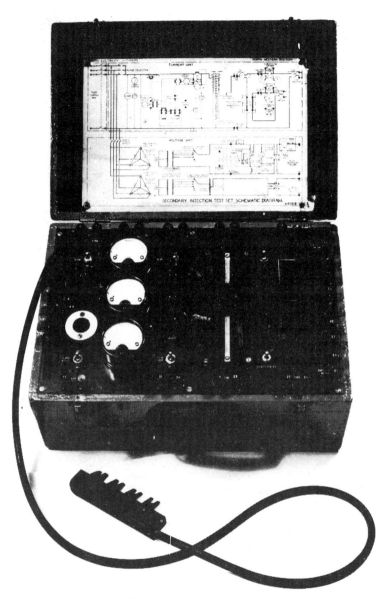

Fig. 18.8C   *Test gear – current box*

if too much resistance is introduced in series with the primary of the transformer some distortion of output wave form will result. On the other hand, the resistor in series with the relay on the 'mains direct' side will give a good waveshape – provided, of course, that the voltage supply is sinusoidal to begin with.

A small 240/110 V transformer is included in the current box to give a supply for a timing clock.

The external 240/30 V 20 A transformer draws its supply from two pins of a four-pin socket mounted in the side of the current box, and feeds the 30 V output back into the other two pins on the same socket, from where it runs to output terminals for testing 5 A relays.

(*e*)   *Voltage box:* This plugs into the current box on a multipoint plug containing the three-phase four-wire 415 V supply and various contactor leads. Two selector switches allow any pairs of phases or any phase-to-neutral to be applied separately

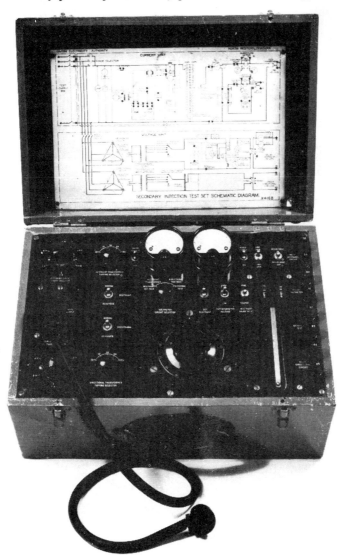

Fig. 18.8E   *Test gear — voltage box*

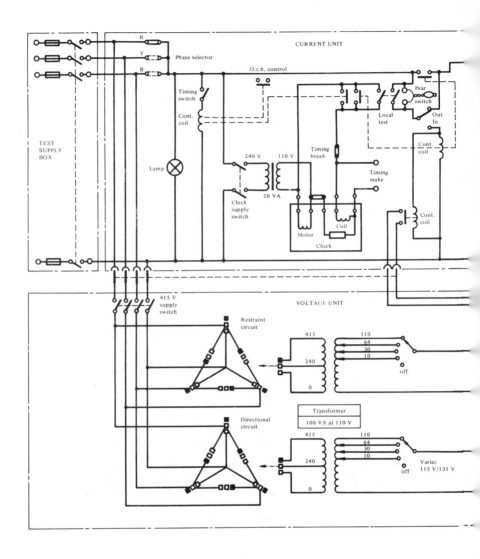

Fig. 18.8D   *Secondary injection test set circuit diagram*

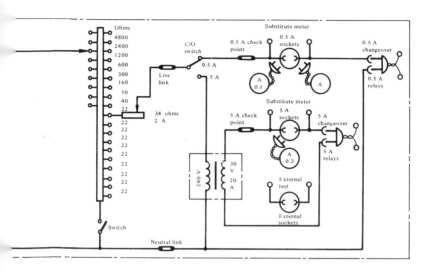

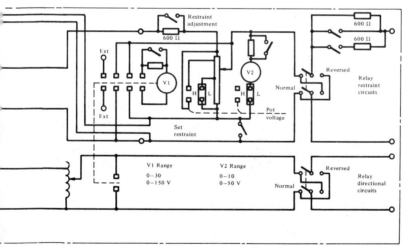

to internal transformers and Variacs for feeding:

(i)   relay directional circuits,
(ii)   relay restraint circuits (collapsible to simulate fault conditions).
Fig. 18.8E shows the voltage box, and Fig. 18.8D shows its connections.

(f)   *Primary injection equipment:* This equipment is designed to pass a heavy current at low voltage through the primaries of current transformers.

One in common use is of 5 kVA intermittent rating; it has both the primary and secondary windings arranged in sections in such a way that the primary can be fed from a 240 V or 415 V supply, and the secondary can give an output voltage of 7 V or 14 V at a current of about 500 A. The current drawn from the mains may, for short periods, be as high as 30 A. Control of the primary circuit can be provided by a 5 kVA Variac on the primary side of the transformer.

Heavy flexible test leads with clamps for fastening to the primary connections are necessary, and a measuring c.t. and ammeter are needed to determine the output current. Because of the low voltage and heavy current, it is essential that all connections are clean and tight.

The equipment (f) above enables primary currents to be simulated by which it can be proved whether the c.t.s are correctly connected to the protection. The relays themselves can be injected with smaller currents from the secondary injection test equipment and proved to be in calibration. Thus, by the use of this test equipment the whole chain can be proved from the initial primary current to the final closing of the protective relay contact.

(g)   *Instruments and other devices:* In conjunction with the above test equipment, a variety of instruments and other devices may be used. In considering instruments one should consider what quantity they are *required* to measure and what they are *calibrated* to measure. Instruments of the moving iron, dynamometer and hot-wire type will read correctly on d.c.; they will also read correctly on a.c. because they read the r.m.s. value of the current or voltage.

A permanent-magnet moving-coil instrument, however, will incorporate a rectifier if it is to be used on a.c. and is consequently very sensitive to wave shape. Such an instrument responds to the *average* value of a wave, but the scale is calibrated to indicate the r.m.s. value. Reference to Fig. 18.8F shows that a sine wave has a ratio of r.m.s. value to average value of 1·11 (the 'form factor'). Provided, therefore, the instrument is used on a sine wave it will *measure* the average but is calibrated to *indicate* (correctly) the r.m.s. If, however, the wave shape is non-sinusoidal because it contains harmonics, the form factor will be different from 1·11; the instrument will thus give a wrong reading. This emphasises the need to ensure that the right instrument is used for any given application. It is advisable to have the calibration of all test instruments periodically checked.

(i)   *Multipurpose instruments:* Many of these instruments incorporate rectifiers

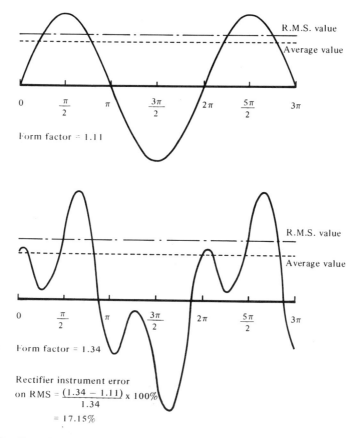

R.M.S. value

Average value

0    $\frac{\pi}{2}$ π $\frac{3\pi}{2}$ 2π $\frac{5\pi}{2}$ 3π

Form factor = 1.11

R.M.S. value

Average value

0    $\frac{\pi}{2}$ π $\frac{3\pi}{2}$ 2π $\frac{5\pi}{2}$ 3π

Form factor = 1.34

Rectifier instrument error

on RMS $= \frac{(1.34 - 1.11)}{1.34} \times 100\%$

$= 17.15\%$

Fig. 18.8F *The effect of waveform on measurements*

which are in circuit when on the a.c. ranges, so consideration should be given to waveshape as already discussed.

On these instruments there is often a 'divide by two' button which doubles the reading if this facility is needed for any reason. Care should be taken to ensure that the button does not stick down and so give too high a reading.

The instrument has different impedances depending on the range in use. It is always desirable when using the instrument on the voltage ranges to have its impedance high compared with any other resistance in the circuit, otherwise the same voltage may be read differently on different ranges of the meter. The number of ohms-per-volt is a measure of the current consumed by the instrument, and is usually marked on the back of the instrument or is given in the literature.

An easy way of calculating the current drawn by a voltmeter at full-scale deflection is to apply the formula:

$$\text{mA for full-scale deflection} = \frac{1000}{\text{ohms per volt}}$$

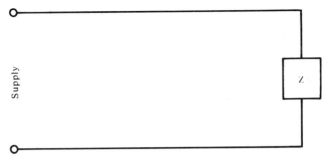

Fig. 18.8G   *Load Z connected to supply*

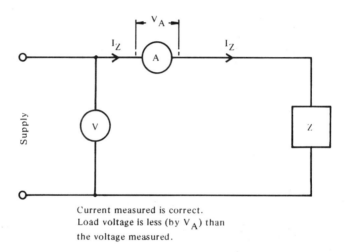

Current measured is correct.
Load voltage is less (by V_A) than
the voltage measured.

Fig. 18.8H   *Voltmeter on supply-side of ammeter*

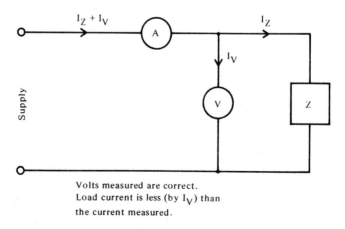

Volts measured are correct.
Load current is less (by I_V) than
the current measured.

Fig. 18.8I   *Voltmeter on load-side of ammeter*

On the current ranges it should again be realised that the meter represents an impedance in the circuit; this impedance is greatest on the lowest current range. A high-burden ammeter can upset the distribution of current in c.t. and relay secondary circuits and may give misleading results when measuring spill currents.

(ii) *Ammeters and voltmeters:* The points discussed in the previous paragraphs really cover most of what need be said about the instruments. However, if an ammeter and voltmeter are being used together to compute accurately the impedance of some circuit it should be remembered that the ammeter has some resistance and that the voltmeter takes some current. Consider Fig. 18.8G. If it is desired to measure the impedance of the load circuit denoted by Z, it could be done by applying a supply and measuring the voltage and the current taken, then dividing the volts by the amps. But where should the voltmeter be connected if a really accurate answer is needed? If it is connected as in Fig. 18.8H the ammeter will read the true current, but the voltage across the load would be slightly less than that read because of the volt-drop of the load current passing through the impedance of the ammeter. If, however, the voltmeter is connected as in Fig. 18.8I it will read the true voltage across the load, but the ammeter will read the load current plus the small current taken by the voltmeter.

In most circuits it makes negligible different which method is used. If the current is heavy then the method of Fig. 18.8I is better because the voltmeter current is infinitesimal compared with the load current. If, however, the load current is small, Fig. 18.8H would be the best method because the volt-drop across the ammeter is negligible compared with the supply voltage.

These examples are quoted as a reminder that accurate resistance measurement is not always as easy as it first appears. The way to connect the instrument is, however, largely a matter of common sense, and the instrument position can if necessary be allowed for in the calculations.

Finally, brief mention might be made of valve-voltmeters which have virtually an infinite impedance and therefore give a true reading even in high-impedance circuits.

(iii) *Wattmeters:* Wattmeters have a current coil and a voltage coil. Often the voltage coil has a resistor in series with it, and if accurate measurements are required it is important to see that the meter is connected up correctly in the way already discussed for ammeters and voltmeters. If extremely accurate measurements are required it may be necessary to allow for the $I^2 R$ losses in the current and voltage coils.

Another point to be watched is the potential of the current and voltage coils. In Fig. 18.8J the current and voltage coils are at the same potential. If, however, the connections were reversed, as in Fig. 18.8K, there is phase-to-neutral voltage between the two coils. If accurate measurements are required, Fig. 18.8K should be avoided because the electrostatic attraction between the two coils can introduce minute errors.

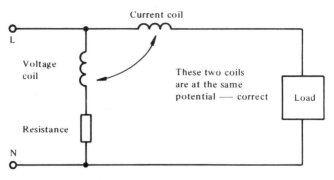

Fig. 18.8J   *Correct wattmeter connections for very accurate measurement*

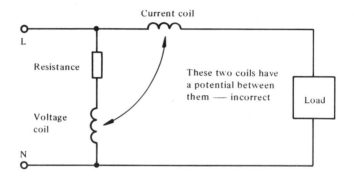

Fig. 18.8K   *Incorrect wattmeter connections for very accurate measurements*

(iv) *Signal generator:* The function of a signal generator is to produce a range of frequencies. Such an instrument should be available when testing carrier equipment. These instruments can be obtained with different frequency ranges, and a model should be selected which will be most suitable for the intended application. For tests on carrier protection a frequency range between 70 kHz and 700 kHz is required; the instrument should have low harmonic-distortion and good frequency-stability.

The maximum output available from frequency generators is normally limited to a few volts. Such outputs are adequate for testing carrier equipment at the protection frequency, but to test the performance of filters at frequencies outside their pass-band and to check the line-coupling equipment, much higher outputs are required. For these tests it is necessary to pass the output from the signal generator through an amplifier with an output of approximately 10 W.

(v) *Oscilloscopes:* An oscilloscope is required when carrying out work on carrier or v.f. equipment, and it can also be used to advantage when the wave form of a 50 Hz test supply is in doubt. Its usefulness arises from the fact that it provides a visual representation of a voltage wave form at a speed limited only by the writing speed of the electron beam.

The deflection of the beam is proportional to the voltage applied to the deflection plates, the signal under test being applied to the Y plates (vertical deflection) and an internal time base to the X plates (horizontal deflection). Internal amplifiers are normally built into the instrument to improve sensitivity. These amplifiers are calibrated, and the instrument can thus be used to obtain an estimate of signal amplitude. In this respect it is essential to confirm from the label on the selector switch that the band-width of the amplifiers covers the range of frequencies of the signals under test. In general, the instrument should be suitable for use with signals of frequencies up to 700 kHz, this being the upper limit of frequencies on carrier systems.

Current wave forms may also be examined by passing the current through a noninductive resistor and observing the voltage drop across the resistor in the normal way. The value of the resistor should of course be small compared with the impedance of the circuit under test, to minimise its effect on the circuit.

The oscilloscope can also be used for frequency comparisons. An approximate estimate of frequency can be obtained from the time-base frequency if a stationary trace is obtained and the number of cycles on the screen counted.

A more accurate method of frequency-measurement is possible by making use of a signal generator. This is connected to the X plates in place of the internal time base, and the unknown frequency is applied to the Y plates. When the two frequencies are identical, a stationary trace, known as the 'Lissajous figure' is obtained in the form of a straight line, ellipse or circle. The shape of the figure depends on the phase relationship between the two signals.

The other points worth mentioning are that the oscilloscope can also be used to measure d.c., and that the common terminal for a.c. and d.c. is usually earthed to the frame of the oscilloscope, which in turn is earthed through the supply lead. Great care should therefore be taken in connecting up a.c. or d.c. supplies to the terminals when this earth is present.

18.9   Records

For the proper management of protective gear, good records are essential as they enable the performance of protective gear to be assessed for long or short-term periods. Typical records are discussed below under their appropriate headings.

18.9.1   Relay settings

For the proper calculation of relay settings, many facts have to be known. Apart from the mathematical ability (including familiarity with symmetrical components) required to do the actual calculations, much information is needed before the calculations can even be started. This information includes:

(a)   *Current transformers:* Ratio, errors, internal resistance, excitation characteristics including knee point voltage.

(b)   *Voltage transformers:* Ratio and errors.
(c)   *Protection:* Types of relays, relay ratings and burdens, setting ranges, operating times, bias characteristics (if any).
(d)   *Primary equipment:* Lengths of lines and cables; impedances of generators, transformers, reactors, lines and cables; types of line construction (as some types of line have different impedance characteristics).
(e)   *Diagrams:* Diagrams of the local system are required so that the requirements for discrimination can be assessed.
(f)   *Fault levels*

(i)   Maximum fault levels need to be known to determine the degree of stability the protection has to have on external faults, and to calculate relay operating times.
(ii)   Minimum fault levels are assessed to ensure that there is always enough current available to operate the protection, and to calculate relay operating times.
(iii)   Data on the infeed from other points on the system are necessary at times.

Relay settings, once calculated, have to be recorded and readily available at all appropriate points — for example, not only at the location where they were calculated but also on site and in the Grid or Area Control Room.

One such system of recording employs typed sheets from which extra prints can be taken. The sheets list the station, circuit, type of protection, c.t. ratios, serial number and ratings of all relays, range of settings available, settings in use, and the date on which the settings were applied.

It is vitally important that these records are always up to date, and the flow of such information should be carefully monitored. Except in an emergency, the passing of relay setting information by telephone is deprecated.

18.9.2   Test results

The recording of commissioning tests and routine maintenance tests has already been described in earlier chapters. It is, however, worth listing the main points again:

(a)   *Commissioning log:* For recording all test results on commissioning and keeping a running record of progress.

(b)   *Block and circuit diagrams:* Block diagrams showing the single-line primary connections of a substation together with c.t. positions, the protection those c.t.s operate and the circuit breakers the protection trips are a ready means of enabling an overall picture of the substation to be readily assimilated.

Circuit diagrams show c.t., d.c. and other circuits in more detail in a simple non-physical form, so that, again, a scheme can be readily understood. Such diagrams are invaluable on commissioning tests, routing maintenance tests and fault investigation.

(*c*)   *Test record schedules:* Schedules are desirable for recording the results of secondary injection, tripping, insulation resistance and other tests. These schedules will vary in design depending on the type of test and whether it is a commissioning test or a routine maintenance test. A commissioning test is usually only done once and usually in great detail, whereas a routine maintenance test will be done many times in less detail.

The schedules can be conveniently contained in binders for a particular station. Commissioning logs are used for tests on new equipment, and routine maintenance logs for tests done subsequently. These latter schedules were discussed more fully in Section 18.5.3.

(*d*)   *Routine maintenance test records:* As mentioned earlier, opinions differ as to the frequency of routine maintenance testing. However, some scheme should be devised of ensuring that the engineer responsible is reminded, well in advance, that tests are due or overdue on a particular piece of equipment. This reminder can take the form of cards, schedules, or even notes on calendars or in diaries. Regular programming is desirable, no matter how recorded.

(*e*)   *Fault record sheets:* To form an assessment of the need for routine maintenance tests, a 'fault history' of all equipment is a good guide. If engineers record, on simple forms, everything found wrong with a particular scheme of protection, or type of relay, auxiliary switch, pilot cable and the like, trends in performance can be watched. In an ambitious scheme the information could be coded on to a punched-card system so that the information, fully cross-referenced, could be reviewed whenever necessary. Such records enable the frequency of routine maintenance tests to be varied to line up with the fault liability of a particular equipment.

The sheets record brief details of the trouble and of the corrective measures applied. If these two classifications are entered under headings on different parts of the same sheet they enable outstanding faults to be seen at a glance in those cases where it was not possible to clear the fault at the time it was found.

(*f*)   *Data storage using computers:* The Central Electricity Generating Board have evolved a central storage system for technical data. A national catalogue of power system data has been produced, and a protection data scheme has been started.

Each piece of primary equipment is identified by a code and all known data appears in coded form. Questions referring to any type of equipment can be answered quickly by the computer.

The same codes are used in the protection data scheme, in which system faults are recorded in code, operations of all relays are tabulated, and information on incorrect performance is given in detail. The information fed into the computer can be used to determine the performance of any type of protection equipment in use.

(g)   *Protective gear operation reports:* The justification for the careful testing of protective gear is its high overall performance. There must be some method of assessing whether it has behaved correctly; to this end a detailed record should be kept of every fault and every protective gear operation, together with the circuit breakers which trip. A careful note should also be made of any failure to trip.

An annual study of these figures enables the protective gear performance to be assessed. The system fault performance can be expressed as the ratio of the number of system faults correctly cleared to the total number of system faults.

It sometimes happens that during work on protective gear or control circuits a mishap occurs and circuit breakers are tripped. This could be due, for example, to secondary wiring or vibration. In assessing the overall performance of protective gear, these unnecessary trips should also be recorded. Here the performance can be expressed as ratio between the number of circuit breakers unnecessarily tripped and the total number of circuit breakers at risk. On the Generating Board's system, such faults are known as non-system faults, because the trips occur at a time when there is no fault on the power system.

The system fault performance thus gives the technical performance of the gear, the non-system fault performance gives the performance influenced by the human element, and the combination of the two gives the overal performance of the protective gear and the staff.

(h)   *Lines of communication:* When dealing with protective gear, attention to detail is of paramount importance. It is therefore essential that all relevant information is fully and clearly recorded. This is not easy with a multiplicity of gear and voltages and a staff which may be dispersed over several thousand square miles.

Day-to-day contact can be made via telephone calls or visits to site, but written information needs further consideration. It is not always realised that the flow of information needs to be two way — from headquarters to site and from site to headquarters.

Relay settings, plant data, circuit diagrams, fault levels, commissioning logs, routine maintenance records, fault record sheets and protective gear performance statistics require a two-way flow of information, and to avoid chaos some system by which this information is channelled to and fro should be devised. The method used will vary to suit different conditions.

For information which usually flows in one direction only, some form of memorandum or circular may be desirable. For communications on protective gear, protection memoranda bearing serial numbers may be issued. In this way, files may be devoted exclusively to these memoranda. Methods of test could form the basis of a numbered series of test circulars to cover different types of protection, testing hints, warnings and the like.

The volume of information so handled can be quite formidable but if several files are used for different subjects, reference to a particular topic can quickly be made.

Index